D0992537

INTERSCIENCE MONOGRAPHS AND TEXTS IN PHYSICS AND ASTRONOMY

Edited by R. E. MARSHAK

INTERSCIENCE MONOGRAPHS AND TEXTS IN PHYSICS AND ASTRONOMY

Edited by R. E. MARSHAK

University of Rochester, Rochester, New York

VOLUME XXI

SUPERNOVAE

I. S. SHKLOVSKY

*Sternberg Astronomical Institute
Moscow, USSR*

*Translated from the original manuscript
by Literaturprojekt, Innsbruck, Austria*

A WILEY–INTERSCIENCE PUBLICATION

John Wiley & Sons Ltd.   **London**   ·   **New York**   ·   **Sydney**

Library of Congress catalog card number 68–56972

SBN 470 78650 7

Made and printed in Great Britain by
William Clowes and Sons, Limited, London and Beccles

Preface

In recent years the outbursts of supernovae have attracted the attention of many researchers. It is now clear that these outbursts play a very important part in the general picture of stellar and galactic evolution. It is not too much to say that the evolution of the chemical composition of matter in the universe is to a large degree determined by supernovae. Modern theories of the origin of the primary cosmic rays are closely connected with various aspects of the problem of supernova outbursts.

The rapid development of radioastronomy and, in recent times, of X-ray astronomy, has led to a significant increase in the extent of our knowledge of the nebulae which form after outbursts of supernovae. We now have a relatively good understanding of the complex physical processes taking place in these nebulae. These processes are highly unusual. Their thorough investigation is of great importance to modern astrophysics as a whole. Take, for example, the discovery of the synchrotron nature of the optical radiation from the Crab nebula which stimulated a considerable number of investigations into the rapidly developing field of metagalactic astronomy.

As yet there exists no monograph on this interesting field of astrophysics. This is obviously explained by the great difficulties involved in the compilation of such a book. The investigations into this fascinating field of astrophysics are based on the application of the most diverse methods and, moreover, the problem itself is far from being solved. As yet nobody knows with certainty the cause of the explosion of certain stars, nor how these stars differ from others ... In this situation it might seem premature to write a book on the problem. The author, however does not agree with this point of view. After all, one may (and indeed must) write books on electricity without knowing the nature of the elementary particles. Numerous aspects of the problem of supernovae outbursts are now more or less fully understood. At the same time, we must, of course, take into account the rapid development of this field of astrophysics. It is quite possible that, within a few years, individual conclusions in this book may appear obsolete and even naïve. This is inevitable with all rapidly developing fields of science.

The author hopes that this monograph will be of value to astronauts and physicists interested in modern astrophysics.

I. S. SHKLOVSKY

Contents

CHAPTER I

General information on supernovae

§ 1   Photometrical and statistical investigations

On August 31st, 1885, in our country's oldest observatory, at Tartu, an epoch-making discovery was made: the astronomer Hartwig discovered a new star near the core of the Andromeda nebula, M 31.[1]   The luminosity of this star was estimated at 6.5, while according to contemporary estimates the integral stellar magnitude is close to 4.5.   From separate casual observations made since at various European observatories one may conclude that on August 17th this star must have been of magnitude 9, while a year previously, in August 1884, there was no object brighter at this position than that of magnitude 15.   Beginning with March of the following year, 1886, this star could not even be observed with the largest telescopes.   On the basis of these observations, Lundmark drew the light curve of this remarkable star[2] (Fig. 5).

One must take into account that up to the beginning of the 1920's the nature of objects, now known as extragalactic nebulae, had not yet been finally established.   In fact, even in Lambert's time (eighteenth century), the conception of "island universes" was applied more and more.   According to this conception the spiral nebulae must be viewed as huge associations of stars, gas and dust nebulae, similar to our own stellar system, the galaxy.   The distance to M 31 was first estimated by Lundmark, in 1919, who obtained a value of 200,000 psc.†[2]   It therefore followed that the absolute magnitude of the nova of 1885 must be -15. It is interesting that this result was then used by the opponents of the conception of the "island universes" as a decisive argument against it....   Shapley, adhering to the contrary conception of "supergalaxies" considered it "a matter of course" that no novae may exist whose absolute magnitude at maximum brightness was so high.[3]   Ordinary novae at maximum have absolute magnitudes of about -6 and -7.

---

† This estimate proved quite good.   It was maintained until 1951 when the entire system of intergalactic distances was enlarged several times.

In the period from 1920 to 1922 it was finally proved that the spiral nebulae and also a great number of elliptic and irregular nebulae with continuous spectra, positioned in high galactic latitudes, were extragalactic stellar systems. Science owes this fundamental achievement of astronomical observation in the twentieth century to the American astronomer Edwin Hubble who made his observations with the greatest modern telescope, the 100-inch reflector of the Mount Chipson observatory. As indisputable proof of the extragalactic nature of spiral nebulae, the spiral arms in M 31 could be resolved into a huge number of stars, including variables and cepheids.

In the course of these investigations it was shown that in M 31 new stars, with maximum magnitudes of up to 15, flare up quite frequently (about thirty times per year).

This fact is an obvious proof of the unusual character of the nova of 1885 whose magnitude was several thousand times greater than the magnitude of "ordinary novae" and was thus only six to seven times lower than the integral luminosity of the giant stellar system M 31.

Several outbursts of bright novae were observed between 1885 and 1920 in extragalactic nebulae, such as the outburst of a new star in June 1895, in the nebula NGC 5253, located in the Centaur constellation,[4] which was of particular interest. This star, to which the name of Z Centauri was assigned, reached a magnitude of 7.2 at maximum luminosity, which is almost five times brighter than the integral stellar luminosity of the NGC 5253 galaxy. At present we know that the stellar system in which the outburst was observed pertains to the category of dwarf systems. Nevertheless, it is astounding that within a short period of time one star should become a hundred times brighter than the hundreds of millions of stars forming the stellar system. Figure 1a shows a photograph of the supernova that made its appearance in the galaxy NGC 3938.

Within the period from 1885 to 1920 about ten novae were discovered which flared up in spiral, elliptical and irregular galaxies. They were sporadically observed, mainly by photographic means. Only in the one case of Z Centauri was a spectrum of very low quality obtained by chance, taken through an objective prism.[4] At the same time, in a series of cases, it was possible to obtain very rough light curves of the corresponding novae through photographic observation. Nevertheless, some important conclusions could be drawn from these fragmental observations. First of all it followed that the brightness of these novae at maximum, equals, and sometimes even exceeds, the integral brightness of the corresponding nebulae. It was also established that there was no explicit connection between the outburst of a nova and the morphological features of the latter. Outbursts may occur in spiral nebulae and in elliptical and irreg-

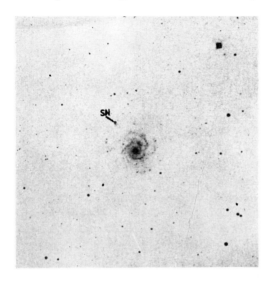

FIG. 1a   Photograph of supernova outburst in the galaxy NGC 3938.[6]

ular nebulae as well. Finally, a rough statistical analysis of the very poor observational material led to the preliminary conclusion that, on the average, one outburst occurs in a given nebula approximately once in every 1,000 years.

All this scanty observational data enabled Lundmark to state a hypothesis as early as 1919, to the effect that, besides the "ordinary" novae, stars flare up in the galaxies from time to time, reaching a luminosity that exceeds a thousand times that of the galaxy concerned.[2] In 1934, Zwicky and Baade gave these stars the name "supernovae."[5]

As to its fundamental characteristics, our galaxy does not differ in principle from other galactic spiral nebulae. It may thus be expected that from time to time supernovae must also make their appearance in it. In this connection Lundmark drew attention to the historic chronicle, containing references to unusual luminosities of stars occasionally appearing on the horizon and then fading away. In particular, he was the first to draw attention to the fact that near an unusually bright star which, according to a Chinese chronicle, flared up in 1054 and was observed even in brightest daytime, there exists an object, remarkable in many respects, M 1 in the Crab nebula, which we shall often discuss in this book.[38]

Let us note, however, that Hubble[48] (cf. § 3) was the first to assume, in 1928, that the Crab nebula was the remnant of the supernova outburst of 1054.

Since supernova outbursts are very rare in our galaxy (last observed by Kepler in 1604, before the invention of the telescope), the investigation of supernovae with the help of modern methods requires their observation in other stellar systems. Though the probability of an outburst in any definite galaxy is very low, a systematic search, following a reasonable programme in a sufficiently great number of galaxies, must meet with some success.

This important problem has been solved by the well-known American astronomer Zwicky.[6,7,8] In 1933, with very modest observation equipment at his disposal (a 10-inch refractor), he began a systematic search for supernovae in extragalactic nebulae. The work became much more successful after 1936 when he obtained an 18-inch telescope of the Schmidt system, designed especially for this survey programme. In this systematic search 175 celestial fields were surveyed. These fields were mainly located near galaxies (M 31, 32, 33, 51, 81, 82, 101, etc.) and a series of galactic clusters (in Ursa Major, Coma Berenices, Leo, Cancer, Perseus, Hydra, Pisces and Centaurus). Within the framework of this systematic programme about 3,000 galaxies brighter than 15^m were observed; among these about 700 were brighter than 13^m. In Zwicky's own words, observations took place "as often as possible."

This planned work showed the first results quite quickly. In the period from September 6th, 1936, to December 31st, 1939, altogether 1,625 photographic plates were exposed and scanned. Taking into account the number of galaxies positioned in the visual field of the telescope and represented on a single plate, the programme of this period corresponds, as can be shown, to 5,150 years of continuous observation of one "average" galaxy. During this time a total of twelve supernova explosions were recorded. Hence it follows that once in 430 years a supernova flares up in an "average" galaxy. Within the same period in 840 brighter galaxies, listed in the well-known Shapley–Ames catalogue, five supernova outbursts were discovered. This gives an average of one outburst per 360 years. The latter estimate is perhaps the more reliable.

Zwicky's work was carried out in close co-operation with other
Californian astronomers. Baade plotted the magnitude curves of the
supernovae discovered during this search[9] while Zwicky and Humason
studied their spectra (cf. § 2).[11] Figures 1 and 2 show the light curves of
the supernovae in NGC 1003 and IC 4182.

These important investigations were broken off when World War II
began. They were recommenced with new vigour in the middle of the
1950's. At the beginning of 1958, the systematic search for supernovae
was carried out with the help of one of the world's greatest telescopes of
the Schmidt system, with a mirror diameter of 48 inches. The result was
a sharp increase in the number of supernova discoveries. Whereas, for
example, a total of fifty-four supernovae were discovered in the period
from 1885 to 1956, eighty-two were discovered between 1956 and 1963.
Zwicky assumes that if the 48-inch Schmidt telescope was used exclusively
for purposes of this programme (and not only on three to six nights per
month as at present), about one hundred supernovae would be discovered
per year.[11] It must still be mentioned that according to Zwicky, in spite
of the great many newly-discovered supernovae, the material does not yet
permit an improvement of the mean frequency data of supernova appearances per galaxy, previously determined by him (on the average one outburst per 360 years in one galaxy of the Shapley–Ames catalogue). This
is explained by the difficulties of accommodating all series of observations
in a single system. On the other hand, systematic observations of supernova outbursts in galactic clusters (which may only be carried out with a
sufficiently large telescope, e.g., the 48-inch Schmidt telescope) supported
the previous conclusion: in these clusters one supernova outburst occurs
on the average every 300 years in each bright galaxy of the cluster.
("Bright galaxies" are determined by the condition $m < m_{max} + 3$,
where m_{max} is the magnitude of the bright member of the cluster itself.)

It had so far been tacitly assumed that all supernovae pertain to a
system of like objects. We now know, however, that this is not so.
Even a simple analysis of the light curves shows that there are great
differences in their shapes. Spectroscopic observations, which will be
considered in the following section, showed that there must exist at least
two types of supernovae, each of them being characterized by its light
curve. Figure 1 shows the light curves corresponding to supernovae of
the type I. A schematic representation of a light curve is given in Figure
2. A steep rise in luminosity with a rather flat maximum is followed by a
sharp drop (within 20 to 30 days the luminosity decreases by two to

three magnitudes). After this the increase of m_{ph} follows an almost linear law for a long time (of the order of 100 days) as long as the exploded star still remains observable. The time interval, τ, characteristic of this curve, amounts to about 40 to 50 days. We must stress the surprising similarity of the light curves after the maximum of the various supernovae

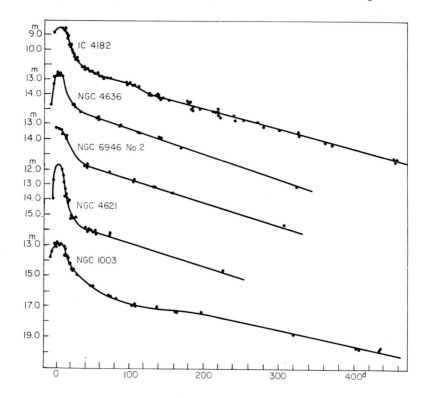

FIG. 1　Photographic light curves of type I supernovae.[13]

of the type I. According to Baade,[12] beginning with the moment of decline 100 days after the maximum, the apparent photographic magnitude of supernovae of this type increases by 0.0137 per day.

Moreover, we must not forget that individual light curves of supernovae of this type display considerable differences near the maximum. It must also be borne in mind that the light curves yield the apparent photographic magnitude of the star as a function of time. The amount of the bolometric correction for supernovae of this type and its possible time dependence are still unknown.   An argument in favour of the assumption that the bolometric correction is independent of time is the absence of noticeable changes in the photographic part of the spectrum of supernovae which flared up in IC 4182, in the period from 70 to 339 days after the maximum (Fig. 10).   If the bolometric correction is a constant, the light curve shows the true time dependence of the luminosity of the supernova.

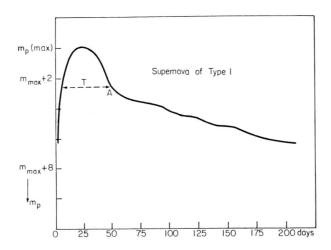

FIG. 2   Schematic representation of light curve of type I supernova.[11]

In contrast to supernovae of the type I, the light curves of the other supernovae (which the majority of investigators consider a single class and denote as type II, though Zwicky classed them into five types altogether—see the following section) differ considerably from one another.   Figure 3 shows the light curves of the type II supernovae, obtained by Baade.[12]

The great differences between the light curves of the various supernovae of this type are obvious.   As to the general features, the difference in the light curves of supernovae of types I and II is that the curve of the type II has a "broader" maximum than that of the type I.   The post-maximum luminosity drop of the type II supernovae usually amounts to about 1.5 magnitudes, i.e., the decline is slower than with the type I supernovae; it is often followed by a "plateau."   Thereafter, in the "final stage" the light curves of supernovae of the type II are as a rule

much steeper than those of the type I supernovae. One may find very
peculiar light curves which differ essentially from the "average" curve
described above. For example, the light curve of the supernova which
appeared in NGC 4725 cannot be discerned in its post-maximum part

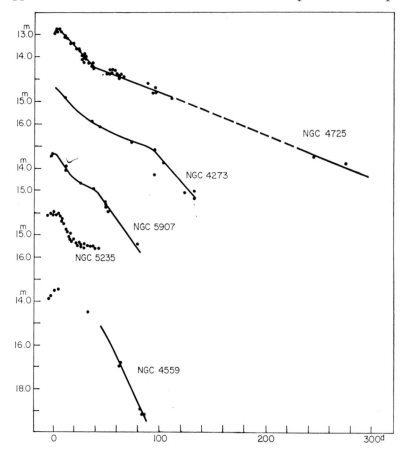

FIG. 3   Photographic light curves of several type II supernovae.[13]

from that of a type I supernova, whereas the spectrum is typical of a type
II supernova.

The great variety in the light curves of the type II supernovae may
indicate that these supernovae do not represent a uniform group of
objects. Some of the light curves are very peculiar. For instance, the

supernova of 1961, in NGC 1058[32] manifested a slow decrease in luminosity for 110 days after its discovery, then, for the next 30 days, luminosity increased by 1.5 magnitudes. Thereafter the luminosity again began to fall (in 90 days by 4.3 magnitudes) and finally remained constant. The absolute magnitude of this supernova reached 17.1 at maximum. The spectrum looks like the ordinary spectrum of a type II supernova (see below), only the emission lines are narrower.

No less remarkable are the light curves of the supernovae in NGC 5457, NGC 5236 and NGC 6946 (see Fig. 4). The first two galaxies in which supernovae made their appearances belong to the type Sc; the third is an irregular stellar system. The three light curves are all rather similar.

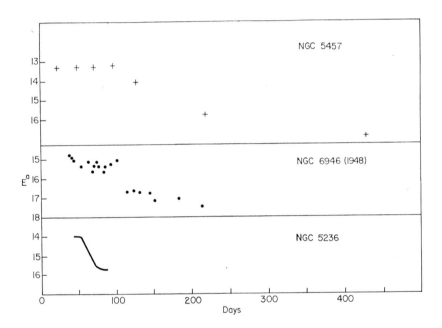

FIG. 4   Light curves of supernovae in NGC 5457, NGC 5236 and NGC 6946.[13]

The initial decrease in luminosity occurs very slowly, then a relatively quick drop of 1.5 magnitudes occurs, followed by another slow decline which, however, is somewhat faster than the first one. As to their spectra, these objects are fairly typical of supernovae of the type II. The absolute magnitudes at the moment of discovery, however, differ essentially from those of supernovae of the type II, amounting to -15.2, -13.2 and -14.7, respectively. We cannot, however, exclude the possibility that these supernovae were already in a post-maximum state when they were observed for the first time.

On estimating the absolute magnitudes of supernovae, interstellar absorption has only recently been taken into account.[15,16] Minkowski, using a very simplified procedure of taking interstellar absorption into account in our galaxy (for all supernovae $\Delta m = 0.25$ cosec b_{II}, which is obviously too low) and roughly estimating the light absorption in the galaxy where the supernova appeared, gives the following absolute magnitudes of some supernovae of types I and II (cf. Tables 1 and 2).

TABLE 1   Absolute Photographic Magnitudes of Supernovae of the Type I

Object	m_{max}	0.25 cosec b_{II}	Type of Galaxy	b/a	A_n	$m_{max,0}$	$m - M$	M_g	M_{max}	$M_{max,0}$
NGC 1003	13.0	0.86	Sc	0.24	1.3	10.8	29.3	-17.2	-16.3	-18.5
4214	9.5	0.25	Irr	0.9	—	9.2	28.4	-16.3	-18.9	-19.2
4486	12	0.25	E0–1	0.79	—	11.7	30.4	-20.7	-18.4	-18.7
4621	11.8	0.25	E5	0.48	—	11.5	30.4	-19.4	-18.6	-18.9
4636	12.5	0.25	E0–1	0.74	—	12.2	30.4	-19.8	-17.9	-18.2
5253	8.0	0.52	Irr	0.29	—	7.5	27.3	-17.3	-19.3	-19.8
5668	12.2	0.30	Sc	0.95	0.3	11.6	31.2	-19.0	-19.0	-19.6
IC 4182	8.5	0.25	Irr	1.00	—	8.2	27.2	-13.7	-18.7	-19.0
Anon 13^h08^m	14.1	0.0	SBc	—	0.2	139	32.4	-16.9	-18.3	-18.5

The fifth columns of Tables 1 and 2 give the ratio of the minor axis to the major axis of the visual appearance of the corresponding galaxy. This ratio determines the angle made by the basic plane of the galaxy and the plane of the map. The quantity b/a serves as a rough criterion for A_n, the light absorption in the galaxy in which the supernova made its appearance. If b/a is small, the galaxy is seen almost "from the edge" and the dust matter located in the zone around the base plane of the galaxy will be strongly absorbed. For a supernova outburst at the periphery of a galaxy this estimate of absorption would tend to be too high. $m_{max,0}$ denotes the supernova's apparent photographic magnitude at maximum luminosity, M_g the absolute photographic magnitude of the galaxy in which the outburst occurred.   The absorption values for the two supernovae listed in the last lines of Tables 1 and 2 were taken from [16] and [17].

TABLE 2   Absolute Photographic Magnitudes of Supernovae of the Type II

Object	m_{max}	0.25 cosec b_{II}	Type of Galaxy	b/a	A_n	$m_{max,0}$	$m - M$	M_g	M_{max}	$M_{max,0}$
NGC 3938	13.7	0.27	Sc	0.90	0.3	13.1	29.8	-19.0	-16.1	-16.7
4157	14.5	0.28	Sb	0.12	1.8	12.4	31.1	-19.7	-16.6	-18.7
4273	14.4	0.27	Sc	0.67	0.7	13.4	30.2	-18.0	-15.8	-16.8
4559	13.5	0.25	Sc	0.41	0.8	12.4	29.3	-18.0	-15.8	-16.9
4725	12.8	0.25	Sb	0.55	0.8	11.5	30.2	-17.4	-17.4	-18.5
5907	13.4	0.32	Sb	0.06	1.8	11.3	29.3	-18.3	-15.9	-18.0
7331	13.6	0.8	Sb	0.23	1.2	11.6	29.9	-19.7	-16.3	-18.3

We can see from Table 1 that the luminosities of the type I super-novae are very similar and extremely high.   The record in luminosity was reached by the supernova of 1885 which appeared in NGC 5253.   If the bolometric corrections with type I supernovae were the same as with the sun (as a matter of fact they may even be much higher, see below), the maximum luminosity of each supernova of this type was higher than that of the sun by a factor of 10^{10}!   The total amount of energy emitted in this outburst was of the order of 10^{50} erg.   Such an amount of energy would be emitted by a star equal in mass to the sun during the entire time of its evolution, i.e., for several thousand million years.

It is interesting that the luminosity of the supernova which appeared in NGC 4182 exceeded that of the irregular dwarf galaxy in which it flared up by five magnitudes.   The supernova of type I, observed in 1921 by Balanowski near the core of the elliptical galaxy NGC 4486,[18] is also of interest.   Today this galaxy is known as one of the brightest radio sources of Virgo A.

Figure 5 shows the visual light curves of several supernovae.   The full line represents a light curve typical for supernovae of the type I. The light curve of S Andromedae which we discussed at the beginning of this section is quite different from both the typical light curve of super-novae of type I and from the light curve of supernovae of type II, shown in this figure.

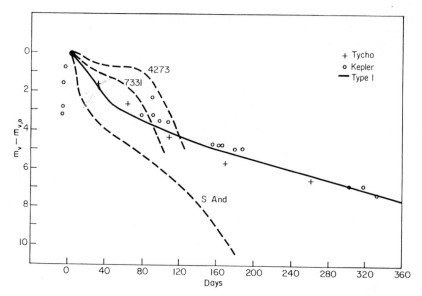

Fig. 5   Visual light curves of several supernovae.[13]

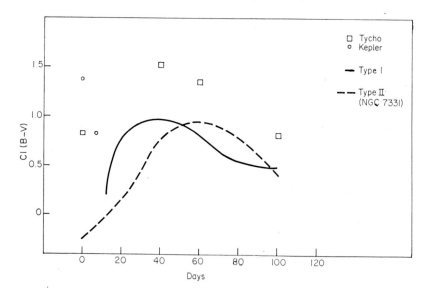

Fig. 6   Time dependence of colour index of supernovae of types I and II.[13]

Figure 6 shows the time dependence of the colour index for supernovae of types I and II. These curves have been drawn on the basis of
investigations by Michalas[16] (for supernovae of type I) and Arp[15] who
studied the luminosity variations of the type II supernova which appeared
in AGC 7331. With both types of supernovae, the colour index is low,
near the maximum. This indicates that the apparent magnitudes not
corrected for interstellar light absorption are close to the photographic
magnitudes. Taking interstellar absorption into account, supernovae of
both types have a small (~ 0.15–0.20) negative colour index at maximum.
A still greater difference for the two types of supernovae must show the
colour index U–B. According to Arp[15] the colour index U–B of the
supernova of type II which exploded in NGC 7331 reaches high negative
values near the maximum. This is in accordance with observations of
spectra of supernovae of this type which are very intense in the ultraviolet range. The corresponding data for type I supernovae (cf. [16]) are
still very scanty.

There is as yet only one paper by Bertola in which the change in
luminosity in the type I supernova which appeared in November 1962
in NGC 1073 has been studied.[17a] The results of photoelectric observations of this supernova in the UBV system are shown in Figure 7. It may
be interesting to note that the maximum is reached at different times
for different colours. The light curve maximum of the ultraviolet light
was observed on December 6th, with the blue light on December 7th and
for the visual range it was observed on December 10th. In the post-
maximum stage the rate of change in brightness was also different in the
different ranges of the spectrum; it was 0.08 per day in the visible, 0.12
per day in the blue range and 0.13 per day in the ultraviolet. Thus the
decrease in luminosity of the supernova is accompanied by a change in
colour towards red.

Above, when discussing the frequency of supernova outbursts in the
various galaxies, we did not differentiate between the supernovae of types
I or II. It is, however, very likely that the two types are manifestations
of two quite different phenomena. It is therefore necessary to study
separately the statistical characteristics of both types of supernovae.

In past years several investigations have been devoted to this
problem. Van den Bergh in his statistical analysis used nineteen supernovae of type I and thirteen of type II,[17b] Yu. P. Pskovskiy thirty-three
and twenty-six, respectively,[17c] and Bertaud nineteen and twelve,
respectively.[17d] All three investigators arrived at the same conclusion, a

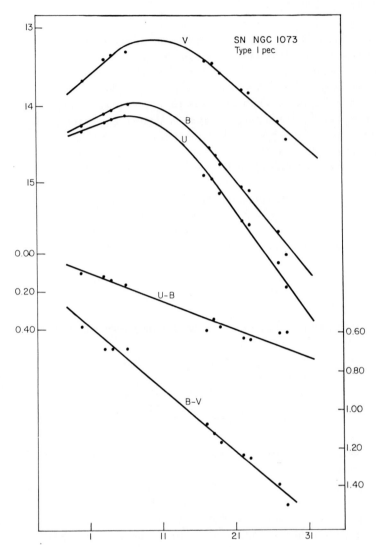

F$_{\text{IG}}$. 7   Photoelectrical observations of the supernova outburst in NGC 1073.[17a]

very essential first result; namely that supernovae of type II appear only in spiral stellar systems of the types Sb and Sc. Supernovae of type II with like frequencies appear in galaxies of all types including elliptical ones. In those rare cases where outbursts were observed in irregular

galaxies, the supernovae were of type I. Previously Zwicky came to
the conclusion that there was no marked correlation between the frequency
of supernova outbursts and the type of the galaxy. This result, however,
was obtained without classifying the supernovae into types.

It is significant that supernovae of the type II appear only in spiral
systems and there, as a rule, in the arms of the spiral structure. It
indicates that the stars exploding in this way are comparatively young
objects, not over 10^8 years old. On the other hand, the supernovae of
type I, exploding particularly in elliptical galaxies, are very old, since
modern theories assert that the process of stellar formation in the elliptical
galaxies, deprived of interstellar matter, has long since come to an end.
Stars whose mass exceeds $1.2M_\odot$ have already reached the end of their
evolutionary track and, most probably, have long ago turned into white
dwarfs or cold neutron stars (cf. § 18). In this case the mass of stars
exploding for any reason must be smaller than $1.2M_\odot$ and their age must
be about 10^{10} years.

The statistical investigations make it possible to determine the
dependence of the outburst frequency of supernovae on the absolute
magnitude of the galaxy of the corresponding type. It is quite possible
that for a galaxy of given type the outburst frequency of supernovae is
inversely proportional to the mass of the galaxy. In other words, the
outburst probability per unit mass might be a constant quantity. Thus,
for example, in the galaxy M 33 (in the Triangulum), with a comparatively
small mass, outbursts of supernovae cannot occur once per 300 years (as
in giant galaxies) but only once in several thousand years.

The absolute magnitude of supernovae at their maximum depends
essentially on the system of intergalactic distances accepted. Minkowski,
analyzing the data given in Tables 1 and 2 (obtained on the assumption
of Hubble's redshift constant amounting to $H = 100$ km/s-Mpsc),
found that the mean apparent absolute photographic magnitude of supernovae of type I is equal to $M_{max} = -18 \pm 0.3$, $\sigma = 0.3$, where σ is the
dispersion of absolute magnitude. Taking into account the interstellar
absorption of light in our galaxy, and in the stellar system where the outburst took place, yields $M_{max,0} = -19.0 \pm 0.3$, $\sigma = 0.7$. Minkowski
does not exclude that supernovae of type II may constitute a non-
uniform group of objects for which he obtained $M_{max} = -16.3 \pm 0.3$,
$\sigma = 0.8$; $M_{max,0} = 17.7 \pm 0.3$, $\sigma = 0.8$. The correction for interstellar absorption is greater in the case of supernovae of type II, since in
this case light absorption in the "atomized" arms of the galaxy where the

outburst occurred is much more intense than in the regions of outbursts of supernovae of type I (elliptical galaxies, the central parts of spirals). Note that a rough estimate of M_{max} for the supernova which flared up in 1054 in our galaxy (cf. § 3) yields a value of about 18. It should also be noted that Minkowski's estimates of M_{max} should not of course be viewed as final. They will be subject to several improvements, although the quantity $M_{max,0}$ itself will hardly be changed very much.

In his estimates of the outburst frequency of supernovae given above, Zwicky made no distinction between supernovae of type I and supernovae of type II. Based on the results of systematic searches for supernovae, undertaken by Zwicky, Minkowski found that, on average, one outburst of a type I supernova in a given galaxy occurs once in every four hundred and fifty years.

This estimate is mainly based on observations of outbursts in the giant clusters of galaxies in Virgo, the one nearest to us (it is possible that our own galactic system moves into this cluster). Within the survey period five outbursts of supernovae were observed in this cluster, one of them belonging to type II. It must, however, be remarked that the statistical material used by Minkowski was very poor. On the other hand, from the results of searches for supernovae down to some limiting magnitude m, conducted in the years from 1937 to 1941, taking into account that with supernovae of type II the absolute magnitude M_{max} is higher by almost 2, Baade found that the outburst frequency of supernovae of type II exceeded that of type I by a factor of 6 to 7. Hence it follows that, on the average, a supernova of type II appears in a given galaxy (giant spiral galaxy) once in every 70 years. This method of estimation, however, depends heavily on the value chosen for M_{max}. It is therefore very desirable to find other independent methods of estimating the outburst frequency of supernovae of type II. In this connection it may be of interest to draw attention to the fact that at present we already know several galaxies in which, within the last 50 years, two and even three outbursts of supernovae were observed. In the galaxy of the type Sc in NGC 3184, for instance, three supernova outbursts were observed: two in 1921 and one in 1937. In four Sc-type galaxies in which three outbursts have been observed, Bertaud established the mean time interval between the outbursts at 18 years. In each of the two galaxies two outbursts were observed: in NGC 2841 (Sb) with an interval of 45 years and in NGC 4303 (Sc) with an interval of 35 years. It is essential that the overwhelming majority of supernovae appearing, "multiply" in these galaxies (almost always appearing much later as spirals), pertain to type II. On the other hand, these galaxies, in which repeated outbursts of supernovae were observed, do not possess any other peculiar character-istics. This forces us to draw the conclusion that the outburst frequency of supernovae of type II is comparatively high, and in all cases several times higher than that of supernovae of type I. Just taking into account interstellar absorption in galaxies in which an outburst had occurred places supernovae of both types in different positions, even if their M_{max} had been equal. In § 7 we will give yet another independent argument in favour of a comparatively higher frequency of outbursts of supernovae of type II. Note, however, that this problem has not yet been fully solved and there are still some authors who even today assume that the frequency of supernovae of type II is of the same order or even smaller than that of supernovae of type I (cf., for example, [19]). To us, however, their considerations seem unconvincing.

At the end of this section we shall discuss an interesting problem connected with the enormous luminosity of the supernovae at maximum. It is well known that Nova Persei, which appeared in 1901, was observed to be surrounded by a varying nebula which was explained as being caused by dispersion of the spherical light wave, emitted during the explosion, in interstellar dust. Analogous luminous phenomena may also be observed around other novae (cf., for example, [20]). The theory of this effect was developed in 1939 by Couderc.[21] But a natural question arises: Can analogous effects in principle be observed around old super-novae? The power of a light signal from supernovae, however, is ten thousand times greater than that from ordinary novae. This problem was considered by Zwicky[22] and the author of the present book[23] who treated this problem quantitatively.

The effect of the reflection of a light signal from a supernova is schemat-ically represented in Figure 8. According to [21] the surface brightness of such a "flash" (or "light echo") is determined by the expression†

$$I = \frac{\Phi(\alpha) L \, \Delta t}{R^2(\omega^2 + r^2)} \qquad (1.1)$$

where $\Phi(\alpha)$ describes the reflective properties of the intergalactic medium, $r = t/r$ where t is the time (in years) after the outburst, R is the distance (in light years) to the nebula, ω the angular distance of an element of the

† In 1965 the same results were obtained by Van den Bergh[358] from independent considerations.

nebula to the point of the outburst, L is the luminosity of the exploding star at maximum and Δt is the effective duration of the outburst.

For supernovae the product $L\,\Delta t$ is 10^4 to 10^5 times higher than for ordinary novae. On the assumption that we can today record extended objects whose surface luminosity is thirty times lower than the brightness of the varying nebula around Nova Persei, and that the reflective condi-

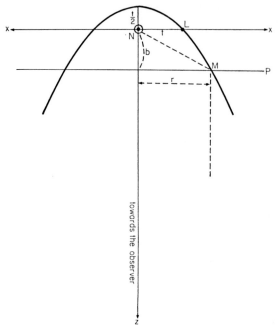

Fɪɢ. 8   Schematic diagram explaining the appearance of a light echo during the outburst of a supernova.[21]

tions of interstellar dust around supernovae are the same as around Nova Persei, we may conclude from (1.1) that the limiting "age" of the light front around a supernova is about one thousand times greater than around Nova Persei. Since the nebula around the latter has been observed for about six months, we may conclude that under favourable conditions the light front around supernovae may be observed for at least several hundred years. Under extremely favourable conditions this period may be much longer.

It is therefore interesting to search for very faint varying nebular discs of irregular structure, in the first place, around the supernovae which appeared in our galaxy in 1572 and 1604 (cf. § 3), and also around the

FIG. 9a, Photograph of the ring nebula in galaxy NGC 5457.

FIG. 9b. Schematic sketch of the ring nebula in galaxy NGC 5457.[24]

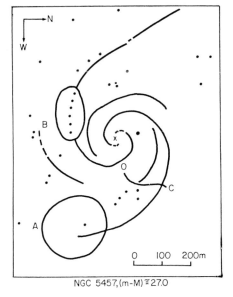

NGC 5457,(m-M) ≅ 27.0

remnant in Cassiopeia A of an outburst of a type II supernova (see § 5). Such nebulae must be sought within the limits of several degrees around the corresponding supernova.

It is to be expected that these light fronts of supernovae which exploded several hundred years ago will be successfully observed in the bright galaxies nearest to us. Possibly they are already under observation. Recently, in the galaxies M 31, NGC 5194–95, NGC 628, NGC 5457 and NGC 7741 very interesting disc-like nebulae[24] were discovered. Figure 9a shows a photograph of the galaxy NGC 5457, in which we see several of these nebulae; their arrangement is schematically shown to the same scale in Figure 9b. However, quite probably most of these formations have other origins. In particular, those which have a diameter of the order of 1,000 psc or more are known not to be light fronts of previously exploded supernovae. Only nebulae with radii less than 100 psc can be presumed to be "flares" of supernova outbursts. If our hypothesis is right, we may expect that these nebulae are unstable since the conditions of reflection in interstellar dust are highly inconstant.

§ 2   The spectra of supernovae and their interpretation

Even though spectroscopic observations were carried out in 1885 when S Andromedae flared up and the spectrum of Z Centauri was obtained with the help of an objective prism, there were virtually no spectroscopic investigations of supernovae up to 1937. The systematic search for supernovae initiated by Zwicky in 1936 was accompanied by spectroscopic studies. In 1937 two bright supernovae appeared in IC 4182 and NGC 1003. From these objects Minkowski obtained spectrographic records of the individual evolutional stages of the supernovae[25] which are as yet unsurpassed. Whereas S Andromedae and Z Centauri were observed with slitless spectrographs of very low dispersion, in the case of the supernova of 1937 slit spectrographs were used for the first time. The dispersion of the various spectrographs varied within wide limits, from 37 Å/mm at Hγ to 850 Å/mm at Hα.

The spectral range investigated covers the interval from 6711 Å to 3700 Å. Unfortunately these spectra have not been calibrated. The spectrum of ζ Aquilae (spectral class B9, $m_v = 3.0$), however, obtained on the same plates and with the same spectrographs, permits a calibration. In spite of the lack of an exact calibration, the fundamental particulars of the spectra and their variations could be explained reliably enough.

The supernova in IC 4182 reached its brightness maximum on August 14th, 1937 ($m_v = 8.5$). The first spectrogram was obtained on August 22nd, 1937, i.e., eight days after the maximum. Altogether a great number of spectrograms were obtained which enabled the evolution of its spectrum to be followed up to 339 days after the maximum. Still more successful proved the observation of the supernovae which appeared in NGC 1003. The first spectrogram of this supernova was obtained on September 12th, 1937, two days before the maximum. Its spectrum was tracked until 115 days after the maximum.

The spectra of both supernovae displayed an astonishing similarity in the fundamental details and in the character of their variations with time. Figures 10a and 10b show some of the spectroscopic records of both supernovae. Figure 10c shows spectra of the supernova which appeared in NGC 4496 in 1960, as obtained by Bloch, Chalonge and Dufay.[26] Unlike Figure 10b, Figure 10a shows the intensity distribution of the various bands (but not the density).

First, we see that the spectra consist of very broad partly over-lapping emission bands. As stressed by Minkowski, it is essential that this character of the spectrum (superposition of broad bands) is also observed in the early pre-maximum stage of evolution of supernovae. Later on Minkowski observed the spectrum of the supernova seven days before its maximum. Here too it displayed the characteristic band structure. No essential changes were observed in the spectrum when the supernova passed through its brightness maximum. The narrow bands, observed during an earlier stage of evolution of the supernovae (50–100 days after the maximum), have a width of about 100 Å. Then about two weeks after the maximum one may, in a purely phenomenological manner, divide the spectra into two parts. While the range of $\lambda > 5,000$ Å undergoes essential changes (the bands appear and vanish almost as in the spectra of ordinary novae), the range of $\lambda < 5,000$ Å maintains its structure quite steadily. In this range, apart from three or four less intense peaks, a broad intense maximum is observed for a long time at about $\lambda \sim 4,600$ Å. This entire system of peaks is displaced as a whole towards the red part of the spectrum. In the course of time the intensity ratios in the "long-wave" and the "short-wave" parts of the spectrum differ widely, which might indicate an independent origin of these emissions. At first the long-wave part of the spectrum ($\lambda > 5,000$ Å) is very intense. About 40 days after the maximum it becomes predominant. After 160 days, however, its intensity becomes minimal, only to rise within a further 20 days to almost its initial value. During the last stages of spectral

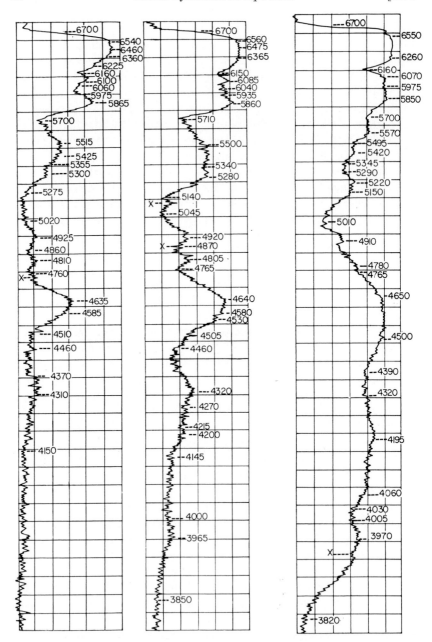

FIG. 10a   Tracings of spectra of the supernova in IC 4182 at various instants of time.[25]

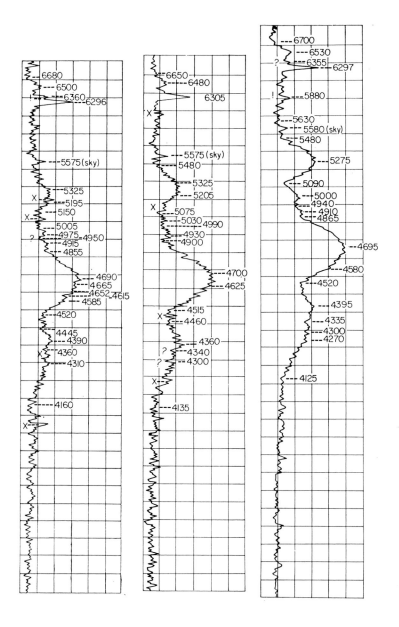

Fig. 10a   Tracings of spectra of the supernova in IC 4182 at various instants of time.[25]

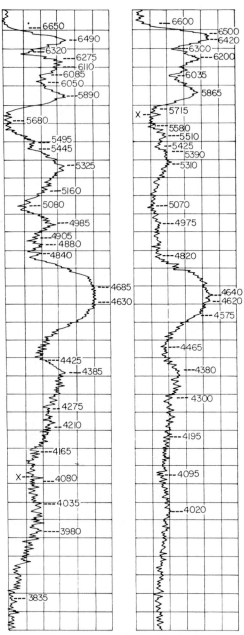

Fig. 10a   Tracings of spectra of the supernova in IC 4182 at various instants of time.[25]

evolution the "red" emission gradually fades.   In the case of the supernova which exploded in IC 4182, this last evolutionary stage is characterized by two narrow bands ($\Delta\lambda \sim 50$ Å) which are observed in the red part

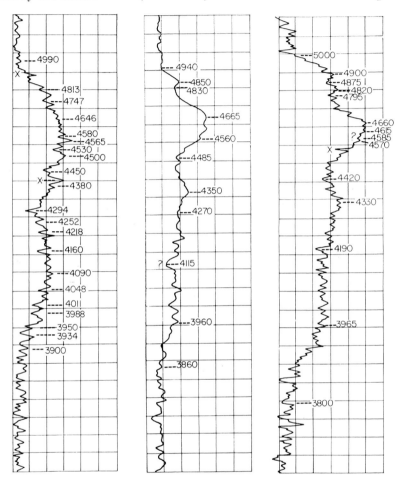

FIG. 10b   Tracings of spectra of the supernova in NGC 1003 at various instants of
time.[25]

of the spectrum, near λ 6300 and λ 6360.   These lines of the supernova
spectrum tend to remain stable.   Minkowski identified these two relatively
narrow emission bands with the well-known forbidden lines of oxygen,
observed in the radiation emitted from the nocturnal sky and in the polar

2 + s.

aurorae. Besides the good coincidence of the wavelengths the intensity ratio also speaks in favour of this identification.

Unfortunately, these two bands are so far the only details which can be identified with a more or less high reliability in the spectra of supernovae of this type (I). The possible interpretation of spectra of supernovae of the type I will later be discussed in greater detail.

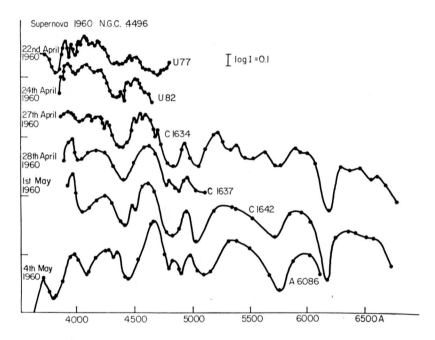

Fig. 10c   Spectra of supernova in NGC 4496 at various instants of time.[26]

In 1940 Minkowski obtained the spectrum of a supernova which flared up in the galaxy NGC 4725. This spectrum was quite dissimilar to the spectra of the supernovae in IC 4182 and NGC 1003, discussed above.[27] Spectra of this kind were later obtained from several supernovae, e.g., the supernova outburst in 1941 in NGC 4559, a fact that enabled Minkowski to class them into a separate group, known as "supernovae of type II," in contrast to the objects whose spectra are similar to the spectra of the supernovae in IC 4182 and NGC 1003, called "supernovae of type I." Moreover, it was established that the light curves of the supernovae of both types were essentially different (see the previous section).

It is a characteristic feature of the spectra of type II supernovae that they are intense continuous spectra with very bright ultraviolet edges before the maximum and during the first days after it. In the maximum stage neither emission nor absorption bands can be observed. The colour temperature of this continuous emission is close to 40,000°K, i.e., it is almost the same as that of the hot stars of class O. A week after the maximum a weak emission band appears around Hα. Thereafter the continuous spectrum gradually fades and the ultraviolet part becomes less intense. At the same time very broad emission bands and absorption bands appear. These may, with sufficient certainty, be identified as the lines of hydrogen, helium and other elements. The extremely large width of the bands corresponds to the scattering of the emitted atoms' velocities, amounting to $7-8 \times 10^8$ cm/s. The spectra of supernovae of the type II are at this stage generally similar to the spectra of ordinary novae in the post-maximum stage of development. There are, however, also important differences. Firstly, the width of the emission bands in spectra of supernovae of the type II is much larger than in the case of ordinary novae. Secondly, there are no bands corresponding to forbidden transitions, whereas in the spectra of ordinary novae such bands are observed soon after the maximum. This difference is freely explained by the density of the emitting substance which is considerably higher in the case of supernovae than with ordinary novae at corresponding instances of time after the maximum. On the other hand, we may draw the conclusion that the mass of ejected matter is much greater with supernovae of the type II than with ordinary novae. A rough estimate of the lower limit of mass of the shell, ejected in the explosion of such a supernova, may be obtained in the following way: let us assume that in the case of ordinary novae the forbidden lines appear 10 days after the outburst, whereas in the spectra of supernovae of type II they are still absent even 100 days after it. Moreover, the radial velocities of the gases in a supernova outburst are three to four times as high as in the case of an ordinary nova. Hence it follows that with supernovae, the shell dimensions at which the mean gas density was the same as with ordinary novae 10 days after the outburst, must be at least thirty to forty times as high. Consequently the volume occupied by the shell of a supernova of type II will now be at least a thousand times as large as with ordinary novae and quite the same will be true for the mass of the shell.

Since in the case of ordinary novae the gas mass ejected in the outburst amounts to 10^{-5} to $10^{-4} M_\odot$, according to estimates given in[28], we may immediately suppose that the lower limit of the gas mass ejected during an explosion is of the order of $1 M_\odot$. Hence follows the conclusion that the mass of supernovae of the type II must be sufficiently large, in any case much greater than the mass of the sun. These stars must therefore be young stars. This provides a natural explanation for the fact that these stars explode exclusively in spiral stellar systems of later types, rich in interstellar gas, where an intense process of stellar formation takes place.

The above estimate for the mass of gas ejected in the outburst of a supernova of type II is of course only a rough one. Modern astrophysics, however, has also other independent methods at its disposal which permit an estimation of the mass of gas ejected in the outburst of a supernova of type II. An application of these methods leads to precisely the same results (see §§ 5 and 6). So we are now already in a position to draw a very important conclusion: an essential difference between supernovae of type II and supernovae of type I is the great difference in their mass. While the supernovae of type II have a mass which is considerably greater than the mass of the sun, the mass of supernovae of type I hardly exceeds the solar mass by 20 per cent. It is well known that stellar evolution is essentially determined by the mass of the stars. Observations also show that the rotation of a star is closely connected with its mass (massive stars, as a rule, rotate very rapidly). The evolutional tracks of supernovae of types I and II in pre-outburst stages must therefore differ essentially. It is, however, likely that the causes of explosion and the nature of its course vary according to the different types of supernovae.

In the past it has been stressed that supernovae of the type II may hardly be considered as a uniform group of objects. At the same time in the group of very similar objects, denoted as supernovae of type I, one may occasionally observe considerable deviations from the average characteristics. This applies to both the light curves and the spectra. Recently Zwicky suggested a new classification of supernovae which he himself considers preliminary.[11] Apart from the two types of supernovae described above, another three types are distinguished:

Supernovae of type III. A representative of this type is the supernova which appeared in 1961, in NGC 4303. In qualitative respects the spectra of supernovae of this type resemble the spectra of supernovae of type II.   There are, however, essential quantitative differences.   First of all, the continuous spectrum with the very bright ultraviolet end can be observed for several weeks after the maximum with type III but only for a few days with type II.   The emission bands of hydrogen have an unusually large width, corresponding to a spread of the velocities of ejected gases, amounting to 12,000 km/s.   According to Greenstein,[12] the density of the gas clouds ejected and their dimensions are so great that even several weeks after the maximum only those spectral bands may be observed that are emitted from the part of the shell facing the observer (that is the part approaching him).   This, in particular, results in a displacement of the bands towards the ultraviolet part of the spectrum by an amount corresponding to the velocity of approach, which is of the order of 6,000 km/s.   After this displacement has come to a standstill, the band width doubles and the band profile corresponds to a velocity distribution ranging from $-12,000$ km/s to $+12,000$ km/s.

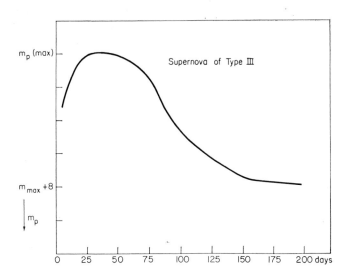

FIG. 11   Schematic light curve of supernova of type III.[11]

According to the results of observations described above, the supernovae of type III differ from supernovae of type II by the much greater ejected mass of gas shell and higher radial velocities of ejection.   Zwicky, without giving details of his calculations, assumes that the mass ejected in such giant explosions is one hundred times greater than the solar mass. Possibly this estimate is too high but in any case the mass of gases ejected in such an explosion of a supernova of type III must exceed those ejected by a supernova of type II by at least an order of magnitude. Figure 11 gives a schematic representation of the light curve of a supernova of type III. Attention should be drawn to the fact that about 150 days after the outburst, when the magnitude has reached a value of 8, the luminosity variation slows down. For comparison, the light curve of a supernova of type II is also shown schematically in Figure 12.

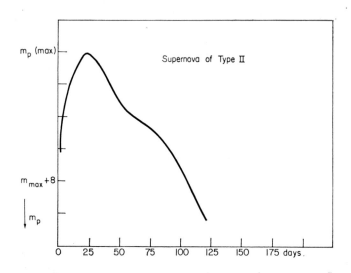

FIG. 12   Schematic light curve of supernova of type II.[11]

Supernovae of type IV. Their spectra are in many respects similar to the spectra of supernovae of type I, but some interesting differences have been observed in the details. For example, the ultraviolet part of the spectrum is very intense near the maximum, which is not usually observed with supernovae of the type I. The emission bands, which display a considerable development some time after the maximum, differ strongly from the corresponding bands in the spectra of supernovae of type I as regards both the wavelength and the intensity variations. Just as in the case of supernovae of type I, not a single band could be identified in the spectrum of supernovae of type IV. It must, however, be

mentioned that at present it is not yet clear whether the supernova which
appeared in NGC 3003 is a representative of some individual class of
objects or simply a peculiar object.

Supernovae of type V are objects similar to the well-known star
η Carinae (Argo Navis) whose outburst was observed in 1843. Recently
Zwicky observed an analogous object in NGC 1058 and investigated its
spectrum.[29] In its fundamental characteristics this spectrum resembles
the spectra of ordinary novae. The radial velocity of the gas clouds
ejected in the explosion reaches 2,000 km/s, almost the same as in the
case of ordinary novae; a fundamental difference, however, consists
in the fact that even 18 months after the outburst no forbidden lines were
observed in the spectrum of this object, which indicates a very great mass
of gases ejected, rather of the order of several solar masses or more.
The light curve of this star, shown in Figure 13, looks quite unusual.

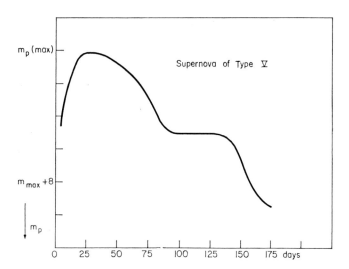

FIG. 13   Schematic light curve of supernova of type V.[11]

The features attracting our attention are the very slow increase in
luminosity and the symmetry of the ascending and descending parts of the
light curve. For the present it is, however, not yet clear whether objects
of the type of η Carinae may be considered as being supernovae. In our
opinion the essential difference being the fact that at the minimum of

brightness η Carinae has a visual magnitude equal to 8, whereas at maximum, during its outburst in 1843, it was of $m_v = -1$, that is only nine magnitudes brighter. Supernovae, however, are characterized by very great differences $m_{min} - m_{max}$. Zwicky considered it one of the characteristic features of supernovae that the condition $m_{min} - m_{max} >$ 17 was satisfied. The supernova of 1054 had an $m_{max} \approx -5$ while now no stars brighter than $m = 15.5$ are found in its place. There is still another essential difference between objects of the type of η Carinae and supernovae. At present it is established that all nebulae formed as the result of outbursts of supernovae are fairly powerful sources of non-thermal radio radiation (cf. Chapters II and III). The nebula around η Carinae, however, is not such a radio source. If we assume that the generation of a considerable quantity of relativistic particles (responsible for non-thermal radio radiation of the "remnants" of supernovae) is an important concomitant of supernova outbursts, objects of the type of η Carinae cannot be such stars. Note by the way that the nebulae formed around ordinary novae are not radio sources either.

Since we do not see any qualitative differences between the characteristics of supernovae of types II and III and since we do not consider we are justified in viewing the peculiar supernova which appeared in NGC 3003 as a representative of a new type of supernovae, we will assume in what follows that we have two fundamental types of supernovae whose characteristic features have already been described in present and former sections. In this connection it must be borne in mind that supernovae of the type II may differ essentially from one another as regards their masses and the velocities of the gas clouds ejected.

As mentioned above, the fundamental emission and absorption bands in the spectra of type II supernovae have been identified in a sufficiently reliable way. The "pre-maximum" and the "maximum" spectra may be interpreted as being caused by an "expansion" of the photosphere of the hot star up to dimensions of 10^{14} to 10^{15} cm, which is ten times as large as the radius of the earth's orbit. The further spectral evolutions are explained in the same way as in the case of ordinary novae, with the only essential difference that the mass of the ejected gas shells is ten thousand times greater in the case of supernovae of type II. Figure 14a shows the spectrum of a supernova of type II, which appeared in NGC 3938, and Figure 14b shows the tracing of this spectrum.[31]

The problem of interpreting the spectra of supernovae of type I is particularly difficult. As repeatedly mentioned, the emission bands observed in this spectrum could not yet be identified in a universally adopted manner. As early as 1938, Wipple and Payne-Gaposhkin achieved a theoretical construction of the so-called "synthetic" spectra,[30] based on the assumption that the gases ejected in a stellar explosion were of a "normal" chemical composition. The ejection occurs at a speed of 6,000 km/s. Owing to the strong Doppler broadening the emission bands are partly overlapped. To simplify the calculations, the line profiles were assumed to be of parabolic form. The construction of these "synthetic" spectra was based on the results of observations of ordinary stellar spectra. Figure 14 shows a spectrum obtained in this way. An attentive consideration of the synthetic spectrum, however, shows that it differs essentially from the spectra of supernovae of the type I, given in Figure 10. Thus, for example, the five characteristic emission bands in the blue part

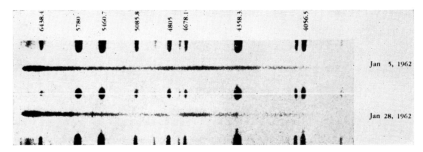

FIG. 14a   Photograph of spectrum of type II supernova in NGC 3938.[31]

of the spectrum are lacking and there is no characteristic depression at λ 6,150, etc. At the same time, as indicated by Minkowski,[19] these synthetic spectra are very similar to the spectra of supernovae of type II. This, however, was to be expected since Wipple and Payne-Gaposhkin, when constructing the synthetic spectra, mainly utilized the spectrograms of ordinary novae whose spectra are qualitatively similar to the spectra of supernovae of type II.

A paper,[32] recently published by McLaughlin, contains, in our opinion, a first serious attempt at interpreting the spectra of supernovae of type I. Attention is focused on spectrograms of the supernova which appeared in 1954, in NGC 4214. Though as to its fundamental characteristics (light curve, general contour and evolution of the spectrum) this supernova pertains without any doubt to type I, it displays a series of very

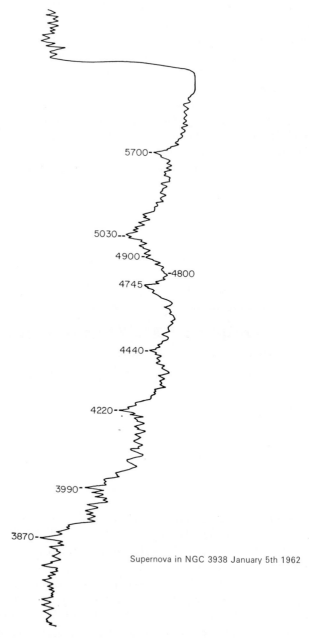

Supernova in NGC 3938 January 5th 1962

FIG. 14b   Tracing of spectrum of supernova in NGC 3938.[31]

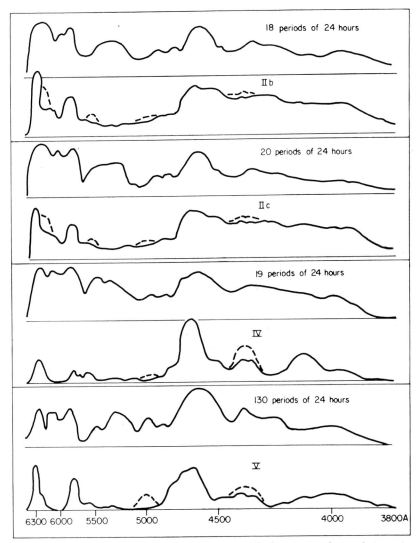

Fɪɢ. 14   Synthetic spectra of supernovae.   Dashed curves: observed intensity distribution.[30]

interesting peculiarities.   Photographs of its spectra, taken at different instants of time, are shown in Figure 15.   The spectrum obtained on June 6th, 1954, is of particular interest.   The emission bands were very faint, though about 50 days had passed since the maximum.   On the other hand, there are some conspicuous details which can hardly be interpreted other than as broad and deep absorption bands. Figure 16 shows "smoothed" spectroscopic records of the supernovae in NGC 4214 (February 24th, 1954) and in NGC 3992; the latter exploded in the spring of 1956 and is a "normal" supernova of type I. Apart from the general similarity of these two spectra, we may recognize marked differences. For instance, the "normal" supernova of type I has in its spectrum two rather narrow peaks at 4,800 and 4,900 Å, while the supernova in NGC 4214 has a peak at λ 4,980, edged towards the short waves by a deep minimum. A further analysis of the spectrum of the supernova of NGC 4214 enabled McLaughlin to draw the conclusion that the "apparent" continuous spectrum was caused by a superposition of a series of broad emission bands of approximately equal intensities. Though the deep and broad minima at λ 3,800 and λ 4,900 may partly be explained as gaps between emission bands, McLaughlin has arguments speaking in favour of the assumption that strong absorption must here play a dominant part, eliminating individual spectral lines. A "key" to the interpretation of the spectrum suggested by him is the clearly developed deep minima in the spectrum at λ 3,960 and λ 4,390, observable in the spectrogram of Figure 15. McLaughlin assumes that these minima are the result of an absorption of the lines of neutral helium (λ 4,026 and λ 4,472) strongly shifted towards the violet side. The amount of the displacements, $\Delta\lambda \sim$ 65–80 Å, corresponds to a speed of the ejected gases approaching the observer of about $-7,500$ km/s. McLaughlin identified a great number of more or less distinct minima in the spectrum of the supernova in NGC 4214 with the displaced lines of chiefly He I and several other elements (e.g., C II, O II, Si III).

It must be stressed that all fundamental absorption bands, observed in hot stars of spectral class B (with the exception of hydrogen stars), could be observed in the spectrum of the supernova in NGC 4214 as minima with a certain intensity distribution. In this case the amount of the violetwards displacement of the lines varied between about 6,100 and 8,000 km/s. The relative intensities of the minima, interpreted as absorption bands, are almost the same as those observed with some hydrogen-deficient stars of the previous subclasses B. The intense minimum, observed in the spectrogram of Figure 15, at λ 5,719, is interpreted as an absorption band caused by the well-known helium line at λ 5,876. According to McLaughlin two absorption components were observed in certain cases. Therefore, in the case of the absorption caused by the helium line at λ 5,876 two components are observed with ray velocities of − 6,100 and 8,000 km/s, respectively.

It is interesting also, that, in the spectrum of a "classic" supernova of type I, obtained 41 days after the maximum, McLaughlin found minima

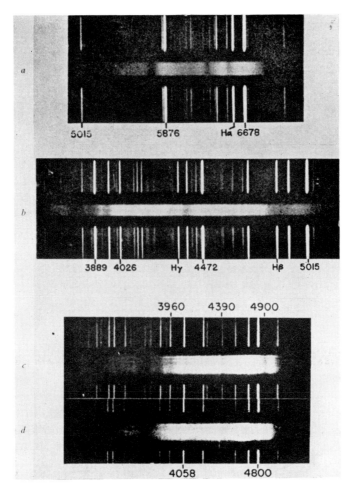

Fig. 15   Photographs of spectra of the supernova in NGC 4214 (*a, b, c*).   (*a*) June 6th, 1954, red-green part of spectrum; (*b*) June 6th, blue-ultraviolet part of spectrum; (*c*) June 24th, blue-ultraviolet part of spectrum; (*d*) May 24th, 1957: Spectrum of the supernova in NGC 4374.[32]

which he explained in the same way. Thus, for example, the very sharp minimum at $\lambda\,5{,}708$ (see Fig. 15) was explained by an absorption at the [He I] line of $\lambda\,5{,}876$. In this case the speed of the absorbing shell must exceed 8,000 km/s.

Besides the minima, McLaughlin explained the broad and flat maxima in the spectra of both the supernova in NGC 4214 and the supernova in IC 4182. The centres of these broad bands ($\Delta\lambda \sim 100\text{--}200$ Å) coincide with the lines of He I (e.g., $\lambda\,5{,}876$) and N II.

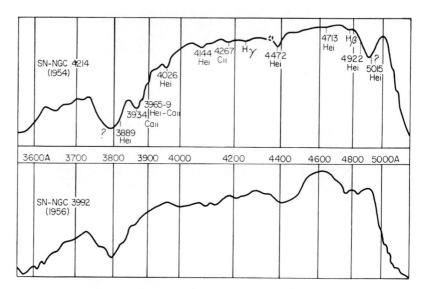

Fig. 16 "Smoothed" tracings of spectra of the supernovae in NGC 4214 and NGC 3992.[32]

McLaughlin assumes that the intense emission bands in the range $5{,}100 > \lambda > 3{,}900$ Å are also caused by a superposition of helium bands. He connects this emission with a group of bright helium lines, beginning with the line at $\lambda\,5{,}116$ and ending with that at $\lambda\,3{,}889$. It is possible that the sudden break of the spectrum at $\lambda\,3{,}900$ is connected with absorption caused by helium atoms moving with a velocity of 6,000 to 7,000 km/s.

The very deep minima at $\lambda\,3{,}800$ and 4,900 are explained by McLaughlin—partly at least—by the presence of "displaced" absorption lines of [He I], at $\lambda\,3{,}889$, $\lambda\,3{,}965$ and $\lambda\,5{,}016$. These lines possess the particularity of metastable lower levels. This may result in a considerable overpopulation of these levels whereby absorption is essentially intensified.

In this way both emission and absorption observed in the spectra of supernovae of type I are explained by McLaughlin chiefly by transitions in He I atoms. If his interpretation is correct we must draw the conclusion that stars exploding as supernovae of the type I must be very poor in hydrogen.

Minkowski discovered a systematic redshift of the emission bands in the spectra of supernovae, in the range of $\lambda < 5{,}000$ Å. In connection with this, McLaughlin pays attention to the systematic decrease with time of the violetward shift of absorption lines, which he had discovered in the spectrum of the supernova in NGC 4214. It is possible that the effect discovered by Minkowski may be explained to some degree by an absorption in lines with variable redshift. It is also possible that the redshift observed with the emission bands is connected with a gradual decrease in opacity of the part of the shell that moves away from us.

The identification of the spectra of type I supernovae, suggested by McLaughlin, is of course still far from presenting a final solution to the problem. Minkowski, in particular, subjected McLaughlin's paper to a critical consideration.[33] He stresses the difficulties connected with the problem of identifying the spectra of supernovae of type I where the individual details are very different and uncertainly determined. An identification based solely on a coincidence of wavelengths is therefore not sufficient to serve as a serious argument in favour of the interpretation proposed. But his more concrete objections (with the exception of one), in our opinion, do not seem to be convincing. For example, Minkowski pays attention to the absence of the helium line $\lambda\,4{,}388$ $(2p^1\text{--}5D^1)$, whereas the line $\lambda\,4{,}144$ $(2p^1\text{--}6D^1)$, according to McLaughlin, explains one of the minima. It must, however, be mentioned that the minimum which, according to McLaughlin, is caused by an absorption at the line $\lambda\,4{,}144$ is very weak. A more serious objection of Minkowski's concerns the interpretation of the deep minimum at $\lambda\,6{,}311$ as the displaced line of N II, $\lambda\,6{,}482$. If this interpretation were right, one could expect to find another minimum of at least the same depth, connected with the line N II, $\lambda\,3{,}995$, resulting from a transition from the same level. There is, however, no such minimum. This objection of Minkowski's disproves the interpretation of the minimum at $\lambda\,6{,}311$ Å (which is a characteristic detail of the spectra of type I supernovae) as an N II line. This minimum might rather be a simple gap between two emission bands.

In spite of the objections discussed above, McLaughlin's paper is the first serious attempt at analyzing spectra of supernovae of type I, because until recently no interpretation had been given. It is obvious that a final solution of the problem may be found in the way indicated in McLaughlin's paper. Investigations of spectra of supernovae which are not "classic" representatives of the type I would be of particular significance. Precisely this method was used by McLaughlin with indubitable success.†

It has already been mentioned that the supernova which appeared in IC 4182, in its last stage of evolution, shows [O I] lines in its spectrum. This problem is of particular interest and we may only wonder why it has not yet been studied quantitatively. Unfortunately, owing to the absence of a calibration it is not possible to obtain an accurate evaluation of the intensities of these lines and their variations with time. Therefore we may obtain only a rough estimate. The tracings of the spectrum given in Figure 10 enable us to draw the following two conclusions. (i) The intensities of the lines of [O I], λ 6,300–6,363, 339 days after the maximum, reached several per cent of the total intensity of the whole spectrum. (ii) Beginning with the 184th day after the maximum, when the [O I] lines were observed for the first time, their relative intensity (compared to the other emission bands) has increased continuously. If we take into account the general decline of the supernova during this period, we may conclude that the intensity of the [O I] lines remained constant for a comparatively long period of about 150 days. The latter fact may be interpreted in the following way. Because of the relatively high electron concentration in the expanding shell, collisions of the second kind, de-activating the excited level $^1D_2$, remain effective throughout this period. This indicates that the population of the level $^1D_2$ is determined by Boltzmann's formula

$$n\left(^1D_2\right) = n(^3P) \frac{g_2}{g_1} e^{-\chi/\kappa T_e}, \tag{2.1}$$

where the ratio of the statistical weights is $g_2/g_1 = 5/9$. Under these conditions the emission at the lines of [O I] will be determined by the number of oxygen atoms in the shell and the electron temperature T_e, and will not depend on the density which drops as r^{-3}. Since the excitation potential of the [O I] lines is not high (1.96 eV), the T_e-

† See footnote on page 133. [Morrison]

dependence will be weak and in first approximation the luminous power of the shell at the [O I] lines will be constant in spite of its considerable expansion.

Note that 339 days after the maximum the emission in the [O I] lines amounts to two per cent of the entire emission. Since at maximum this supernova had an absolute magnitude of -19 (cf. Table 1) and after 339 days it had faded to a magnitude of 7.5, our coarse estimation of the luminous power in the [O I] lines yields

$$L_{[O\ I]} = 2 \cdot 10^{43} \cdot 10^{-3} \cdot 2 \cdot 10^{-2} = 4 \cdot 10^{38} \text{ erg/s}.$$

On the other hand

$$L_{[O\ I]} = n\,^1 D_2 A_{D \to P} \cdot h\nu \qquad (2.2)$$

where the probability of a spontaneous transition is $A_{D \to P} = 10^{-2} \text{ s}^{-1}$. Hence we obtain a value of the order of 10^{52} for the number of excited oxygen atoms in the shell while the total number of atoms (at $T_e \sim 10^4$) will be $\sim 3 \cdot 10^{52}$. The mass of oxygen in the shell will amount to $\sim 10^{30}$ g, i.e., $5 \cdot 10^{-4} M_\odot$, a rather insignificant value. If the shell displays a normal chemical composition, its mass will be of the order of $0.1 M_\odot$. Note that the mass of the gas fringes of the Crab nebula is of the same order of magnitude (cf. § 14). Our estimate of the mass is of preliminary character. It might be important to improve it on the basis of good spectrophotometrical material.

In § 18 we shall return to the discussion of the interpretation of spectra of type I supernovae.

§ 3   Galactic supernovae

Outbursts of supernovae in our own stellar system, the galaxy, are of particular interest for astrophysics (and not only astrophysics). From investigations of the frequency of supernova outbursts in other galaxies we may draw the conclusion that in every stellar system of the type of our galaxy one outburst occurs in several hundred years. Consequently we may say that this is a rather rare event. It is quite natural to assume that such outbursts must also take place in our own stellar system. In this case the visual brightness of the exploding star must be very great. For example, if somewhere in the galaxy, at a distance of 5,000 psc from the sun, a supernova of type I explodes with an absolute magnitude of $M_v = -18.5$, its visual magnitude m_v must amount to -5, i.e., it will be

brighter than Venus and may be seen perfectly by daylight.   If we take
interstellar absorption into account, its magnitude is reduced by 1 to 1.5
but it is still a bright object.

As such an outburst is a very rare event, it is not surprising that none
was observed for the last three and a half centuries of the "telescopic"
era of astronomy.   But for many centuries and even millennia men have
admired the starry sky and studied it.   And it is quite natural that in
remote times such unusual events as the appearance of a new and very
bright star in the sky and its gradual fading could not remain unnoticed.
Since in many early civilizations the positions of the planets with respect
to the constellations were connected with the fate of man and nations, a
systematic "celestial service" was an affair of state and sufficiently well
developed.

In Chinese chronicles ("Cheng-Wang") each dynasty had an astronomical department where all unusual celestial phenomena were briefly
described for the reign of this dynasty.   The authenticity of these reports
is indisputable.   It may be sufficient to indicate that, *without a single
exception,* all appearances of Halley's comet within the last two thousand
years are reported in the Chinese chronicles.   In ancient Chinese astronomy distinction was made between "unusual" stars or "guest-stars"
(novae) and comets.   But when studying the old Chinese chronicles there
is a certain danger of confusing novae with comets.   In this case it
may be valuable to study the circumstances of observation from which
important information can be gained (immobility in the sky with respect
to other stars, proximity to the galactic equator).

Biot, who in 1846 translated part of the 294th book of the encyclopedia
Ma T'uang-ling (*Wen-Syan-Tung-Kuo*) written in the thirteenth century,[34] was a pioneer in the study of this material which is extraordinarily valuable for astronomy.   In this big treatise the old Chinese
observations of comets and unusual stars were compiled for the period
from the second century B.C. up to A.D. 1203.   Humboldt, in Volume III
of his *Cosmos* (1850), was the first to publish a catalogue of novae observed
within the last 2,000 years.[35]   He used Biot's investigations as well as
various Arabic and European sources.

Williams, studying authentic Chinese sources, published a catalogue
of ancient Chinese observations of comets, among which we also find
observations of novae.[36]   Williams' book contains very valuable chrono-
logical tables and detailed celestial maps with contours of the constellations, traditional for ancient Chinese astronomy, which, however,

do not in the least resemble the present ones.   In 1919 Zinner compiled a
more complete catalogue of the novae mentioned in various chronicles.[37]
In 1921, Lundmark, who was a pioneer in supernova research and the first
to separate them from the ordinary novae, compiled a comprehensive and
interesting catalogue for which he used mainly Chinese sources.[38]

The greatest triumph of this historic astronomical research was the
identification of the famous Crab nebula as the remnant of the supernova
which appeared in 1054.   Later on we shall discuss it in detail.   After
this identification further investigations were carried out.   Baade and
Minkowski succeeded in observing very faint peculiar nebulae at the places
where supernovae had appeared in 1572 and 1604.   This research was
given new impetus after 1949 when radio sources were discovered at the
sites of previously exploded supernovae.   It is quite natural that attempts
were made to identify some of these radio sources with formerly exploded
supernovae registers in old chronicles.   In particular, the author of the
present book[39,40] was also engaged in these researches.   In 1954 we
addressed to the Chinese Academy of Sciences a request to organize a
study of old chronicles with the aim of obtaining additional information on
previously exploded novae.   Our Chinese colleagues reacted promptly
to this request and this resulted in interesting investigations.   In the old
chronicles indications as to outbursts of more than thirty-five novae were
discovered, some of which were unknown in the West.   Great work was
done in order to permit accurate dating and to determine the approximate
positions of these novae.

Recently Goldstein in the U.S.A. conducted a great project on old
Chinese, Japanese, Arabic and European chronicles, as a result of which
he succeeded in a verification of the supernova of 1006 and an approximate
determination of its co-ordinates.[42,43]

In this way the supernova research proved to be surprisingly entwined
with philology and orientalism. . . .   In what follows we will discuss in
detail all known data on outbursts of supernovae in our own galaxy.   We
will cite a series of passages from the old chronicles in order to impart the
peculiar atmosphere of these fascinating studies to the reader.

1. *The supernova which flared up on December 7th, 185*, seems to be
an authentic object.   Biot and Williams translated the Chinese chronicles
in which this unusual phenomenon has been described: " In the Chung-
P'ing period, in the second year, in the tenth moon, on K'uei Hae's day,

an unusual star appeared in the middle of Nang-Mang [α and β Centauri and neighbouring stars (author's note)]. It was of the size of a bamboo mat and showed subsequently five colours. Its luminosity decreased gradually towards the sixth moon of the following year [that is until July 186 (author's note)] when it disappeared." This unusually bright star (Lundmark estimated its magnitude as amounting to -6) was seen very low above the horizon (since its declination was $-60°$). The optical phenomena in the atmosphere, connected with this event, may explain some details of the description of this stellar explosion (the comparison with a bamboo mat, the indication as to the change of colours). Many centuries thereafter, such a highly qualified observer as Tycho Brahe described the colour effects during the outburst of the supernova of 1572. According to Lundmark, the supernova of 185 had the following approximate co-ordinates: $\alpha = 14^\mathrm{h}2$, $\delta = -60°$. This event was also found by Hsi Tse-Ts'ung to be mentioned in the chronicle of *Early Han*, a source which is older than *Wen-Hsien-T'ung-K'uo*, used by Biot and Williams, whose translations were used by Lundmark. Let us quote a passage of this chronicle: "Kueihai, October of the second year of Chung-P'ing (Early Han Dynasty), a guest-star appeared in Nang Mang, of the size of half a mat. It was of five colours. Then it faded gradually and vanished in the following year" (translated into Russian by Hsi Tse-Ts'ung). It is quite possible that Ma T'uang-ling used this passage when compiling his encyclopedia. It is an essential fact that the nova of 185 had a galactic latitude close to zero. As in this case the luminosity of the star was very high, probably it was a supernova and not a nearby nova. Otherwise its galactic latitude would have been arbitrarily high, since in the case of novae with such light curves the absolute magnitude amounts to $M_v \sim -7.5$ to 8, and with $m_v \sim -6$ the distance to an ordinary nova would have been only 30 psc.

2. *The supernova of 369.* In Lundmark's catalogue this star has the high "reliability mark" 3. In the 294th book of Ma T'uang-ling's encyclopedia the following is said about this star (translation by Biot): "In the period of T'ai-Ho, in the fourth year, in the second moon [that is in March A.D. 369 (author's note)] an unusual star was observed near the western wall of the Blue Palace (Tse-K'ung)." According to the ancient Chinese astronomical terminology, the "Blue Palace" means the inclined circle enclosing the non-setting stars.

Let us also cite the chronicle *Shih-K'o* (translated by Williams[36]): "During the reign of T'ieh-ying, in the fourth year of the epoch of T'ai Ho, in the second moon, an unusual star was to be seen in Tse-K'ung, near its western border. In the seventh moon [that is in August 369 (author's note)] it faded."

Undoubtedly, both chronicles speak of one and the same star. We may obtain more accurate indications as to the position of this star's outburst if we take into account that it was observed near Peking, whose latitude is 34°. Hence it follows that the star's declination must have been about $+56°$. Furthermore, the star was observed in March when the solar declination was close to zero. It is quite natural to assume that it was observed in the evening, in any case before midnight. Hence we may deduce that its right ascension must have been close to 23^h. Lundmark, in a rather arbitrary estimate, assumed its magnitude to be -3. So we may draw the conclusion that this supernova appeared in the constellation of Cassiopeia.

3. *The supernova of 1006.* The data available to us on the unusual brightness of the stars observed in China in 185 and 369 are, in fact, extremely sparse and we cannot yet say with absolute certainty that these stars were real objects (though it is a very probable assumption); however, as regards the extraordinarily bright star that flared up in the southern sky in the *spring of 1006*, we have at present sufficient information at our disposal. As long ago as 1956, on the basis of all the data then at our disposal, we arrived at the conclusion that this was a supernova.[44]

Indications as to the appearance of this star, which was very bright at that time, may be found in the chronicle by Ibn al Atir (thirteenth century), Bargebraus (same century but later) and in the European chronicle of the monk Epidanus, who died in 1068. Some of these sources were already known to Humboldt who included the star of 1006 in his list of novae.[35] In 1891, Schönfeld, who collected all the data contained in the sources mentioned above, came to the conclusion that this must have been a nova. Of course, Lundmark entered it on his list.[38]

The story of the search by the various authors for proof of the outburst of a very bright star in 1006 which, by now, is beyond any doubt, reminds us of a detective story. We shall now enter into details.

In Ibn al Atir's chronicle it is said that "... in this year [Anno Hegirae 396 (author's note)] at new moon, in the month of Shaban a big star appeared, similar to Venus, at the left side of the Iraq Kibla [Kibla is the direction from the point of observation towards Mecca]. On the earth its rays were similar to those of the moon and it remained in the sky until the middle of the month of Dsul-kada, then it died away." Ibn al Atir's knowledge obviously stemmed from an older source, the manuscript *Kitab al Muntasam* by Ibn al Yavsa, who died about A.D. 1200. We read in this manuscript that "...at the left of Kibla a big star appeared which, in size and brightness, resembled Venus. Its radiation in the sky was like that of the moon. It flared up on a Friday night, at new moon in the month of Shaban, and remained there without moving until the middle of Dsulkad, when it disappeared" (translation by Goldstein[42]).

It is possible that the comparison of this star's light with that of the moon indicates that terrestrial objects, illuminated by this star, cast shadows. The dates mentioned in the chronicles may be recalculated from the Arabic calendar to the European one. The star was observed for the first time on May 3rd, 1006, and died away on August 13th of the same year.

Recently Goldstein published new and important data on this star which he had found in old chronicles.[42] The most interesting information is contained in the comments of the Egyptian astrologer Ali ben Ridwan on the translation of the astronomical treatise of Ptolemy, *Tetrabiblos*. Let us cite this interesting text: "I will give you a description of an appearance I observed at the beginning of my school days. This phenomenon appeared in the zodiacal sign of Scorpius, in opposition to the Sun. At this time the Sun was 15° away from Taurus, and the described phenomenon was 15° away from Scorpius. It was very bright, of round form and its size was 2.5 to 3 times larger than that of Venus. Its light illuminated the horizon and was strongly flickering. Its magnitude in brightness was somewhat greater than one-fourth of that of the Moon. It rotated together with the vault of heaven until the Sun entered the sign of Virgo. This star was also observed by other scientists right after I had discovered it...." Later on Ali ben Ridwan gives the longitudes of planets, the sun and moon at the moment when this astonishing star was discovered and, based on his astrological researches, he prophesied very unpleasant events for his contemporaries.

The significance of this report which contains valuable astronomical information consists, first of all, in the fact that it was written by a witness who observed this surprising phenomenon. First of all, the longitudes of planets, sun and moon, given by Ali ben Ridwan, permitted a reliable determination of the moment of outburst of this star. It was found that this constellation of celestial bodies could have been observed only on April 30th, 1006. It has been established that the author of the comments to *Tetrabiblos* died in 1061 so that the events described by him must in fact have occurred at the time of his youth. As to its longitude the surprising star coincides with the planetary nebula in NGC 5882. From the brilliant descriptions of its brightness and size one may draw the conclusion that the visual magnitude of this star must have been at least -8, possibly even -10. Another important fact follows from Ali ben Ridwan's text, namely that the mysterious object did not move relative to the other stars while the sun moved from Taurus to Virgo, which excludes that the object observed was a bright comet.

It is interesting that this star has also been mentioned in European chronicles. The Swiss monk Epidanus, in a chronicle in which various events up to 1044 are listed, describes a new unusually bright star, which appeared in 1006.[42] According to these annals the star was to be seen for a period of three months in the southern part of the sky. It altered its magnitude, the brightness fluctuated and sometimes it disappeared entirely (?). If the observations were made in Switzerland (latitude $47°5'$) the star must have been visible above the southern point of the horizon.

Note that Humboldt already included in his list the unusually bright star which, supposedly, was observed during the reign of Caliph Al Momun, in 872, in the constellation of Scorpius, by the astronomers Hali and Jafar ben Muhammed Albumasar.[35] Goldstein, however, showed convincingly that the astronomer Hali, mentioned by Humboldt, must have been identical with Ali ben Ridwan and that this bright star had been observed in 1006, not in 827.

I suppose that the most valuable information about this star could be obtained from Chinese, Japanese and even Korean chronicles. The contents of a lecture given by the head of the Astronomical Department of the Emperor's Court (there was in fact such an institution in old China!) on May 30th, 1006, contained in Ch'ing Li K'uo's book presented to the Emperor in 1044, seems to be of particular interest. We may read: "...At the first day of the fifth month in the third year of the period of Chin-T'ieh [that is on May 30th, 1006], the head of the Astronomical Department related how, at the first hour of the night, the second day of the fourth month [May 1st, 1006], east of K'yu-Lu, in the western part of Ch'yu K'uong, there appeared a bright star of yellow colour. Its brightness

grew steadily. It stood in the third degree from T'i.... The star
then intensified its luminosity." Thereafter the head of the Astronomical
Department, referring to the yellow colour of the star, predicted very
favourable events for his sovereign in the near future, obviously differing
in his opinion from his distant colleague in Cairo, Ali ben Ridwan.

The report cited above contains very valuable information as it
allowed the co-ordination of the "guest-star" to be essentially improved:
it was in the constellation of Lupus, its equatorial co-ordinates (within an
accuracy of 3°) were: $\alpha = 15^h13^m$, $\delta = -45°28'$ (1950), a position rather
close to that of NGC 5882. These co-ordinates agree well with the Arabic
observations described above. It is interesting that in 1006, because of
the precession, the right ascension was almost 40^m less.

Obviously, we must not believe the suggestion that the star was of
"yellow colour" since this "colourimetry" had been governed by
"astrological principles" (a yellow colour could serve as a basis of optimistic
predictions).

It follows from Chinese chronicles that the "guest-star" which flared
up in 1006 must have been observed for at least a period of ten years, which,
in fact, is very interesting. Information on this may be found, for
example, in the official history of the Sung Dynasty, *Sung-Shih*. Let us
cite, for example, the following passage: "...At K'eng-Chieh's day, in the
fourth moon, in the ninth year of the period of Ta Ch'ung Ts'ya-Fu
[May 15th, 1006] an unusual star was seen." The implication of the
context is that the writer meant the "guest-star" which appeared in 1006.
There are also other Chinese sources from which we may conclude that this
star must have been observed for several years after it had made its
appearance in the East, at dawn in November–December and setting
below the horizon in the southwest in August–September. This is also
in agreement with the star's position in the constellation of Lupus.

Finally, there are independent Japanese chronicles containing important information on the brightness and colour of this star. In 1230, the
Samurai scientist Sadaye Fujiwara observed the outburst of a new star.
By the way, at present this star attracts our attention in connection with
a problem of radio-astronomy (see § 15). The observation of the "guest-
star" of 1230 induced Fujiwara to compile a list of previously appeared
novae, as far as these events were still alive in the people's minds. The list
is contained in the chronicle *Mei-Getzuki*. According to Fujiwara's list,
such "guest-stars" appeared in August 642, in February 877, May 891,
June 930, May 1006, in the summer of 1054, in May 1166, and in June

1181.   The event we are interested in is described in the following words:
"...On the second day of the fourth moon, in the third year of Kanko's period, on the day of Nesunoto Tori [May 1st, 1006] a big 'guest-star' appeared, similar to Mars, bright and scintillating.   It appeared at the end of the preceding night, in an exactly southern direction."

Another, older, Japanese chronicle of 1011, *Ishidao Yoki*, contains a list of the most important events in the reign of the Emperor, where we find the following passage: "...On the twenty-eighth day of the third month, on Tsusinoe-Nesumi's day (April 28th, 1006), a 'guest-star' appeared in the constellation of Kikan.   Its light was white–blue.   The official of the Astronomical Department, Abe Yoshimaze, reported on it." This report contains an important indication as to the star's colour, thus revising an error in Chinese chronicles.   Finally, we know several chronicles that contain suggestions that even at the end of September 1006 this "guest-star" was still sufficiently bright and that its observations were systematically reported to the Emperor.

It is thus beyond any doubt that at the end of April 1006 an unusually bright star flared up in the constellation of Lupus.   The main problem is now whether this star was a supernova or, possibly, just a very bright nova.   The latter possibility is not very probable.   In fact, in the first half of the twentieth century three nova were observed that were brighter than magnitude 0 (Nova Persei, 1901, Nova Aquilae, 1918 and Nova Puppis, 1942).   We shall therefore assume that such novae appear about once every 20 years.   A simple calculation shows that novae brighter than −3 must appear, on the average, about once every 1,000 years, and novae brighter than −6 once every 50,000 years.   On the other hand, the probability of an outburst of a nearby supernova is not high either (see § 17).   In § 15 we shall return to discuss the nature of the "guest-star" of 1006.

4. *The supernova of 1054.*   In history this star played a leading part. The remnant of this cosmic catastrophe, the Crab nebula, is an object to which almost one-third of the present book will be devoted.   In Lundmark's catalogue of historical novae, mentioned above, we find under number 36 the "guest-star" that flared up on the horizon on July 4th, 1054, and was registered by Chinese observers.   This object was mentioned for the first time by Biot.   As already mentioned, Biot's main source was the encyclopedia of Ma T'uang-ling.   In brief notes to his catalogue, Lundmark indicates that the "guest-star" of 1054 was "situated near

NGC 1952," that is the Crab nebula. Owing to a peculiar coincidence of circumstances, in the very same year when this paper of Lundmark was published, two very important investigations of the Crab nebula were carried out. Lampland discovered the variability of this nebula[46] and Duncan found that individual parts of it moved in radial directions.[47] From Duncan's observations it immediately follows that this "flying apart" must have begun about 900 years ago (for details see § 10).

One would think that these simultaneous investigations must have led immediately to the recognition of the genetic connection between the "guest-star" of 1054 and the present Crab nebula. Nevertheless, neither Lundmark nor Duncan arrived at this conclusion! Only in 1928, the outstanding American astronomer Hubble expressed clearly that from the present angular dimensions of the Crab nebula and the measured velocity of its expansion it follows that this nebula must have originated about 900 years ago. At the same time, referring to Lundmark, Hubble points out that near the Crab nebula a bright exploding star was observed by Chinese astronomers about 900 years ago, and this explosion must be viewed as the source of the Crab nebula. Unfortunately, Hubble's article was published in a journal which did not attract the serious attention of specialists.[48]

In 1938 Hubble's conclusion was reiterated by Lundmark, who in this connection stressed that the "guest-star" ought probably to be viewed as a supernova.[49] Apart from the old Chinese sources he also made use of independent new Japanese sources contained in Yba's investigations, published in 1934.[50] New and extraordinarily important information contained in the Japanese chronicles was the statement that the "guest-star" of 1054 was as bright as Jupiter. Since in 1938 the distance to the Crab nebula was already known (cf. § 10), Lundmark drew the conclusion that the absolute magnitude of the nova of 1054 (without taking interstellar absorption into account) was -13. On the basis of this result he assumed that the "guest-star" of 1054 was not an ordinary nova, but a supernova.

In fact, Lundmark's paper showed with a high degree of probability that a supernova was observed in 1054 in our own galaxy, which exploded at a distance of somewhat more than 1,000 psc from the sun. If some additional proofs had been necessary to finally confirm this highly probable hypothesis, they were found a few years later. In 1941 Oort, who thought it necessary to study further the old Chinese sources, in order to find a final proof of the reliability of observations of an unusually bright "guest-star" in 1054, interested the outstanding orientalist Duyvendak, a professor in Leyden, in this problem. Duyvendak studied reports on this celestial phenomenon, unknown until then, and published his comments on them in the American astronomical journal *Pacific*.[51] At this time such a publication involved great difficulties, as the Netherlands were occupied by Hitler's troops. Duyvendak's paper removed the last doubts (if there had been any) as to the supernova of 1054, and confirmed that it had been a real object, to be viewed as the origin of the Crab nebula. We shall give here a translation of some of the old Chinese texts published by Duyvendak.

The original text, used by Ma T'uang-ling and later on translated by Biot,[34] is contained in the chronicle *Sung-Shih* (*History of the Sung Dynasty*): "In the first year of the Shih-huo period [1054], in the fifth moon, on the day of Ch'ih-Ch'iu [July 4th] a guest-star appeared about several inches south-east of T'ieng-K'uang [Taurus]. Over a year later it gradually became invisible." Moreover, there is still another passage in the annals of *Sung-Shih*: "On the day of Sing-wei, in the third moon of the first year of Ch'yang-Yu's period [April 17th, 1056], the head of the Astronomical Department reported that a guest-star appeared one morning in the eastern sky, in the fifth moon of the first year of the Shih-huo, and remained all the time in T'ieng-K'uang, but had now ceased to be visible." This very interesting report demonstrates how carefully the old Chinese astronomers made their observations. For almost two years, as long as it was possible, they observed the unusual star. They, however, answered for their service with their lives! It was valuable that the star remained all the time near the constellation of T'ieng-K'uang. Thus we may conclude that it cannot have been a comet. We may now determine the time of its decline down to the magnitude of 6 when it ceased to be visible. This took 21 months.

Moreover, in the chronicle of Sung Hai-Yao we find the following indication in the notice that the star ceased to be visible: "...Initially this star remained visible in the fifth moon of the first year of the Shih-huo period [June 9th to July 8th, 1054] in the eastern sky, in the constellation of T'ieng-K'uang. It was seen in the daytime like Venus, with an omnilateral shine. Its colour was red–white. It was visible during the day for altogether 23 days."

In this chronicle of Sung Hai-Yao we may also find the following colourful description of the epoch in which this astonishing event occurred: "On the twenty-second day of the seventh moon in the first year of the Shih-hou period [August 27th, 1954], Yang Wei-T'e told the following: 'I make my kowtow. I observed the phenomenon of a guest-star. Its colour was slightly iridescent. Following an order of the Emperor, I respectfully made the prediction that the guest-star does not disturb Aldebaran; this indicates that . . . the country will attain great power. I beg to store this prediction in the Department of Histography.' " At this time Yang Wei-T'e was the head of the Department of Astronomy.

Not only in China but also in the capital of medieval Japan, Kyoto, was this unusual star observed. It was mentioned in the Japanese chronicles *Mei-Getsuki* and *Ishi-dao-Yoki*. Let us cite a passage from *Mei-Getsuki*: "In the middle of the ten-day period of the fourth moon of the second year in the Ten-ki period, between May 20th and 30th of 1054, and in the following days, a guest-star was observed in the orbit of Orion. It was seen on the eastern horizon. Its radiation resembled a comet with short rays in T'ieng-K'uang and it was about the size of Jupiter." Oort showed Duyvendak that the star could not have been observed between May 20th and 30th, 1054, since it was too close to the sun (at present, owing to the precession, the sun is near the Crab nebula, at whose position the guest-star of 1054 flared up in the middle of June). The date of the Japanese observations must therefore fall in the period of June 19th to 29th, 1054, i.e., 16 to 6 days before the first Chinese observations. Hence we may conclude that in Japan this star was observed before its brightness maximum.

It is astonishing that neither an Arabic nor a European chronicle contains any information about the appearance of this unusual star. As we have seen above, however, Arabic chronicles mentioned the appearance of the nova of 1006. This star was also observed in Europe in spite of the fact that it flared up in the far south; which seems to indicate that the nova of 1006 must have been much brighter than the nova of 1054. It is rather strange that nothing has been found on observations of this star in the *Kiev Rus*. In 1054 Yaroslav Mudryy died and internecine dissensions began. One would think that the appeance of such a bright star, visible by day, must have attracted attention and have been interpreted as a "token": Russian chronicles contain only a series of data of astronomical character (sunspots, eclipses). It is therefore reasonable to assume that documents on an unusual star were destroyed when the Mongols conquered Kiev.

While the European and Arabic chronicles do not tell us anything about this event, it is an astonishing fact that in Northern Arizona two stone pictures were discovered in 1955 (Fig. 17). One of these pictures is in a cave, the other on the wall of a canyon. Each of these consists of two elements, a circle and a rising half-moon. These representations had been carved in stone by Red Indians, almost five centuries before Columbus discovered America. This symbol is extremely rare among American Indians and these figures are very likely to represent a celestial phenomenon, the new moon and with it the unusual brightness of a star. An analysis shows that this event can only have been the outburst of the supernova of 1054.[52] Calculations show that on the morning of July 5th, before daybreak, the moon was 2° to the north of the present Crab nebula, at whose position the unusually bright star had flared up.

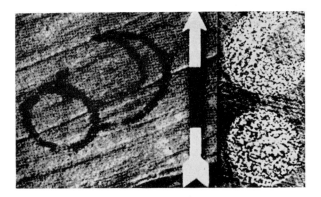

FIG. 17   Rock drawings in Arizona.

Archaeological data speak favourably of the fact that in the period between 900 and 1100 the place where these astonishing representations were found was inhabited by Indians of the Navaho tribe. Finally, the age of the representations, estimated with the help of usual archaeological methods, was found to be ~ 900 years. All these facts may be viewed as supporting the hypothesis that the American Indians engraved pictures of the supernova outburst of 1054.

Let us now analyze the information on the "guest-star" of 1054, contained in the Chinese and Japanese chronicles, from which passages have been cited.

Simultaneously with the paper of Duyvendak, discussed above, Oort sent a paper from Holland, occupied by the Fascists, via the neutral country of Sweden, to the U.S.A.; this paper contained astronomical comments and publications of old astronomical chronicles. Together with the co-author Mayall to whom it had been addressed[53] he published this paper in the same edition of *Pacific*.[54] Let us consider the contents of these comments. In the old astronomical chronicles it is stressed that a "guest-star" similar to Venus was seen. But according to Oort and Mayall, one must not conclude from this remark that a supernova outburst was observed. In fact, for a distance to the Crab nebula of ∼1200 psc (this estimate is independent of interstellar absorption of light, see § 10), the distance modulus will amount to 10.5 and with $m_v \approx -4$ the absolute magnitude is obtained as $M_v \approx -14.5$. As indicated by Oort and Mayall, however, we must not forget that the old estimates of stellar luminosity might be wrong. On the other hand, a correction for interstellar absorption results in higher luminosity of the star and thus supports the hypothesis that this object was a supernova. It seems to us that on this point Mayall and Oort displayed extreme caution. In particular, they ignored an important independent argument: the very low galactic latitude of the "guest-star" of 1054 which, together with its high luminosity, virtually excludes the possibility of interpreting it as an ordinary nova.

A more reliable estimate of the visual magnitude at maximum of the star of 1054 may be obtained from that part of the chronicle where we read that the star could be seen in the daytime for 23 days. We may write the simple relation

$$m_{\max} = \Delta m + m_i$$

where Δm denotes the difference in stellar magnitude between luminosity maximum and the end of visibility by day and m_i is the limiting stellar magnitude of an object which can just be observed with the naked eye in daylight. The quantity Δm may be obtained by analyzing the light curves of supernovae (see § 1). From the light curves of the supernovae in NGC 1003, NGC 46 and IC 4182 we may draw the conclusion that within 23 days after the maximum the luminosity of the supernova had dropped by 1.5. Note that Oort and Mayall happened to compare the light curve of the star of 1054 with those of the supernovae of type I mentioned above to which to all appearances the "guest-star" belongs. At this time the division of the supernovae into two types (cf. § 2) had not yet been generally accepted.

In order to determine m_i more accurately the authors make use of the assertions of experienced observers watching Venus in the daylight. One found that, provided the angular distance from the sun was not too small, it was possible to see an object of the magnitude -3.5. At the moment when the star ceased to be observable, its distance to the sun amounted to about $50°$, i.e., it was sufficiently far away. Hence we may draw the conclusion that the visual magnitude at maximum, at which the "guest-star" of 1054 was seen, amounted to -5. This estimate may be verified by means of other independent Chinese observations. According to the chronicles, it was 650 days after the maximum when the star could no longer be observed during the night. On the other hand, from an analysis of the very similar light curves of supernovae of the type I, it follows that within 650 days after the maximum the luminosity of such a star decreases by 11^m (cf. Fig. 4). If we take into account that the star of 1054 ceased to be visible when its visual magnitude dropped below 6, we find that at maximum its luminosity must have been close to -5.

Very interesting data may also be obtained from an analysis of Japanese chronicles in which the luminosity of the "guest-star" of 1054 was compared with that of Jupiter. It seems that, according to Duyvendak's interpretation of the chronicles' texts, the Japanese observations began 6 to 16 days earlier than those in China. In the epoch in which the "guest-star" made its appearance, Jupiter was almost in conjunction with the sun and therefore clearly observable. One must take into consideration that the unusual star was at a distance of 2^h5^m away from the sun and was observed in the morning. Near the conjunction the visual magnitude of Jupiter is equal to -1.3. We may see from the light curve that this may be the magnitude of a supernova, about one week before its maximum; this is in full agreement with the text of the Japanese chronicles.

The analysis of the Chinese and Japanese chronicles yields a convincing proof of the outburst of a supernova in our galaxy in 1054 and permits us as well to say that it must be classed among the type I.

Among the great number of bright stars which suddenly flared up in the sky and which are mentioned in Chinese and Japanese chronicles, the "guest-star" of 1230 is worthy of interest. In the chronicles of the Sung Dynasty we find the following passage: "In Ding-yu [November] of the third year of Shao-ding a comet was seen below the star of T'us in the constellation of T'ien-shih. In Jen-wu [February] of the following year it faded away." In Japanese historical chronicles one may find many passages which indicate that this object must have been a "guest-star" and not a comet. It could be observed from October 1230 until the end of March 1231. The approximate co-ordinates of the outburst are: $\alpha = 16^{\mathrm{h}}20^{\mathrm{m}}$, $\delta = 20°$.

We will now devote ourselves to the epoch in which European astronomy received its impetus. A great number of data on observations of two very bright stars, which appeared in 1572 and 1604, have reached us. The first was studied thoroughly by Tycho Brahe. It attracted the attention of a great many thinkers and philosophers of this time since visually it violated the scholastic conceptions on the "eternity and invariability" of the celestial bodies.

Tycho published his observations in the treatise *De Stella Nova* (1573) and, in more detailed form, including discussions of all observations carried out by other astronomers, in the treatise *Progymnasmata* (1602). Baade analyzed these observations on the basis of modern astronomical concepts in 1943.[55]

The new star, which exploded in the constellation of Cassiopeia, was observed for the first time on the morning of November 6th, 1572 (Julian calendar), by the astronomers Schuler and Wittenberg (Germany). In the days that followed it was observed by many European astronomers. Tycho himself discovered it during the evening of November 11th. In contrast to the other observers, this great astronomer estimated systematically the luminosity of the new star. Let us cite one of Tycho's texts: "... Initially the nova was brighter than any other fixed star, including Sirius and Wega. It was even brighter than Jupiter which rose after sunset so that its luminosity was approximately that of Venus when this planet has reached its maximum brightness.... It maintained approximately its luminosity for almost the whole of November. On a clear day it could be seen by many observers by bright daylight, even at noon.... At night it was often shining through a cloud, covering the other stars. The nova, however, did not maintain its unusual brightness throughout the time of its appearance. It slowly faded and finally disappeared completely. The subsequent stages of its decline took the following course. As already mentioned, in November of 1572 the nova was as bright as Venus. In December it was almost equal to Jupiter and in January 1573 it was slightly fainter than Jupiter but still exceeded in luminosity all stars of first magnitude. In February and March its luminosity was comparable with that of the latter and in April and May it was as bright as a star of second magnitude. In July and August it declined to the third magnitude and its brightness was close to that of the brightest star in Cassiopeia.... At the end of 1572 and in January of 1574 it was hardly brighter than a star of magnitude 5 and in February it reached magnitude 6. Finally, in March, it had become so faint that it could no longer be observed."

We see that this description is sufficient to draw an approximate light curve of the nova of 1572.

TABLE 3   Star Magnitudes in Cassiopeia (1572)

Dates (Julian calendar)		Descriptions of Observations	m_v	Phase (days)
1572	XI–15	Almost as bright as Venus	−4.0	
	XII–15	About as bright as Jupiter	−2.4	30
1573	I–15	A little fainter than Jupiter, but brighter than stars of first magnitude	−1.4	61
	III–2	Equal in brightness to bright stars of first magnitude	+0.3	107
	V–1	Equal in brightness to stars of second magnitude	+1.6	167
	VIII–1	Equal to α, β, γ, δ Cassiopeia	+2.5	259
	XI–1	Equal to stars of fourth magnitude	+4.0	351
	XI–15	Equal to κ Cassiopeia	+4.2	365
1574	I–1	A little brighter than stars of fifth magnitude	+4.7	412
	II–15	Equal to stars of sixth magnitude	+5.3	457
	III–15	Invisible	—	485

A careful analysis enabled Baade to conclude that at maximum, which was reached in the middle of November 1572, the visual magnitude of this star was equal to −4.0 ± 0.3.[55] From estimates of its post-maximum brightness, carried out by various observers, it was possible to find corresponding stellar magnitudes for different dates of observation. These data are compiled in Table 3. Figure 18 shows the light curve, drawn on the basis of these data, of the nova of 1572, called "B Cassiopeia." This curve resembles a light curve of a supernova of the type I (see Fig. 4).

Observations made in the sixteenth century also yield valuable information on the colour of this star and its variations in the course of

3+s.

time.   All observers stressed that near its maximum this star had the
same colour as Venus or Jupiter.

For one to two months after the maximum, as the decline progressed,
its colour became more reddish, like that of Mars and Aldebaran; thereafter it again assumed a whitish colour, like that of Saturn.   Such
changes in colour are typical of supernovae of the type I.

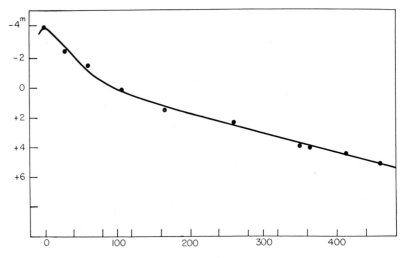

FIG. 18   Light curve of the supernova of 1572 (in Cassiopeia).[55]

From a careful investigation of original observations Bohm[56] found
that the co-ordinates of B Cassiopeia were the following: $\alpha = 0^h22^m4^s.6$,
$\delta = +63°52'30''$ (1950.0).   The accuracy of Tycho Brahe's determination
of the co-ordinates was rather high, namely about $0'.5$.   Figure 19 shows
a photograph of the celestial region in which the supernova of 1572
appeared.   The site of the outburst is marked by a circle.

We can thus verify with certainty that in 1572 to 1574 a supernova
was observed that had flared up in our own galaxy.   In 1952 a rather
powerful radio source was discovered in this place—apparently a specific
attribute of all remnants of supernovae outbursts.   The characteristics of
the remnant of the supernova outburst of 1572 will be discussed in § 15.

Another bright star appeared at the beginning of October 1604, on
the south-western horizon, in the constellation of Ophiuchus, not far from

Mars and Jupiter. Although its position in the sky was quite unfavourable for European observers, it was discovered immediately. It is a fact that many astronomers of this time had expected a conjunction of Mars and Jupiter (which was assumed to fall on October 9th, 1604) and observed them systematically. The new star reached its brightness maximum when it was a little brighter than Jupiter, in the middle of October, then it remained at the brightness of Jupiter until it disappeared in the light of the sun, in November. Thereafter it appeared in the east, at the

Fig. 19   Photograph of celestial area in which the supernova of 1572 exploded.[55]

beginning of January of the following year, 1605. At this time its luminosity had already faded and it was about equal to that of Antares. In the following months its luminosity continued to decrease. One year after its outburst, when it was observed by Kepler, it had already declined to the fifth magnitude.

In the nineteenth and twentieth centuries a series of authors determined the co-ordinates of this star on the basis of analyses of the old observations in the seventeenth century.[56,57,58] According to Bohm these co-ordinates were the following: $\alpha = 17^h27^m38^s.5$; $\delta = -21°26'38''$ (1950) and are likely to have an error of $\pm 1'$.

In 1943 Baade analyzed old visual estimates of the luminosity of this star and drew the light curve for it.[59] The nova of 1604 was first observed in Italy, in the evening of October 9th. Since the astronomers of that time carefully observed this part of the sky, we can be sure that on October 8th its brightness must still have been insignificant, at least below the third magnitude. And in the evening of October 9th its brightness had already risen to about that of Mars.

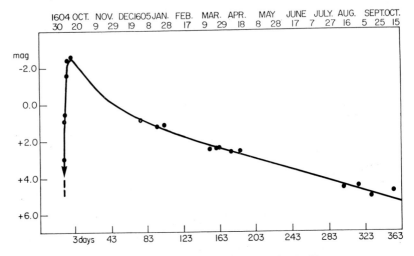

Fig. 20   Light curve of supernova of 1604.[59]

Figure 20 shows the light curve of the Nova Ophiuchi of 1604 as obtained by Baade. The dots mark the luminosity estimates obtained by the various observers, given in the uniform Baade system. The dashed curve shows the light curve of a supernova of the type I, which appeared in 1937 in NGC 482, normalized to the nova of 1604. This diagram removes the last doubts that the nova of 1604 was a supernova of the type I. As already emphasized in § 1, the light curves of different supernova of type I are identical in the period of 80 to 100 days after the maximum, though some differences may be observed in the stage of maximum. The supernova of 1604 is in particular characterized by its very steep pre-maximum rise: within 24 hours its luminosity increased at least tenfold.

This supernova was also observed in China. In the report on the astonishing celestial phenomena observed in the epoch of the Ming Dynasty we find the following passage: "... In the thirty-second year of this epoch, in the ninth moon, on the day of Yi-Ch'ai [October 10th, 1604] a star was seen in the constellation of Wei. It resembled a round ball. Its colour was yellow–red. It was seen in the south-west, for the whole period of the tenth moon [October 27th to November 26th, 1604], then it ceased to be visible. In the twelfth moon, on the day of Sin-Yu [February 3rd, 1605] it re-appeared in the south-west, in the constellation of Wei. In the following year, in the second moon [March 24th to April 23rd, 1605] it appeared once again. In the eighth moon, on T'ing-Mau's day [October 7th, 1605] it died away" (translation by Williams[36]). The constellation of Wei ranges from $\alpha = 16^h40^m$ to $\alpha = 10^h$ and from $\delta = -20°$ to the constellation of the Parrot. The "guest-star" must therefore have flared up near the northern boundary of this constellation. The surprising agreement of the results of observations of the supernova of 1604 in China and Europe where, by that time, astronomical science was highly developed, is an excellent proof of the reliability of astronomical information contained in the old Chinese chronicles.

Just as in the case of the supernova of 1572, three-and-a-half centuries later a rather powerful radio source was discovered at the place of the outburst of the supernova of 1604 (see § 15).

After 1604 another supernova outburst occurred in our galaxy in the constellation of Cassiopeia, at about 1700; this event, however, was not observed anywhere on earth. At this point we find the most powerful (next to the sun) radio source emitting in the meter band. (We will go into details about this extraordinarily interesting object in § 5.) The outburst of η Carinae in 1843 is considered by Zwicky as a supernova. This assumption we do not agree with, since, at this point, there is no sufficiently powerful non-thermal radio source. To conclude this section, let us also point out that in our present century, when astronomical research has the most powerful means at its disposal, no supernova outbursts have so far occurred.

§ 4 The "sling" effect

One may conclude, from an analysis of the observational data available, that supernovae of the type II are relatively young objects with sufficiently great masses. In particular, the so-called "supernovae of type III," displaying extreme characteristic features of type II supernovae, are characterized by ejected shells of more than $100M_\odot$. One may draw the conclusion that pre-outburst supernovae of the type II are main-sequence stars or in the stage of "Kelvinian" gravitational collapse, with masses essentially higher than solar mass. Such stars, however, may only be objects of the early spectral classes O and B.

There are also other arguments supporting the assumption that stars of the early spectral classes (generally speaking, not necessarily all) explode as supernovae of the type II. (We shall discuss this problem in greater detail in § 7.) Moreover, from an analysis of the luminosity functions of newly-formed stars (see, for example, [60]) and a comparison of the outburst frequency of the type II supernovae with these functions, it follows that an essential fraction of the massive hot stars, pertaining to spectral classes earlier than B5, "end their lives" as exploding supernovae of the type II.

Basing his arguments on this, the author of the present book suggested, in 1960, the hypothesis that, in the pre-outburst state, supernovae of the type II are young, massive, hot stars pertaining to spectral classes earlier than B5.[61] Since these stars are formed from interstellar matter, in the form of groups, called "associations," it is natural to assume that supernovae of the type II would as a rule explode in associations. Certain consequences of such explosions, as indicated in [61], may also be observed at present. In particular, in [61] our attention was directed to the fact that a great part of the young massive stars form multiple systems. Therefore, when one of the components of such a system explodes (obviously, the more massive a star, the faster it passes through its evolutionary track), the remaining star may alter its characteristics under the influence of this catastrophe. In [61] our attention was directed particularly to the fact that in the regions of nebular radio sources, considered as remnants of outbursts of supernovae of the type II, stars may be found which pertain to the spectral classes O–B5, the components of multiple systems in which the outburst had taken place.

These ideas have been developed in Blaauw's paper, which is very important for all problems of outbursts of type II supernovae.[62] We shall now discuss this paper in greater detail. It is well known from stellar astronomy that the dispersion of the stars' spatial velocities, which determine the spatial distribution of the stars, depends on the physical characteristics of a given group of stars (spectra, luminosities). The velocity dispersion is least with the massive stars of early spectral classes. For them $\Delta v \sim 10$ km/s. This is immediately connected with their exclusively "plane" spatial distribution. But we have long since known that a certain number of these stars have anomalously high spatial velocities, which, in certain cases, exceed 100 km/s. Baade subjected these "fast" stars of early spectral classes to a careful investigation. First of all he found that they must in no way be considered as the "tail" of some velocity distribution. Just as in the case of a Gaussian velocity distribution, in a distribution of the type of $\exp(-|v|/\eta)$, the number of fast stars is extremely high ($|v|$ is the modulus of the spatial velocity, η is a constant).

Among the O–B stars with anomalously high velocities are the separate group of so-called "runaway" stars. These are stars for which the vector of the spatial velocity passes through some of the known O associations. They are usually far away from the corresponding associations, as a rule more than 100 psc. If we know the magnitude of the spatial velocity of the "runaway" stars we naturally reach the conclusion that, several millions of years ago, these stars had been "extracted" from one or other association and had "runaway" from them with velocities often exceeding 100 km/s. Figure 21 shows a schematic representation of the positions of the stars AE Aurigae and μ Columbae relative to the well-known O association in Orion. Attention must be paid to the fact that both stars and the association "produced" by them are in celestial regions sufficiently remote from one another. It is quite possible that most of these high-velocity stars of early spectral classes are "running away" from one or another association. For a series of these stars this statement is absolutely certain, while for others the corresponding observational data are still lacking.

Blaauw drew attention to two remarkable peculiarities of the high-velocity stars of early spectral classes. Firstly, among these early-type stars there are virtually no binaries (generally speaking no multiple systems). On the other hand, as already shown at the beginning of this section, "binarism" is a widespread phenomenon among the O–B stars. Thus, for example, Baade could convincingly show that according to the data available more than 75 per cent of the stars of class B0–B5 are members of multiple systems. A still higher percentage of stars of spectral class O are members of multiple systems. As regards the high-velocity early-type stars not a single one is a component of a visual binary. We may also draw the conclusion that at least 80 per cent of these stars do not pertain to binary systems whose components are sufficiently close to one another. This percentage is very likely to be much higher. It is only the difficulties connected with the observation of such remote objects that do not permit a definite conclusion that

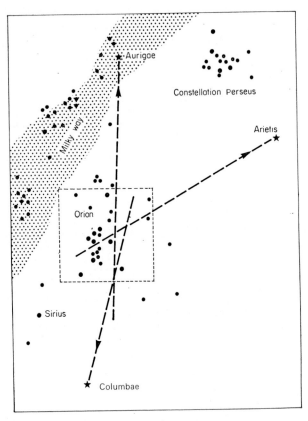

Fig. 21   Schematic diagram explaining the phenomenon of the "runaway stars."

virtually all rapidly flying early-type stars are "singles." The observational data available are, however, fully sufficient to draw the conclusion that the relative number of components of multiple systems are at least five times smaller among the high-speed O–B stars than among the "ordinary" stars of the same spectral classes.

Secondly, the relative number of more massive O stars is at least ten times higher among the high-speed O–B stars than among the "normal" O–B stars. In other words, for some reason or other, the more massive stars of class O fly away comparatively often (usually from O associations).

Following we give a table containing the fundamental characteristics of several rapidly flying stars. In the second column the corresponding numbers of Henry Draper's catalogue are given and the fifth column contains the names of the association from which the corresponding star "flies away." The sixth column contains the "kinematic age" obtained by dividing the distance between the star and the corresponding association by the speed of flight (relative to the association), the seventh and eighth columns contain the absolute visual magnitude and the bolometric magnitude, the ninth column gives the stellar masses as obtained from the theoretical mass/luminosity ratio. In the tenth column the galactic co-ordinates in the old system are given and in the eleventh the distance to the star.

Table 4 must not be considered as complete since the observational data are at present still too scanty, particularly for the southern sky.

The problem of the nature of the stars "running away" from O associations has more than once been considered in literature. In particular, Oort and Spitzer, in 1954 and 1955, explained the extremely high velocities of these stars by the conditions of their formation of a primary gas–dust medium.[63,64] The explanation is based on the so-called "reactive" effect, suggested by Oort. The essence of this effect consists in the following: Let us assume that a star of class O has formed in the outermost part of a gas–dust cloud. Its ultraviolet radiation will ionize the interstellar gas in this cloud up to a certain distance, smaller than the dimensions of the cloud. The gas pressure in the H II zone formed results in a lateral efflux of the gas on the opposite side of the interface of the zones H II and H I (that is in a comparatively dilute gas medium between the clouds). According to the law of momentum conservation a force arises in the interface of the zones H II and H I, which is directed towards zone H I. Under the influence of this force the non-ionized part of the cloud begins to accelerate and, in the end, it gains quite a considerable velocity. At the same time the gas particles may condense to a star which, in this way, will move away from the initially generated star at a high speed.

It must, however, be indicated that, although it looks acceptable at first sight, this "reactive" mechanism of generations of rapidly moving
5*

early-type stars is wrong. This picture, sketched above, would in fact correspond to reality if the interface of zones H II and H I were "solid." But since the primary cloud consisted of compressible gas, the actual reaction must be the formation of a shock wave in the interface of zone H II and H I, propagated in zone H I with a constant velocity of the order of several kilometres per second. It is precisely this phenomenon which may be observed in diffuse nebulae surrounding hot stars. Thus we see that in real interstellar matter any "reactive effect" must not be expected to occur. It is therefore not possible to explain the origin of the rapidly moving early-type stars in this way.

In order to explain the origin of the rapidly moving early-type stars, Blaauw[62] suggested a very elegant hypothesis which, as to the general features, had been formulated several years before by Zwicky.[22] To understand it, let us assume that in an earlier stage of its evolution a rapidly moving O–B star was a less massive component of a binary system. At some instant of time the principal component of this system exploded as a type II supernova so that during the explosion process an essential part of its mass (more than 50 per cent) was dispersed. Let us further assume that the distance between the components was of the order of thirty astronomical units, a value which is most frequently encountered with binary systems, while the linear dimensions of the components are at least by an order of magnitude smaller than the distance between them. Let us denote the mass of the principal component by M_1 (given in solar mass units) and that of the smaller component by M_2 and let a_2 be the orbital radius of the second component around the centre of gravity of the system, given in astronomical units. The velocity of the orbital motion of the second component relative to the centre of gravity of the system will then be equal to

$$ v = 30\left(\frac{M_1}{M_1 + M_2}\right)\left(\frac{M_1}{a_2}\right)^{1/2} \qquad (4.1) $$

If $M_1 \sim 200 M_\odot$, $a_2 \sim 20$ a.u. and $v \sim 100$ km/s. In the destruction of the main component, the substance ejected beyond the orbital radius a_2 will no longer exert a gravitational effect on the component M_2. Therefore, if the process of ejection of matter in the explosion occurs sufficiently fast, the component M_2, whose motion is no longer under the influence of the gravitational force of the rest of the mass, will begin to move, virtually rectilinearly, along the tangent to its orbit at the (small) orbital section in which it had been during the explosion. We

TABLE 4

Name of Star	H.D.	Sp	V (km/s)	Association	t, 10^6 years	M_v	M_b	Mass$_\odot$	l^I	b^I	r, psc
μ Cephei	210,839	O6	64	I Cepheus	?	−5.9	−10.4	87	71°.5	+2°.5	780
ξ Persei	24,912	O7	50	II Perseus	1.6	−5.0	−9.3	50	128.3	−12.0	430
	157,857	O7	50		?	(−5.5)	(−9.9)	(67)	340.7	+11.8	2,400
	152,408	O7–8	110	I Scorpius	?	−7.2	−11.5	160?	311.8	+0.3	2,000
68 Cygni	203,064	O8	49	I Cepheus	5.2	−5.3	−9.7	60	55.4	−4.4	880
α Camelopardalis	30,614	O9	59	I 502(?)	2.0	(−6.4)	(−10.5)	(90)	111.4	+14.9	1,000
AE Aurigae	34,078	O9	106	I Orion	2.7	−3.8	−7.6	24	139.8	−0.9	440
ζ Ophiuchi	149,757	O9	39	II Scorpius	1.1	−4.3	−8.3	32	334.1	+22.1	170
μ Columbae	38,666	B0	123	I Orion	2.2	−3.6	7.3	21	204.5	−25.9	570
	151,397	B0	180	I Scorpius	?	−3.2	6.8	17	312.1	+2.0	2,300
53 Arietus	149,363	B0	115	?	?	(−4.9)	(−8.6)	(38)	337.7	+25.2	2,600
	19,374	B2	59	I Orion	4.9	−2.3	−5.4	10	131.3	−33.0	360
	97,991	B2	156	?	?	(−2.5)	(−5.7)	(12)	231.7	+52.4	760
72 Columbae	197,419	B2	23	I Lacerta	10	−2.8	−6.2	14	44.4	−5.0	540
	41,534	B3	191	I Scorpius	14	−1.5	−4.1	(8)	205.7	−22.2	260
	214,930	B3	73	?	?	(−1.5)	(−4.1)	(8)	56.8	−30.7	440
	216,534	B3	82	?	?	(−1.5)	(−4.1)	(8)	72.1	−8.8	830
	4,142	B5	74	?	?	(−0.7)	(−2.6)	(5)	89.8	−14.7	170
	201,910	B5	58	I Lacerta	2.7	1.5	−4.1	8	52.5	−5.4	480

think it quite justified to denote this interesting effect as the "sling effect." Let us now consider this problem in greater detail.

We shall assume that the orbits of the initial Keplerian movement were circular. Let us further assume that the mass ejected by the component M_1 is dispersed isotropically, in the form of concentric shells, while the mass losses per unit time are constant up to a certain instant at which mass ejection stops. The velocity at which mass is ejected from component M_1 is assumed to exceed by far the velocity of the orbital motion of M_1 around M_2. In our case the velocity of the orbital motion is of the order of 100 km/s, whereas the velocity of gas ejection in the outburst of a type II supernova amounts to several thousand kilometres per second (cf. § 2) so that this condition is always fulfilled.

As long as the shells ejected from M_1 are still inside the orbit of M_2, they exert the same gravitational effect on it as if their entire mass were concentrated in the centre of M_1. After the isotropic shell has extended beyond the orbit of M_2, however, the gravitational effect it may exert on M_2 will be equal to zero. Thus we have the problem of analyzing a Keplerian motion in the case of a continuous reduction of the mass of one of the components. An analogous problem has already been considered long ago in celestial mechanics, under the assumption that the mass losses of component M_1 occur sufficiently slowly.[65,66] In our case, however, the mass losses take place rapidly which makes it necessary to treat the problem in another way. For a series of initial conditions a numerical solution was obtained by Boersma,[67] who worked in close contact with Blaauw.

Let us consider first the simpler case of a sudden ejection of the essential part of the mass of component M_1. The velocity of motion of the component M_2 relative to the component M_1 will be

$$v_{\text{rel}}^2 = 30^2(M_1 + M_2)\left(\frac{2}{R} - \frac{1}{a}\right) \text{ km/s} \qquad (4.2)$$

where R is the distance between M_1 and M_2, a the major semi-axis of the orbit which increases as mass M_1 decreases, while, generally speaking, the motion may change from elliptic to hyperbolic form. The quantity a is determined by the well-known relation of celestial mechanics:

$$a = -\frac{M_1 + M_2}{2E}; \qquad E = T + \Omega;$$

$$E_0 = T_0 + \Omega_0; \qquad \Omega_0 = -\frac{M_1^0 + M_2^0}{R_0} \qquad (4.3)$$

where E is the total energy of M_2 relative to M_1, T is the kinetic energy of M_2 relative to M_1, and Ω is the potential energy. Before the outburst, when the orbit was circular and $a = R_0$,

$$v_{rel,0}^2 = 30^2 \frac{M_1 + M_2}{R_0} \tag{4.4}$$

After the outburst the mass of the component M_1 was equal to qM_1. The initial kinetic energy of M_2 will vary continuously while the potential energy changes suddenly (provided the ejection of gas from M_1 occurs instantaneously), being equal to

$$\Omega = \frac{qM_1 + M_2}{R_0} \tag{4.5}$$

Therefore, right after the explosion of M_1 the entire energy of M_2 (relative to M_1) will be equal to

$$E = T_0 + \Omega_0 + \frac{(1-q)M_1}{R_0} = \frac{M_1(1-q) - M_2}{2R_0} \tag{4.6}$$

If E exceeds zero the motion will be hyperbolic. Obviously, this takes place when the condition

$$q < \frac{M_1 - M_2}{2M_1} \tag{4.7}$$

is fulfilled. We see from (4.7) that in the case of a large ratio $M_1/M_2 > 1$ the motion becomes hyperbolic since $q < 0.5$. If $M_2 > M_1$ the relative orbit always remains elliptic.

Another interesting case is that where before explosion the motion maintains its elliptic character, after explosion the centre of gravity of the system moves relative to the centre of gravity with a velocity equal to

$$v_q = \frac{M_1 M_2 (1-q)}{(M_1 + M_2)(qM_1 + M_2)} v_{rel,0} \tag{4.8}$$

For example, if $M_1/M_2 = 10$ and $q = 0.6$, we obtain $v_q = 0.052 v_{rel,0}$. In the case of great mass losses, when the motion of M_2 goes over to a hyperbolic motion, the ratio of the velocity of M_2 at infinity to the initial relative velocity on the circular orbit will be given by

$$\frac{v_{rel,\infty}^2}{v_{rel,0}^2} = \frac{qM_1 + M_2}{M_1 + M_2} \frac{R}{a} = \frac{M_1(1-2q) - M_2}{M_1 + M_2} \tag{4.9}$$

For example, with $q = 0.3$ and $M_2/M_1 = 0.2$, we obtain $v_{\text{rel},\infty} = 0.4 v_{\text{rel},0}$. We need, however, the velocity of M_2 after the explosion, not relative to M_1 but relative to the initial centre of gravity which was at rest in the system of the gas cloud in which the star was born. For this purpose we have to add the vectors of $v_{\text{rel},\infty}$ and of the velocity of M_1 relative to the old centre of gravity. An analysis, which we will not discuss here, shows that in most of the interesting cases this correction is not essential, i.e., $v_{\text{rel},\infty}$ is close to the velocity of motion relative to the old centre of gravity.

In this way it follows from (4.9) that if the mass loss in the sudden explosion of M_1 is high enough, the component M_2 will move on a hyperbolic orbit and its velocity will consist essentially of the initial relative orbital velocity. As shown above, these calculations were, however, made under the simplifying assumption that during the explosion the mass losses of component M_1 occur instantaneously. In paper [67] the finite duration of the process of material ejection in the explosion of M_1 has been taken into account. In what follows we shall give some results of a numerical integration of the equations of motion, in the form of tables of the orbital characteristics of M_2 after the explosion, as functions of the following parameters: (a) initial mass ratio M_2/M_1; (b) the quantity q; (c) the characteristic of the velocity of mass ejection from M_1, that is the duration τ_c of the process of gas ejection, given in units of the period of revolution, in the course of which M_1 tends to zero.

In the case where the motion after the explosion remains elliptical the velocity of the centre of gravity of a binary system, S_q, relative to the old centre of gravity was calculated, S_q being given in units of velocity of orbital motion of M_2, relative to the old centre of gravity, S_2^0. Moreover, for this case the major semi-axis of the new orbit was calculated, given in terms of the radius of the initial circular orbit.

In a case where after the explosion the motion of M_2 became hyperbolic, its velocity S_2 at infinity was calculated, given in the same units as S_q. The angle Ψ between the directions of motion of M_2 and M_1 at infinity was also calculated (both motions were referred to the old centre of gravity). The velocity S_1 of M_1 at infinity is independent of q and τ_c and is only a function of M_2/M_1: $S_1 = (M_2/M_1)S_2^0$.

In the tables given below the data above the heavy lines correspond to elliptic motion and the data below to hyperbolic motion.

Tables 5–7 enable us to draw several interesting conclusions. If M_2/M_1 is large (e.g., 0.8), hyperbolic motion is only obtained if the

TABLE 5

$M_2/M_1 = 0.05$

q	$\tau_c = 0$	0.2	0.5	1.0	2.0
0.6	0.031	0.031	0.029	0.025	0.015
	2.60	2.57	2.43	2.14	1.78
0.5	0.045	0.045	0.042	0.034	0.019
	11.00	9.56	6.12	3.50	2.23
0.4	0.400	0.379	0.285	0.046	0.026
	83°	82°	80°	15.62	3.15
0.3	0.608	0.584	0.490	0.300	0.037
	85°	85°	84°	80°	6.72
0.2	0.762	0.730	0.621	0.440	0.179
	86°	86°	85°	83°	74°
0.1	0.889	0.847	0.718	0.534	0.327
	87°	87°	86°	85°	81°
0.0	1.000	0.947	0.797	0.606	0.416
	87°	87°	86°	85°	83°

mass losses occur very rapidly, with $q < 0.2$. If the ratio M_2/M_1 is small (e.g., 0.05) the resulting motion is hyperbolic, even if the mass losses occur relatively slowly ($\tau_c > 1$), q being comparatively high (~ 0.3–0.4). The relative hyperbolic velocity M_2, with a small ratio M_2/M_1, amounts as a rule to 50–100 per cent of the initial circular velocity of M_2, the dependence on τ_c being rather strong. The hyperbolic velocity drops as τ_c rises.

With the help of Tables 5–7 we may immediately solve the inverse problem: from the values of M_2 and S_2 (obtained in observations) to find the parameters of a binary system of stars before the explosion, that is the initial mass of the main component M_1 and the major semi-axis of the orbit of M_2 around M_1. Let us consider the following typical cases: $M_2 = 50 M_\odot$ and $10 M_\odot$, $S_2 = 150$ and 50 km/s. The results of the analysis are given in Table 8 in which the upper limits of a and τ_c are compiled.

$M_2/M_1 = 0.20$

q	$\tau_c = 0$	0.2	0.5	1.0	2.0
0.6	0.100	0.099	0.094	0.080	0.047
	2.00	1.99	1.92	1.78	1.59
0.5	0.143	0.141	0.130	0.105	0.055
	3.50	3.39	2.97	2.36	1.85
0.4	0.200	0.196	0.176	0.135	0.067
	0°	44.58	8.98	3.69	2.25
0.3	0.529	0.501	0.383	0.178	0.090
	68°	66°	59°	11.33	3.01
0.2	0.721	0.687	0.564	0.336	0.131
	74°	73°	69°	54°	5.25
0.1	0.872	0.828	0.689	0.475	0.213
	77°	76°	73°	65°	20°
0.0	1.000	0.944	0.786	0.571	0.364
	78°	78°	75°	70°	57°

From Table 8 it follows that the range of the admissible values of a and τ_c is essentially wider for $S_2 = 50$ km/s than for $S_2 = 150$ km/s. The fact that among the rapid early-type stars the number of objects with $S_2 \sim 150$ km/s is not much smaller than that of the slower stars with $S_2 \sim 50$ km/s, indicates that the duration of mass ejection from the exploding stars was comparatively short, most likely less than one year. For the stars with $S_2 = 150$ km/s the limits of a are much narrower than in the case of stars with $S_2 = 50$ km/s.

An analysis of the characteristics of rapid early-type stars (see Table 4) shows that stars with a mass of $M_2 \sim 10M_\odot$ are encountered much earlier than stars with greater masses. At the same time it follows from the luminosity function of newly generated stars that the number of the latter with masses of $M_2 \sim 10M_\odot$ must be considerably greater than of those with masses of $M_2 \sim 50M_\odot$. Blaauw tries to overcome this difficulty with the help of the conditions of formation of stars with great

TABLE 7

$M_2/M_1 = 0.8$

q	$\tau_c = 0$	0.2	0.5	1.0	2.0
0.6	0.229	0.226	0.214	0.180	0.093
	1.40	1.40	1.39	1.35	1.30
0.5	0.308	0.303	0.279	0.218	0.087
	1.63	1.62	1.58	1.50	1.40
0.4	0.400	0.391	0.350	0.254	0.083
	2.00	1.97	1.86	1.67	1.52
0.3	0.509	0.493	0.429	0.292	0.096
	2.75	2.64	2.29	1.89	1.66
0.2	0.640	0.615	0.518	0.336	0.130
	5.00	4.40	3.10	2.19	1.85
0.1	0.800	0.761	0.624	0.391	0.183
	$0°$	21.09	5.10	2.63	2.11
0.0	1.000	0.942	0.753	0.462	0.253
	$37°$	$32°$	19.76	3.37	2.50

masses, in the process of which a certain selection mechanism may be effective which strongly raises the number of stars with great masses M_2.

When the masses of the exploding stars are great (most likely greater than $100 M_\odot$) they must be young stars, i.e., the time-lapse after their generation of interstellar gas–dust matter must be short. It may be considered as most likely that the explosion took place even before the star had reached the main sequence. This indicates that it was in the stage of gravitational collapse. The time t_c of gravitational collapse is determined by the initial mass of the cluster. According to [68]

$$t_c = 10^8 \left(\frac{M}{M_\odot}\right)^2 \frac{R_\odot}{R} \frac{L_\odot}{L} \text{ years} \qquad (4.10)$$

The quantities of radius R and luminosity L of stars which "just" reached the main sequence were calculated theoretically in papers [69] and [70] for various models. Thus, for example, with $M_1 = 250 M_\odot$ we obtain

TABLE 8

S_2	M_2	$M_1 = 83 M_\odot$			$M_1 = 250 M_\odot$			$M_1 = 1{,}000 M_\odot$		
		qM_1	a	τ	qM_1	a	τ	qM_1	a	τ
150 km/s	50	25	—	—	75	2.39	0.027	300	14.2	0.30
		17	0.75	0.00	50	4.40	0.098	200	22.0	0.64
		8	1.40	0.027	25	6.43	0.206	100	30.2	1.22
		0	2.08	0.057	0	8.50	0.342	0	38.1	1.86
	10	25	0.96	0.016	60	2.83	0.060	300	15.7	0.36
		17	1.62	0.043	40	4.40	0.138	200	23.5	0.82
		8	2.29	0.085	20	6.04	0.243	100	31.4	1.37
		0	2.96	0.130	0	7.62	0.371	0	39.6	2.01
50 km/s	50	25	—	—	75	22	0.72	300	128	8.1
		17	6.8	0.00	50	40	2.64	200	198	18.6
		8	12.6	0.72	25	58	5.54	100	272	32.9
		0	18.8	1.54	0	76	9.25	0	343	50.2
	10	25	8.7	0.43	60	26	1.61	300	141	9.9
		17	14.6	1.17	40	40	3.72	200	211	22.2
		8	20.7	2.30	20	54	6.57	100	282	37.1
		0	26.7	3.52	0	69	10.00	0	356	54.2

$t_c = 5 \cdot 10^4$ years whereas with $M_1 = 10 M_\odot$, $t_c = 3.2 \cdot 10^5$ years. Let us assume like Blaauw that the main component M_1 exploded when its radius was about ten times larger than the "equilibrium" radius of a star of this mass on the main sequence. This indicates that the period of time between the formation of the star and its explosion must be very short, only several thousand years. Within this time, when the component M_2 had a comparatively small initial mass, say $10 M_\odot$, its compression was inessential so that its mean density was low, in any case lower than that of the exploding star. In this case the shell ejected by the exploded star literally "disperses" the as yet insufficiently formed star M_2 which is essentially a gas cloud. In the opposite case, when the component M_2 has a great initial mass, e.g., $50 M_\odot$, its collapse will be a sufficiently fast process and at the moment of explosion its mean density has become high enough for the star to "survive," "maintaining its individuality during the explosion of M_1."

This brilliant hypothesis does not of course pretend to provide an exhaustive explanation of a series of fundamental observational characteristics of the rapid O–B stars. It is necessary to analyze in greater detail

the conditions under which a less massive component M_2 may appear
during the explosion of M_1. So far this has not yet been done. By way
of the following simple example we will show that we may here encounter
considerable new difficulties. Let us assume that the mass $M_2 = 50M_\odot$,
$M_t = 250M_\odot$, $a = 30$ a.u. At the time of the explosion of M_1 the radius
of M_2 may be equal to 1 a.u. or even larger since the compression process is
not very advanced. We shall assume as before that the ejection of mass
during the explosion occurs in spherical symmetry. A fraction of $\sim 10^{-4}$
of the ejected mass will then collide directly with M_2. If the ejection
speed amounts to $\sim 7 \cdot 10^8$ cm/s, then the kinetic energy of the gas
"hitting" the component M_2 will be equal to $T = 2.5 \cdot 10^{-2} M_\odot$ and
$a = 10^{49}$ erg. It may be expected that a strong shock wave is propagated
along the photospheric and sub-photospheric layers of M_2, in whose front
the temperature will be extraordinarily high, of the order of many
hundred millions of degrees. At such a high temperature thermonuclear reactions will set in. In any case the conditions in the surrounding
and even in the relatively deep layers of M_2 suffer essential changes; in
particular, the chemical composition may vary. Therefore, at first sight,
it seems strange that several millions of years after the outburst the
component M_2 does not bear any clear traces of the "burn." However,
there might be a difference in the chemical compositions of the rapidly
moving O–B star and the "normal" one, a problem which, as far as we
know, has not yet been studied seriously. It must of course be kept in
mind that convection processes may to an essential degree "smooth" the
traces of the "burn."

Though Blaauw's hypothesis on the existence of a causal relationship
between outbursts of supernovae of the type II and the rapidly moving
early-type stars seems to us to be correct, the particular mechanism
considered in this hypothesis is, obviously, not the only possible way.
The essential element of this mechanism is in fact the supposition of the
symmetrical ejection of matter from the exploding star. The problem
was thus reduced to an analysis of a Keplerian motion in a system where
the mass of one of the components decreases rapidly enough. In fact,
it is difficult to imagine a perfectly spherical-symmetrical ejection of
matter. In the case of explosion effects on a smaller scale—outbursts
of ordinary novae—the ejection of matter is known not to be of spherical
symmetry. The ejected shells are rich in structure, forming an equatorial
belt, "polar caps" and the like, which is naturally explained by the
influence of magnetic fields (cf., for example,[71]). It is beyond any doubt

that in the case of supernovae, mass ejection is not of spherical-symmetrical nature. The irregular structure of the nebular radio source Cassiopeia A also speaks in favour of this conclusion (cf. § 6). In this case the nebula has not yet "had time" to become sufficiently strongly decelerated by interstellar matter so that the observed irregularity of its structure cannot be explained by the conditions of motion in the non-uniform interstellar matter.

If mass ejection occurs asymmetrically, its influence on the motion of the component M_2 will be quite different from the idealized case of the spherical-symmetric ejection considered above.

A simplified problem on asymmetrical ejection of matter by component M_1 looks as follows: At a certain instant of time part $(1 - q)$ of the component M_1 receives abruptly a velocity of $v_1 \sim 5{,}000$ km/s, while the residual part (qM_1) assumes a velocity equal to $(1 - q)v_1/q$ in the opposite direction. Even if $1 - q$ is small (e.g., $1 - q = 0.1$ or even less) the velocity of the residual main part of the star will be much higher than the parabolic velocity. As a consequence the binary system disintegrates. It is quite possible that a rigorous mathematical analysis of this problem (taking into account that the time of mass ejection from M_1 is finite) results in much less rigid conditions for the "departure" of the component M_2 with a velocity of the order of 100 km/s because, nevertheless, the conclusion that the mass of the exploding component M_1 must exceed 100–$250M_\odot$ is undoubtedly a difficulty for Baade's hypothesis.

CHAPTER II

The remnants of supernovae of the type II

§ 5 Optical characteristics of nebulae which are remnants of outbursts of the type II supernovae

For several decades we have known the remarkable system of fine-fibred nebulae NGC 6960 and NGC 6992–5 in the constellation Cygnus (see Fig. 22). The thickness of the individual filaments of these nebulae is as a rule determined by the resolving power of the telescopes, that is ~ 1–2″, while the individual filaments have lengths of tenths of minutes of arc. An important characteristic feature of this nebular system is the system of a hot star in its environment, which may cause the interstellar in the filaments to glow. It was therefore as early as 1946 when Oort expressed the opinion that this nebular system was the remnant of the shell of a supernova which exploded relatively close to the sun, thirty thousand years ago.[72] According to Oort's hypothesis, the expanding shell compresses the interstellar medium in which it moves. The energy released in this process is responsible for the luminosity of the nebula. This hypothesis is supported by the observed expansion of the whole filamentary system with a velocity of 65 km/s at the inner boundary of the nebular system (diameter about 80′), and up to 115 km/s at the outer boundary (diameter 170′). These high velocities of the gas masses clearly indicate the peculiar character of the object and they also permit an effective ionization and excitation of the atoms and ions in the filaments by way of collision. Details of this question will be discussed later on.

We know several celestial nebulae which, in their fundamental characteristics, resemble the system of the fine-fibred nebula in Cygnus. Characteristic features of all these objects are the filamentary structure and the absence of hot exciting stars in their neighbourhood. Some of these objects were discovered by G. A. Shayn and V. F. Gaze during their work on an extensive programme of investigating gas nebulae.[73,74,75] Figure 23 shows a photograph of a system of fine-fibred nebulae in the constellation of Aquarius, which the notation S 147 was assigned to. The "open-work" structure of the fibres of this system of nebulae reminds us of a photograph of particle tracks in a cloud chamber to which a magnetic field has been applied. The angular dimensions of the nebular system S 147 as a whole are very large; they amount to about 5°. Other objects of this type are S 22, IC 443 and NGC 6888.

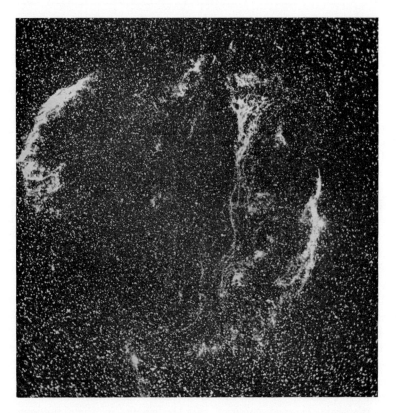

FIG. 22   Photograph of the system of filamentary nebulae in the constellation Cygnus.[75]

An essential characteristic feature of these, as a rule rather faint, nebulae is their emission in the radio-frequency range. Every mass of ionized gas represents a thermal radio source with a characteristic spectrum, where the spectral density of this radio radiation flux is proportional to the optical radiation flux in the lines of the Balmer series (in the case of recombinative excitation of the latter).   The thermal radio-wave emission expected with the fine-fibred nebulae considered above is hardly observed. Moreover, the spectrum of this radio-wave emission (in the cases where it has become known) differs from the spectrum of thermal radio sources

FIG. 23   Photograph of the system of filamentary nebulae in the constellation Aquarius.[75]

(e.g., in the case of the diffuse and planetary nebulae).   The fine-fibred nebulae are consequently non-thermal radio sources.   It is precisely this property that makes it possible to distinguish them with safety from the group of gas nebulae which, in individual cases, also possess a filamentary structure.

The presence of non-thermal radiation, caused by relativistic electrons moving in magnetic fields (the so-called synchrotron radiation)† is a characteristic feature of the remnants of outbursts of supernovae, of both types I and II. It is therefore quite justifiable to corroborate that the fine-fibred nebulae must be remnants of supernovae. As to their

FIG. 24   Photograph of the nebula Cassiopeia A in blue light.[79]

fundamental characteristics (spatial distribution, mass of ejected shell and its initial velocity) these objects must be remnants of supernovae of the type II. It must be emphasized that the corresponding supernova outbursts occurred long ago; as will be shown in § 7, several thousand years may be assumed to have elapsed since then.

† The problem of the non-thermal radio-wave emission of filamentary nebulae will be discussed in greater detail in § 6.

Among this group of objects there exists a conspicuous, though optically very faint, nebula in the constellation of Cassiopeia A, the most powerful radio source in the sky. Let us now analyze in detail the fundamental results of the optical observations of this object (the results of radio-astronomical observations will be discussed in § 6).

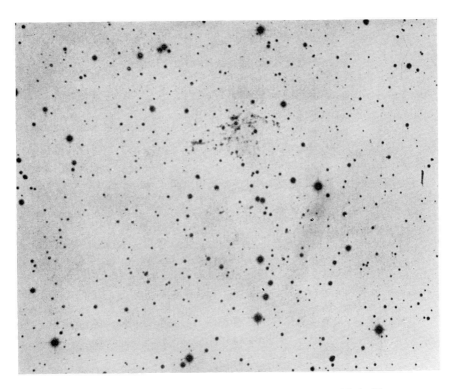

FIG. 25   Photograph of the nebula Cassiopeia A in red light.[79]

Well after Rayle and Smith had discovered Cassiopeia A in 1948, it was not possible to identify it with any optical object. Only at the end of 1951, after Smith had succeeded in essentially improving the co-ordinates of this radio source,[76] Baade and Minkowski, using the 5-metre telescope of the observatory on Palomar mountain, obtained photographs of a faint nebula which could be identified with the radio source.[77] In many respects this nebula proved to be a unique object.

Figure 24 shows a photograph of the region around Cassiopeia A, taken
with blue-sensitive plates. We can see only a single emitting object,
with an extension of 2′.8, located at an angular distance of about 2′
from the co-ordinates of the "centre of gravity" of the radio source
(when this photograph was taken, it was not yet known that Cassiopeia
A is an extended source of about 5′). A quite different picture is to be
seen on the photograph obtained with a red-sensitive plate (sensitivity
range λ 6,400–6,700 (cf. Fig. 25)). This photograph, apart from the
details seen on the blue-sensitive plate, shows us a great number (altogether more than 200) of very small (length $< 30''$) fringes and star-
like emitting objects. Some of them are very bright, others are hardly
discernible. These "nebula flakes" are arranged in a circle whose
diameter amounts to 6′.3. The co-ordinates of the centre of this circle
are the following: $\alpha = 23^h21^m11^s, 38$, $\delta = 58°31'52''$, 9(1950.0), while the
co-ordinates of the centre of gravity of the radio source Cassiopeia A,
referred to the same epoch, are $\alpha = 23^h21^m12^s.0 \pm 1^s$, $\delta = 58°32'.1$
$\pm 0'.7$.[76] Moreover, as ascertained later on, the angular dimensions of
the source Cassiopeia A resemble the dimensions of the zone over which
the nebular "flakes" scattered. This removes all the last doubts as to the
correctness of the identification.

At the centre of the region containing the nebular "flakes" we find a
faint star of photographic magnitude 18.9. It is, however, hardly possible
to assume this star (or any other of the faint stars found in this region)
to be the source exciting the nebula. The spectrum of the nebula, which
we shall describe presently, speaks against the possibility.

Baade and Minkowski obtained the spectra of a great number of the
nebular filaments with the help of a nebular diffraction spectrograph, used
together with the 5-metre telescope. They obtained two types of spectra
which differ essentially from one another. The first type of these spectra
is shown by comparatively small condensations with sharp contours which
may only be seen on the photograph taken with the red-sensitive plate.
The number of these condensations is relatively low, about 20. Figure 26
shows the spectrum of one of the brightest condensations. This shows
clearly the Hα emission line and on either side of it the forbidden lines
of ionized nitrogen, at λ 6,548 and λ 6,584. The relative intensities of
the lines λ 6,548, Hα and λ 6,584 are 1.5:1:4.5. Moreover, in the spectrogram we see a weak forbidden emission line of neutral oxygen, at λ 6,300,
blended with the corresponding lines of the spectrum of nocturnal sky.
The ray velocities in the spectra of this type are comparatively low (of

the order of thirty km/s) and, as a rule, negative. The line width corresponds to a velocity spread of the emitting atoms of about 400 km/s.

The spectrum of the condensations and the filaments of the other type, which are much more numerous (about 200) is quite different from that described above. The condensations of this type show in the photographs a much more "diffuse" form and are conspicuous on both blue-sensitive and red-sensitive plates. Figure 27 shows the spectrum of one

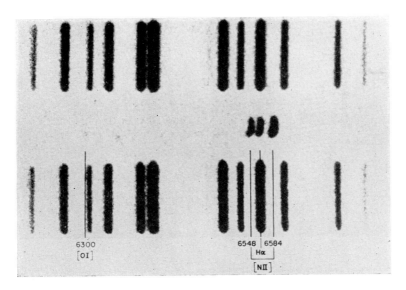

FIG. 26   Spectrum of the "stationary" condensations in the nebula Cassiopeia A.[79]

of the brightest filaments of this type. This spectrum has a completely unusual form. We can only observe the components of the red line of [O I] at λ 6,300 and λ 6,364 and the well-known nebular doublet of [O III] (λ 4,959 and λ 5,007). A remarkable feature is the complete absence of the Hα line and, what is particularly important for further discussion, the forbidden line of ionized oxygen, λ 3,727. Note that this line is also absent in the spectrum of the condensations of the first type. In many planetary nebulae the intensity of the [O III] lines is considerably higher than that of the Hα line. In our case, however, the unusual feature consists in the anomalously high intensities of the lines [O I] and Hα. In nebulae the [O I] lines are usually very weak. Still more peculiar are

width, structure and displacement of the lines.   Each line consists of one
intense component and three weaker components.   As a matter of fact
we have one very broad band with four intensity peaks.   The ray velocities in this band vary from $-1{,}000$ to $+3{,}000$ km/s.   The spectra of
other condensations of this type display a still greater shift of the wavelengths of spectral lines.   Though the lines [O I] and [O III] equal one
another as to the general band structure, they differ considerably in detail.

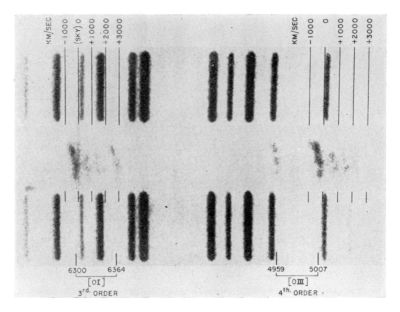

FIG. 27   Spectrum of the "diffuse" condensations in the nebula Cassiopeia A.[79]

A comparison of photographs of nebulae obtained in 1951 and 1953
showed that the diffuse filaments of the second type possess a considerable
proper motion and vary in intensity while the "red" condensations,
whose spectra are of the first type, are virtually stationary.

Right after the identification of Cassiopeia A with a peculiar nebula
we interpreted it as the remnant of a supernova.[39]   Minkowski did not
agree at all with this explanation but viewed this nebula as a unique
object.[79]   In 1955, however, after a careful analysis of the radiation
velocities and the proper motions of a great many filaments and con-

densations of the second type, he accepted our point of view as to the nature of the nebula Cassiopeia A.[80]

The spectrum and the motion of this nebula are of course unique and dissimilar to both the Crab nebula (the remnant of a type I supernova) and the fine-fibred nebulae we considered above. The latter, however, are "old" remnants of supernovae of the type II, strongly decelerated in interstellar matter, while the nebula Cassiopeia A is a very young object

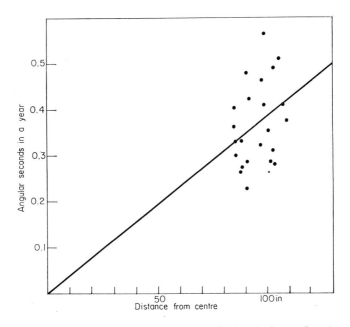

FIG. 28   Proper motions of the condensations in Cassiopeia A as a function of the distance to the centre of the nebula.[81]

(see below). It was thus found that Cassiopeia A and the filamentary nebulae are objects of one and the same nature, in different stages of evolution. Since outbursts of supernovae of the type II are really rare events and Cassiopeia A, as we shall show in what follows, is about 270 years old, i.e., its age is of the order of the mean interval of supernova outbursts, this object must of course be unique in our stellar system since in the early stages of evolution the characteristics of remnants of outbursts evolve very rapidly (cf. § 7).

The fact that the system of condensations of the second type in the nebula Cassiopeia A is rapidly expanding follows from both the proper motions of the condensations and the radiation velocities. Figure 28 shows the dependence of the proper motions on the distance to the centre of the system of condensations, as obtained in 1958 by Minkowski.[81] Though the dispersion of the points is considerable, the fact that the system of condensations expands is established quite reliably. The mean expansion ξ is determined from the relation $\xi = S/r$, where S denotes the proper motion of the condensation, given in angular seconds per year, and r is the angular distance of the condensation from the centre of the system. If this expansion has occurred all the time at a constant rate, it must have begun at about A.D. 1700 $\pm$ 14, and this estimate coincides with the outburst of the supernova. There arises the interesting question, why was it not observed at this time. In the times of Newton and Bradley, European astronomy was at a sufficiently high level and the non-setting constellation Cassiopeia can be observed throughout the year. Below we shall discuss this problem in detail.

The diagram of Figure 29 shows the dependence of the radiation velocities on the distance from the centre of the system of condensations. The expansion diagram shows clearly that the velocity of approach of the condensations is markedly lower than the velocity of withdrawal. The rear part (with respect to the observer) of the condensation system flies away from us at a speed of 7,400 km/s while the front part approaches us at a speed of about 6,000 km/s. The thickness of the expanding system of condensations may be determined from the spread of the patches in Figure 29. It proved to be equal to 18″, that is about ten times smaller than the system's radius.

Knowing the proper motions and the radiation velocities of the condensations it is easy to determine the distance of the object. It was found to amount to 3,400 $\pm$ 300 psc which is in excellent agreement with the results of independent radio-astronomical observations in the 21-cm band; they will be discussed in § 6. The diameter of the entire system of condensations exceeds 4 psc. The object is at a distance of 140 psc from the galactic plane.

The spectra of the condensations in the nebula Cassiopeia A have not as yet been interpreted. This important work is rendered very difficult by the fact that, by far, not all the results of Minkowski's spectroscopic

observations are published. There exists only a very fragmental indication that, besides the lines described above, the spectra of the non-stationary, rapidly moving condensations (of second type), lines of [O II],
[S II] and [Ne III][80] were discovered. One may only guess that it was
the [O III] line which was discovered at λ 4,363, whose intensity ratio to the
"principal" nebular lines [O III] is $N_1 + N_2$, and which permits the determination of the electron temperature of the nebula's emitting plasma. In
the spectra of some condensations of type II the line [S II] λ 6,713 is the

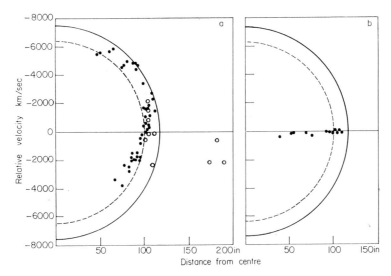

Fig. 29   Radial velocities of the condensations in Cassiopeia A as a function of the
distance to the centre of the nebula.[81]

most intense, a fact that, in our opinion, indicates the great part played by
interstellar absorption. The incidental remark that in the spectra of
condensations of this type there is no trace of Hα lines and, in particular,
none of [N II] lines, is exceedingly important. Unfortunately the results
of these important observations have not yet been published although
more than ten years have elapsed.
    There are two papers which contain attempts to interpret the spectra
of the Cassiopeia A nebula. The first is due to Minkowski and Aller[82]
and the second to Chamberlain.[83]   These papers, however, are in our

opinion unreliable and cannot give us a correct idea of the physical conditions in the nebula. Among other things it is a fact that they do not all account for light absorption (which, as we shall see in what follows, is very strong) and this renders them incorrect. As regards a detailed critical comment on these papers, we will not pursue it any further here. We want only to indicate that the hypothesis, proposed by Minkowski and Aller, on the absence of ionization equilibrium in condensations of the second type is not beyond criticism. The fact is that from the almost equal intensity of the lines [O I] and [O III] it follows that the concentration of the neutral and doubly ionized oxygen atoms is almost the same. The presence of such a great number of O^{++} ions, under the natural supposition that ionization is the result of electron impacts, requires a high electron temperature of $T_e \sim 40,000°$. With such a high value of T_e it is, however, difficult to understand why such a great quantity of neutral oxygen is to be observed. This is precisely the reason for Minkowski's and Aller's hypothesis on the absence of ionization equilibrium. At the same time they tried to explain the low intensity of the line $\lambda\,3,727$ by the influence of collisions of the second kind which require an electron concentration $N_e > 10^4\,\mathrm{cm}^{-3}$. But with this N_e the recombination time is $\tau = 1/N_e\sigma_2$, where $\sigma_2 \sim 4 \cdot 10^{-13}$ is the recombination coefficient of [O III], cf. [84]. Substituting $N_e = 10^4$ we find that $\tau \sim 2.5 \cdot 10^8$ s or eight years, which is much shorter than the age of the nebula. This essential discrepancy in the paper of Minkowski and Aller was first pointed out by Chamberlain.[83]

Realizing the difficulties of the task which are chiefly caused by the absence of detailed information on the character of the spectra of Cassiopeia A we will try—in a quite preliminary way—to interpret the results of the observations published. Let us first consider the stationary condensations of the first type. From the spectrum shown in Figure 26 it follows that the intensity of the line [O I] $\lambda\,6,300$ is much lower than the intensities of the forbidden lines of nitrogen. Since, according to [77], the total intensity of the latter is six times higher than that of $H\alpha$ which is at least ten times higher than that of $\lambda\,6,300$, it is obvious that the intensity of the [O I] line is at least fifty times lower than that of [N II]. Moreover, the excitation cross sections and potentials of these lines are quite similar while the abundance of oxygen in interstellar matter is two to three times higher than the abundance of nitrogen. Hence, results the natural conclusion that both nitrogen and oxygen must exist predominantly in the form of singly charged ions. The same holds true also for hydrogen.

We may assume that for N, O and H the ratio $n_i/n_0 \sim 10$. This conclusion is also supported by the fact that the lines [O III] cannot be observed in the spectra of condensations of this type. Consequently the number of ions of [O III] must be comparatively low. If ionization is due to electron impact (and, obviously, this is so), it can be shown that $T_e \sim 15,000°$. In these estimates we assumed that the relative abundance of oxygen and nitrogen is the same as in interstellar matter. The fact that condensations of the first type are explained as compressed interstellar matter surrounding the supernova, speaks in favour of the correctness of this assumption.

As the majority of oxygen atoms must be in the state of [O II], its abundance being several times higher than the abundance of nitrogen, there arises the fundamental question, why in the spectra of these condensations no [O II] line is observed at λ 3,727. The hypothesis that in one and the same condensation the emission ranges of [O I] and [N II] do not agree cannot explain the absence of the λ 3,727 line, because wherever nitrogen atoms are present in the form of singly charged ions, oxygen atoms will also be present in the very same state of ionization. In this case the intensity of the λ 3,727 line must be several times higher than the intensity of the [N II] lines. The spectrograms of the "stationary" condensations, however, do not display any [O II] lines. According to [82] in the spectra of the "diffuse" condensations the intensity of the λ 3,727 line is at least five times lower than the intensity of the lines of [O I] or [O III].

Since the density of the negative shown in Figure 26 is much higher than that in Figure 27, one may draw the conclusion that if the intensity of λ 3,727 were one-fifth of Hα it would have been observable. Since the total intensity of the nitrogen lines is six times that of Hα and oxygen is about three times more abundant than nitrogen, we may draw another conclusion: the intensity of the line λ 3,727 is at least one hundred times lower than expected.

It seems to us that the only reasonable explanation of this very low intensity is the influence of interstellar light absorption. As interstellar absorption $A_\lambda \sim \lambda^{-1}$, it is easy to show that the difference in absorption between λ 6,584 and λ 3,727 by five magnitudes corresponds to absorption in the range of the nitrogen lines $A_{6,584} = 6^m.6$ while the absorption about λ 3,727 reaches the huge value of $11^m.6$. At about $\lambda = 5,000$ A absorption will be equal to $A_{5,000} = 10^m$. This high magnitude obtained for the absorption in the direction towards Cassiopeia A requires some discussion.

4 + s.

Minkowski and Aller, in their first attempt to interpret the spectrum of Cassiopeia, denied the possibility of an influence of interstellar absorption on the relative line intensities of Cassiopeia A.[82]   However, as soon as possible in the following year, Minkowski emphasized that the absorption in the direction of this nebula was strong and of "flocculate" character.[80] Assuming, for example, that without absorption the brightness of the diffuse condensations in the central part of Cassiopeia A was the same as that in the periphery of the nebula, he estimated the absorbed magnitude in the central part as $A_{ph} \simeq 6^m$.   That the absorption in this zone must be very considerable follows from an analysis of a count of the stars. By means of the "classic" method Greenstein found that absorption must in any case be higher than $2^m.5$.   Our estimate of $A_{ph} = 10^m$ is based on visual estimations of the relative line intensities and therefore it is of course not very accurate.   However, after accounting for all possible errors of this method, absorption in the photographic range will hardly be less than 8^m, and in the visual range—less than 6.5^m.   This conclusion will also follow from other communications.   Above we drew attention only to the fact that it cannot be viewed as unimportant that the supernova which exploded at about A.D. 1700 was never observed.   If the absolute photographic magnitude of this supernova was -17 (cf. § 1) and, consequently, its visual magnitude was -16.5 [since the spectra of type II supernovae near their maximum are of a very "early" type (cf. also Fig. 8)], then, with a distance of 3,400 psc, its visible magnitude, without any absorption, must have been about -3.5!   It is thus only the influence of the strong interstellar absorption that can explain the fact that this supernova was never observed.   This outburst would hardly have remained unnoticed if its visual magnitude had been brighter than 4. Hence it follows immediately the estimated lower limit of $A_v > 7.5$ which corresponds to an absorption at $\lambda\,3{,}727$ with $A_{3,727} > 10$ which is in perfect agreement with our estimate.

What are the physical conditions of the gas present in the "stationary" condensations?   The electron temperature was estimated above. Let us now estimate the density of the gas.   Since the hydrogen in these condensations is ionized, the $H\alpha$ emission can be shown to be caused mainly by recombination (and not by collisions as Chamberlain assumed[83]). Let us estimate the $H\alpha$ line intensity in the spectrogram shown in Figure 26.   We may agree in assuming that it is ten times as intense as the line $\lambda\,6{,}300$ (just as well as this ratio may be several times higher).   On the other hand, the nebular line $\lambda\,6{,}300$ has about the same intensity as the corresponding line in the spectrum of nocturnal sky. For the latter we assume an intensity of 100 Rayleigh (i.e., 10^8 photons emitted in a unit column per second, in all directions). Assuming the absorption in this spectral range as $A \sim 6.5$ magnitudes, we find that the emission in the unit column passing through the condensation amounts to about 310^{11} photons/s. For a condensation which is 2.10^{17} cm in diameter (that corresponds to an angular diameter of 4″) we then find that about 10^{-6} photons are emitted per second and per unit volume in all directions. Applying the well-known formulas of recombinative luminescence of hydrogen, we may now estimate the electron concentration as $N_e \sim 310^3$ cm^{-3} which, for a normal chemical composition, corresponds to a mean density of $\sim 10^{-20}$ g/cm^3. The total mass of the condensation is thus obtained as $M \sim 3 \cdot 10^{31}$ g. If about twenty of such condensations are observed, their total sum will be of the order of $0.3M_\odot$. Note that the mass of interstellar gas contained in a sphere of a radius of 2 psc is equal to $M_{\mathrm{gas}} = 8 \cdot 10^{56}\bar{\rho}$. If $\bar{\rho} \sim 10^{-24}$ g, $M_{\mathrm{gas}} \sim 8 \cdot 10^{32}$ g, which is quite similar to the above estimate of the total mass of stationary condensations. Combining this with the fact that the radiation velocities of these condensations is a hundred times lower than that of the diffuse condensations while the chemical composition is obviously normal, we naturally arrive at the idea that the stationary condensations consist of interstellar gas which was compressed, heated and broken up into individual dense clusters when interacting with the expanding shell of the supernova. Some theoretical aspects of this problem will be discussed later.

The relative intensities of the lines [N II] and Hα are explained by the comparatively high value of T_e in the condensation and the fact that the N atoms are preferably in the state [N II]. Since the emission of spectral lines occurs at the expense of the intrinsic energy of the electron gas, the latter must cool down if no energy is supplied to it from within. The line emission per unit volume must be 10^{-5} photons/s or $\sim 5 \cdot 10^{17}$ erg/s while the intrinsic energy of the electron gas per unit volume amounts to $\varepsilon \sim 3/2N_e kT_e \sim 3 \cdot 10^{-8}$ erg/cm^3; from this we may conclude that the cooling period will be $\tau \sim 20$ years, that is much shorter than the time for which the condensation exists. The condensation must therefore be heated continuously by some mechanism; the possible nature of this process will be discussed in § 8.

Let us now discuss the spectrum of the diffuse non-stationary condensations. As we see from the spectrogram of Figure 27, the intensities of the lines [O I] and [O III] are approximately equal, whereas, according to [82], the intensity of the line [O II] λ 3,727 is at least five times lower. According to [81] this type of the line λ 3,727 was observed in several condensations though, obviously, it is fairly weak. Taking into account that the differential absorption between λ 3,727 and λ 5,000 may reach two magnitudes, and that between λ 6,300 and λ 3,727 even four to five magnitudes, we may conclude that without absorption the intensities of the lines λ 6,300, λ 3,727 and λ 4,959 must correspond to the approximate ratio of 1 : 20 : 5. This, of course, is quite a rough estimate. But we get the impression that most of the oxygen atoms in diffuse condensations are in the state of [O II].

The flat maximum in the distribution of the oxygen atoms with respect to the states of ionization of [O II] is a characteristic feature of the ionization equilibrium if ionization is caused by electron impact. An analogous situation is known to be observed in the solar corona.[85] According to a theory developed in [85] the most frequent state of ionization depends only on T_e and is independent of N_e. If the ionization maximum of oxygen is near [O II], and the number of [O III] is not too small a fraction of that of [O II], $T_e \sim 40,000 - 50,000°$, i.e., it is much higher than in the stationary condensations. This high electron temperature in the diffuse condensations at once gives rise to serious difficulties. If we assume that in these condensations the abundance ratio of oxygen and hydrogen is normal, that is of the order of 1,000:1, we find that owing to the exceeding closeness of the ionization potentials of these elements the number of neutral atoms of hydrogen should be about 10^3 times higher than that of oxygen. With $T_e \sim 40,000°$ the third quantum level of hydrogen would be excited very frequently by means of electron impacts. For this reason the intensity of the Hα line should be higher by at least one order of magnitude than that of λ 6,300, whereas in fact this line is completely absent in the spectra of diffuse condensations.

There are two ways of avoiding this difficulty. Firstly, we may suggest that in the diffuse filaments the relative abundance of the elements differ essentially from the average. In particular the relative hydrogen concentration must be 1 per cent or less compared to the normal. In this connection we must stress that, in contrast to the stationary condensations, which are most likely clusters of compressed interstellar gas, the diffuse condensations must possess the same chemical composition as the shell of the exploding star, which may differ greatly from the average. One may, however, suppose that the relative abundance of hydrogen and heavy elements will not differ considerably from the normal ratio, while the relative abundances of the heavy elements may display some peculiarities. Note that in the spectra of type II supernovae in the post-maximum stage the hydrogen lines belong to the most intense lines (cf. § 1).

The second way of avoiding the difficulties connected with the interpretation of the emission lines [O I] and [O III] is based on the assumption that these lines come from different but closely neighboured zones of the diffuse condensations. This hypothesis is supported by the differences observed in the band structures of [O I] and [O III] bands, whose general profiles are similar. Adopting this "two-component" model of condensations, we shall assume that in "hot" zones with $T_e \sim 30,000 - 40,000°$ the lines of [O III] and other ions are emitted and in the "cold" zones the lines [O I]. Let us first consider the conditions in the "hot" zones of the diffuse filaments. The parameters necessary to calculate the intensities of the forbidden lines are all given in the nomograms and tables of [86]. The emission in an arbitrary nebular line may be given in the form

$$I_\lambda = I_{H\beta} \frac{n_i}{n_p} \theta(N_e, T_e) \tag{5.1}$$

where $I_{H\beta}$ is the intensity of the hydrogen line Hβ in the case of a recombinative mechanism of excitation. $I_{H\beta}$ is used as the reference intensity. $I_{H\beta} = n_p N_e \cdot 1.22 \cdot 10^{-25}$ erg/cm$^3 \cdot$s, n_i is the concentration of the ions which emit the line we are interested in, and n_p is the proton concentration. The quantity $\theta(N_e, T_e)$ for the line λ 3,727, which is a very weak function of N_e if $N_e < 10^4$ cm^{-3}, may be obtained from the graph given in [86] for $T_e = 40,000°$ and $N_e < 10^4$ cm^{-3}, $\theta = 10^6$. Assuming that $n_i/N_e = \alpha = 10^{-3}$ we find

$$\varepsilon_\lambda = N_e^2 \cdot 1.22 \cdot 10^{-22} \text{ erg/cm}^3 \cdot \text{s} = N_e^2 \cdot 2.3 \cdot 10^{11} \text{ photons/cm}^3 \cdot \text{s} \tag{5.2}$$

When we assume that the intensity of the line λ 3,727, free from the influence of interstellar light absorption, is given by $I \sim 3 \cdot 10^{11}$ photons/cm$^2 \cdot$s and the length of the column is $\sim 3 \cdot 10^{17}$ cm, we obtain $\varepsilon_\lambda \sim 10^{-6}$ photons/cm$^3 \cdot$s and hence, by way of a comparison with (5.2), we find that $N_e \sim 2 \cdot 10^2$ cm^{-3}, a value which is rather small. With this value of N_e the measure of nebular emission, $ME = N_e^2 l$ (where $l \sim 0.1$ psc, the thickness of a filament), will be low, i.e., of the order of $4 \cdot 10^3$. In the case of zero absorption the surface brightness in the Hα line would be about the same as with the ordinary diffuse nebulae. We must take into consideration that such faint objects of this type have a surface brightness that corresponds to $ME \sim 10^2$. Therefore, if the absorption in the band of Hα exceeds four magnitudes, the Hα emission of the nebula cannot be discovered. In this way the absence of hydrogen lines in the spectra of non-stationary condensations finds quite a natural explanation.

The fact that the line $\lambda\,3{,}727$ can be seen in some diffuse filaments at the boundary and cannot be seen in the stationary condensations is explained firstly by the high value of $T_e \sim 40{,}000°$; with this T_e the value of $\theta(T_e, N_e)$ is ten times higher than in the case of $T_e = 15{,}000°$. Moreover, it must be borne in mind that absorption in the region of the nebula is locally variable and may be lower in the direction of the individual filaments than in the direction of the central part of the nebula.

We see then that we can explain the absence of the Hα line in diffuse condensations by a comparatively low value of N_e and strong absorption of the light; it is, however, less easy to explain the absence of the [N II] lines because of the presence of an [O II] line, even though it is weak. In our opinion the only reasonable explanation could be provided by the assumption that the nitrogen content is anomalously low in these condensations which, most likely, are expanding parts of the shell thrown out during the explosion. In this connection we should like to note that certain early-type stars have an anomalously low content of nitrogen. Since we have every reason to assume that pre-outburst supernovae of type II are massive hot stars, we can understand that no nitrogen was found in the non-stationary filaments of Cassiopeia A: before the outburst the star belonged to the type of Wolf–Rayet stars which are nitrogen deficient.

Let us now consider the conditions in the "cold" zones of the diffuse condensations which emit the [O I] lines. Since the intensity of these lines depends on the product $N_e \cdot n_0 C(T_e)$, where the concentration of the neutral hydrogen atoms, the electron concentration and the temperature are unknown, the problem is quite indefinite. T_e must be $\lesssim 10{,}000°$, otherwise the Hα line must be observed (with "normal" relative abundance of oxygen and hydrogen!). If we suppose that ionization is maintained by electron collisions with hydrogen atoms, we obtain $n_0/n_H < 3\cdot10^{-2}$ with $T_e < 10^4$. If the observable intensity of the line $\lambda\,6{,}300$ is about 10^{10} photons/cm$^3\cdot$s we obtain $n_0 N_e = 0.25$ with $\theta = 10^4$ (see [86]). If, for example, $n_0 = 0.2$ (i.e., the gas density in the cold part of a diffuse condensation is the same as in the hot part), $N_e \sim 1$ cm^{-3}, which is not in contradiction with the above estimate of the ionization at

$T_e \leqslant 10^4$ degrees. It is, however, quite possible that the gas density in the cold parts of the diffuse condensations is much higher and N_e correspondingly smaller.

We will now estimate the total mass of the filaments. For this purpose we must know the total volume occupied by them. If the angular dimension of an average diffuse condensation is $\sim 5''$, and if there are 200 of them, it is easy to calculate the total volume; we obtain $\sim 2 \cdot 10^{54}$ cm^3, that is $\frac{1}{500}$ of the entire volume occupied by the radio source of Cassiopeia A. With $N_e = 2 \cdot 10^2$ cm^{-3} the mean density is $\sim 5 \cdot 10^{-22}$ g and the total mass $\sim 10^{33}$ g or $\sim 1 M_\odot$. To this we still have to add the mass of the "cold" part of the filaments which emits the [O I] lines. This mass may exceed considerably the mass of the "hot" parts of the filaments.

Our estimate of the mass of filaments is of course very rough owing to both the uncertainty in the determination of the total volume of the filaments and the uncertainty in the estimation of the density of their "cold" components: An estimate of $\sim 1 M_\odot$ for the total mass is in all probability too low. We are probably justified in assuming the mass to be of the order of several (maybe ten) solar masses, which is in good agreement with estimates of the shell masses ejected in the outburst of a supernova of type II.

Besides Cassiopeia A which is a "young" nebula that formed when a supernova of type II exploded, several fine-fibred nebulae are observed which are comparatively "old" remnants of such outbursts. We shall now discuss in greater detail the interpretations of their spectra found in the literature.

The first serious attempt to interpret the spectra of systems of fibrous nebulae in the constellation of Cygnus was made by S. B. Pikel'ner in 1954.[84] Working with the nebular spectrograph of the Crimean Astrophysical Observatory he obtained original observational material which, for that time, was of high quality. It must, however, be noted that a nebular spectrograph yields a high average picture of the spectrum but the individual characteristic differences in the spectra of the filaments (the existence of which was recently proved by Parker[87]) cannot be observed with this method. The dispersion was so low that, for example, the lines [N II] and Hα overlapped. The fundamental peculiarities of the spectrum of fibrous nebulae are, however, quite clearly observable. The brightest line in the spectrum is the [O II] line λ 3,727 which is much stronger than the [O III] lines. Note that light absorption in the direction of the system of filamentary nebulae is low, which is mainly due to their relative proximity. The [O III] lines, which in the spectra of planetary nebulae are weak because of the high ionization, are strengthened here. We saw that a similar picture of the spectrum can be obtained from the "hot" parts of the diffuse filaments of Cassiopeia A. The spectra of the filamentary nebulae are in general characteristic of a comparatively low degree of ionization, which is a usual feature of the spectra of diffuse nebulae, and of a high intensity of the forbidden lines, which is natural in the spectra of planetary nebulae. In the following chapter we shall see that this character of the spectrum is observed in the filaments of the Crab nebula.

TABLE 9   Ionization of Elements

	$T_e = 30,000°$	$40,000°$	$50,000°$
$\dfrac{O\ II}{O\ I}$	50	356	—
$\dfrac{O\ III}{O\ II}$	$1.7 \cdot 10^{-3}$	0.084	1.1
$\dfrac{N\ III}{N\ II}$	$1.2 \cdot 10^{-2}$	0.36	3.1
$\dfrac{S\ III}{S\ II}$	0.252	4.1	24.6
$\dfrac{H\ II}{H\ I}$	140	560	2,300

Now we may ask whether it is possible to explain the observed relative line intensity in the spectra of filamentary nebulae by a steady emission of gas with "normal" relative abundance of elements at a certain temperature T_e. In the case of Cassiopeia A, the fact that in the spectra of the diffuse filaments the lines [O I] and [O III] are present while Hα is absent, at once excludes this possibility and requires the introduction of a "two-component" model of diffuse condensations. The spectrum of the filamentary nebulae in Cygnus is much more "normal": the lines [O I] are absent while the Balmer lines are observed. It is therefore not possible to reject immediately the possibility of steady emission from ionized gas. It proves necessary to conduct careful investigations and this is what was actually done by S. B. Pikel'ner. The calculations were carried out for sufficiently high temperatures as otherwise the presence of ions could not be explained.   First we shall give the highly valuable table of the ionizations of various elements by electron impact at different temperatures.

Knowing the ionizations of the various elements and the excitation cross-sections for electron impact of the various lines we can calculate the relative intensity of the latter (the intensity of Hβ is taken as the intensity unit).

TABLE 10   Relative Intensities of Different Lines

$T_e = 30,000°$		$40,000°$	$50,000°$	Observations
[O I] λ 3,727–3,729	374	570	432	25
[O III] λ 4,959–5,007	0.3	25	225	4.7
[S II] λ 6,711–6,728	65	22	3.7	2.8
[N II] λ 6,582–6,548	48	50	22	6.2
Hα	4.1	3.9	3.8	

In the last column of Table 10 we find the results of these observations.   It is evident that, whatever T_e, a steady emission of gas cannot yield a spectrum similar to the observed one.

We may conclude from this that the radiant gas of the filaments is at different temperatures.   In particular this may be the case when the filaments represent regions of interstellar medium behind the front of the shock wave, which gradually cool down.   Pikel'ner, dealing with this problem, was the first to develop a theory of the luminescence of gas behind a shock wave under the conditions of interstellar medium.

Immediately behind the front of a strong shock wave the gas temperature is very high.   In an ideal monatomic gas it is, independently of the nature of the interstellar medium, determined by the formula

$$\frac{3}{2} kT = \frac{9}{32} m_H V^2 \tag{5.3}$$

where V is the velocity of the front relative to the non-perturbed medium. For example, with $V \sim 10^7$ cm/s (this speed is observed in expanding filamentary nebulae), $T \sim 230,000°$.   The density of the interstellar gas behind the front is raised discontinuously.   If we ignore the losses in intrinsic energy of the gas to radiation (adiabatic case), the gas density

4*

behind the front increases by a factor of 4. If the gas is rapidly cooled down by the emission of radiation the deviation from adiabatic conditions will be great and the density of the medium behind the front may rise to a considerable level. But calculations show that under the conditions that exist in the filamentary nebulae the compression of the gas behind the shock wave may be considered as adiabatic with sufficient accuracy.

Owing to the high temperature arising on the passage of the shock wave, heavy particles (atoms, ions) are produced at first. This indicates that the oriented velocity of the wave is transformed into disordered thermal velocity of the atoms. Herein results the content of Equation (5.3). Initially the electrons do not raise their temperature (unless, of course, the velocity of the wave amounts to several hundred kilometres per second). By means of collisions, however, the heavy particles gradually transfer their energy to the electrons. Therefore, in a given fixed volume element behind the front of the shock wave, the initially very high ion temperature will drop and the electron temperature will rise. While raising their temperature the electrons will suffer inelastic collisions with atoms and ions, thus ionizing and exciting them. In this way the electron energy is lost. From a certain moment on when the energy transfer from the heavy ions to the electrons cannot compensate these losses any longer, T_e begins to drop. Figure 30 shows the change with time of the state of the gas behind the shock wave front for two values of the initial ion temperatures. These curves were calculated in [84] from the energy balance of the electron gas and the ion gas. In these graphs the degree of ionization of hydrogen was also plotted as a time function. The calculations were carried out on the assumption that the initial degree of ionization of hydrogen is $x = n_e/n_H = 0.01$. We see from these curves that the degree of ionization of hydrogen is comparatively low. The development of this process in the course of time is characteristic of it. As long as x is small the energy losses and the "thermal contact" between the heavy particles and the electrons are low. In this stage T_i and T_e vary quite slowly. As x increases the rate of change of the characteristic rises until the energy resources of the gas are exhausted. In this way the temperature behind the wave front drops gradually. The emission of the filaments (provided they can be treated as the wave front) corresponds to a different gas temperature. Integrating the radiation from the gas behind the wave front (on the assumption that each volume element radiates according to its temperature) we may obtain the theoretical values of the

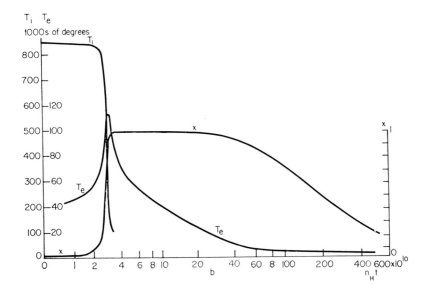

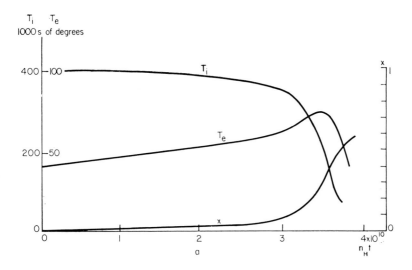

FIG. 30   Variation with time of the state of the gas behind the shock wave front.[84]
T_i, T_e in thousand degrees.

relative intensities of the various spectral lines; this has been done in [84]. Table 11 contains the relative intensities of the most important emission lines calculated in this way and also the empirical values.

TABLE 11

| | One Wave | Two Waves | | | |
T_i	850,000°	380,000°	400,000°	450,000°	Observations
[S II]	1	2.3	1.9	1.2	2.8
[N II]	1	2.6	2.3	1.3	2.8
[O III]	5	0.84	1.6	7.4	4.7
[O II]	9	11.8	15.1	12.4	25

From this table we see that the theoretical values of the relative intensities agree quite well with the observation values.

The absolute values of the intensities of spectral lines in filamentary nebulae, however, require a particle concentration of about 300 cm^{-3}. At the same time, owing to the quasi-adiabatic compression of the interstellar medium its density may increase only fourfold. To co-ordinate the theory with the observations, S. B. Pikel'ner makes two suppositions. First, he assumes that the initial mean concentration of hydrogen in the non-perturbed interstellar medium was ~ 20 cm^{-3} which corresponds to the concentration in the relatively dense interstellar gas clouds. But in this case the particle concentration behind the front will amount to only ~ 80 cm^{-3}, which is insufficient. He therefore states the interesting hypothesis of an intersection of the fronts of shock waves which are propagated at a certain angle with respect to one another. The second wave enters the already compressed gas and causes an additional compression and heating. The glow zone in the intersection of the two surfaces will thus be a one-dimensional structure. The state of the gas in the intersection of the two waves was determined by means of a numerical method and then the line intensities were calculated. The relative intensities obtained are given in Table 11.

Intersecting waves may form when a shock wave is propagated in a non-uniform medium. Since the velocity of propagation of a shock wave depends on the density of the non-perturbed gas, the wave fronts become deformed when propagation occurs in a non-uniform medium. The optical analogue is the propagation of light in a non-uniform medium.   The non-uniformities of the medium exert a focusing effect on the medium which results in an intersection of the fronts.   If this is the actual mechanism, the filaments will arise where the density of the interstellar matter is higher.

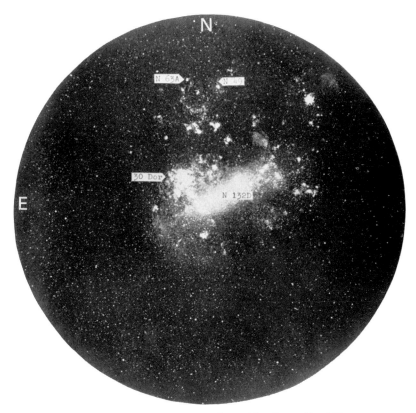

FIG. 31   Photograph of the Large Magellanic Cloud.[88]

This, in general outline, is the theory of glow of the filamentary nebulae worked out by S. B. Pikel'ner.   It is beyond any doubt that the gas in the filaments radiates because of electron impacts.   It is, in particular, the great differences in the spectra of the individual filaments, discovered by Parker,[87] that support this.   It is also certain that we cannot explain the glow of the fibres by assuming a steady emission of the gas whatever we assume for the temperature. Parker himself, trying to interpret the spectra of the filamentary nebulae in Cygnus, was led to the two-component model of the filaments. In the "hot" component ($T_e \sim 10^5$) the [O III] lines are emitted, in the "cold" component,

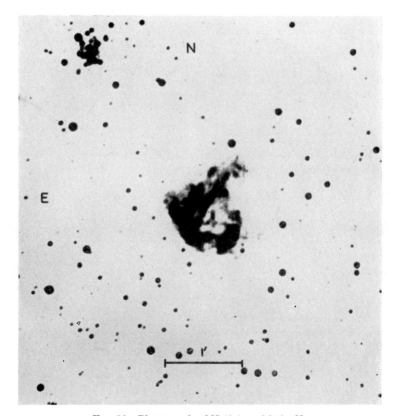

FIG. 32   Photograph of N 49 in red light.[88]

where $T_e = 1.7 \cdot 10^4$, the lines of the other ions and also the Balmer series of hydrogen are emitted. Like Pikel'ner, Parker connects the observed thermal non-uniformity of the filaments with the propagation of a shock wave, but he did not carry out any serious calculations. It must be remarked also that other filamentary nebulae have spectra which resemble the "loop" in Cygnus.

The problem of the remnants of supernovae of type II in other galaxies is of particular interest. The only stellar system in which such objects could still be observed is the Large Magellanic Cloud. All other galaxies, disregarding the Small Magellanic Cloud, are too far away from us. It is not impossible that remnants of supernovae of type II will also be discovered in the Small Magellanic Cloud, a galaxy which is peculiar in many respects.

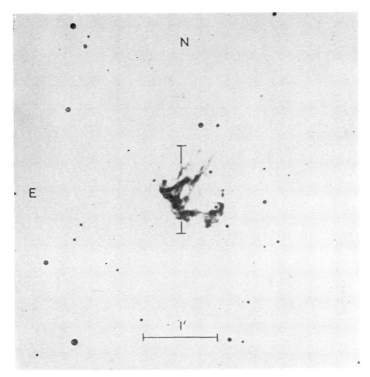

FIG. 33   Photograph of N 49 in blue light.[88]

Recently Westerlund and Mathewson conducted a very interesting comprehensive investigation of the remnants of type II supernovae in the Large Magellanic Cloud.[88] Altogether three such objects were discovered which were identical with the emission nebulae N 49, N 63A and N 132D in Henize's Catalogue. Parallel observations were carried out at the

66-metre radio telescope of the Parks observatory and the 74-inch reflector of the observatory on Mount Stromlo in Australia. The fact that these nebulae could be identified with radio sources of non-thermal emission proves that these objects are in fact remnants of supernovae and

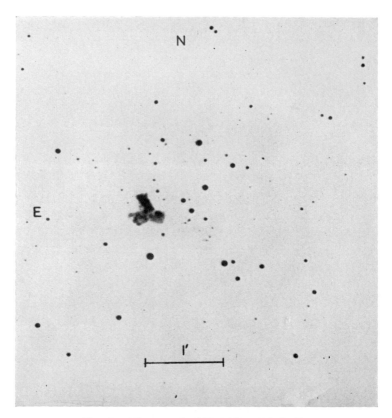

Fig. 34   Photograph of N 63A in red light.[88]

not merely bright gas nebulae, as there are many in the Magellanic Clouds which are rich in interstellar gas and young hot stars (see the following section, § 6).

Figure 31 shows a photograph of the Large Magellanic Cloud; the marks indicate the positions of the nebulae which are remnants of supernova outbursts. Figure 32 shows a photograph of N 49, taken in red light and Figure 33 is N 49 photographed in blue light. The photograph of Figure 34 shows the nebula N 63A in red light.

These remnants of supernovae, which are the first that were discovered in another stellar system, are so important and valuable for us because their distances are well known. They are, naturally, equal to the distance of the Magellanic Clouds, that is 55,000 psc. There are only three galactic remnants of supernova outbursts whose distances are known with a high degree of accuracy, namely Cassiopeia A, the filamentary nebulae in Cygnus and the Crab nebula. For the other objects a statistical method of estimating their distance has been worked out which will be considered in § 7. The knowledge of the accurate distances to the supernova remnants enables us to determine their fundamental characteristics (dimensions, luminosity, etc.) with high reliability.

N 49 and N 63A are in a region which is very rich in hot blue giants and clouds of interstellar neutral hydrogen. As we see from the photographs of Figures 32 and 33, the nebula N 49 has a distinct fibrous structure. Because of the great distances only such filaments which are thicker than 0.5 psc can be resolved. The insufficient resolution of course does not permit the observation of that "open-work" structure, as is possible with S 147 or the filamentary nebulae in Cygnus. If these were photographed in a resolution of ~ 1′, they would show about the same form as N 49.

It is necessary to stress that N 49, N 132D, the filamentary nebulae in Cygnus and IC 443 display a very complex photometrical structure. These nebulae are characterized by open shells. It is interesting that in all these cases the shell is "torn" in a direction which faces a region of relatively high density of interstellar gas. In the case of the filamentary nebulae in Cygnus this direction is perpendicular to the galactic plane and in the Magellanic Clouds it is opposite to local condensations of interstellar gas clouds.

The structure of N 63A differs from those of N 49 and N 132D. It is characterized by three bright condensations. The impression is as if the material had been ejected from a common centre in three directions. The intensity distributions in red and blue light are quite different for one and the same nebula, which indicates that the conditions of excitation are different.

The angular dimensions of N 49 in red light are rather high, namely 67″, which corresponds to linear dimensions of 18 psc, whereas the linear dimensions of N 63A and N 132D are only 7 and 6 psc, respectively.

From the photograph of a part of the Large Magellanic Cloud, shown in Figure 31, we see that N 63A is a member of an association of young hot stars. The brightest stars in this association have an absolute visual magnitude of $M_v = -6.2$ which, according to the mass-luminosity relationship, corresponds to a mass of $\sim 40 M_\odot$. The total mass of the stars in this association amounts to about $10^3 M_\odot$ and their age is of the order of 10^6 years.

N 49 is also a member of a fairly extended association, though this is not so obvious as in the case of N 63A. This association contains a cluster of young stars in whose neighbourhood N 49 is located. This structural detail of the Magellanic Clouds is entirely embedded in a relatively dense cloud of neutral interstellar hydrogen. As regards N 132D it cannot yet be said definitely whether this nebula belongs to the association. Interstellar absorption in this region of the Magellanic Clouds is obviously very intense.

The Australian researchers working with the 74-inch telescope succeeded in obtaining several good spectrograms of N 49, N 63A and N 132D (Fig. 35). In these spectra the emission lines Hα, [N II], [S II] and [O I] are clearly seen. In the nebula N 49 each line displays a quite irregular variation in a direction perpendicular to the dispersion. This indicates the "flocculent" character of the nebula (compared with the spectrum of Cassiopeia A).

The differences in the radiation velocities for one and the same spectral line but from different emitting condensations reaches 100 km/s in the case of N 49. This indicates that the nebula expands relative to the surrounding interstellar gas at a rate of 50 km/s. From this we may conclude that the shell was essentially slowed down. The shells in N 63A and N 132D were still more decelerated.

The character of the spectrum and the relative line intensities in these nebulae in the Large Magellanic Cloud are nearly the same as in the filamentary nebulae of Cygnus (or IC 443, see above). The lines are mainly excited by means of electron impact. We shall not go into details as to the interpretation of the spectra; it is almost the same as in the case of the filamentary nebulae in Cygnus (see above). According to the final results of the authors of [88] $T_e \sim 15{,}000$–$20{,}000°$ and the electron concentration in the filaments is $N_e \sim (3 \text{ to } 5) \cdot 10^4$ cm^{-3}, which seems to us to be rather high.

In §§ 7 and 8 we shall return to a discussion of the characteristic features of these exceedingly interesting objects.

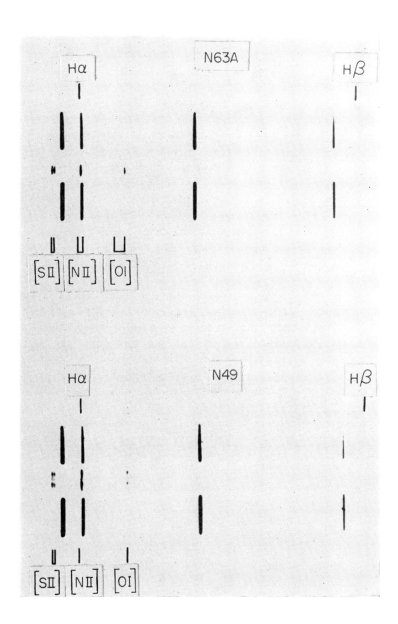

FIG. 35   Spectra of the supernova remnants in the Large Magellanic Cloud.[88]

§ 6   Radio-frequency emission from remnants of supernovae of type II

Twenty-two years ago, in 1946, one of the greatest discoveries in the twentieth century was made in the field of astronomy. Studying the intensity distribution of cosmic radio emission over the firmament on the 4.7-metre band, Hey, Phillips and Parsons discovered a discrete radio source in the constellation Cygnus.[89]   Two years later, Ryle and Smith, who studied this source at a frequency of 81.5 Mc with the help of a two-antenna interferometer with a base of 500 m, discovered another still more powerful source in the constellation Cassiopeia. The approximate co-ordinates of this source were $\alpha = 23^h 17^m$, $\delta = +58°$, the spectral flux density at this frequency was $F_\nu = 2.3 \cdot 10^{-22}$ W/m^2·c/s. In 1951, with the help of an interference method, Smith succeeded in obtaining more precise co-ordinates of this source, which enabled Baade and Minkowski to identify it as a peculiar nebula, the remnant of a supernova of type II.

The enormous technical potential which is at the disposal of modern radio-astronomy permits the detection of at least twenty thousand discrete radio sources in the sky. The weakest of these sources emit fluxes which are about ten thousand times weaker than those from the source in Cassiopeia mentioned above which is the most powerful source. The power of the latter is such that its flux in the band of $\nu = 100$ Mc is almost the same as that of the quiescent sun. It must still be stressed that the sources in Cygnus and Cassiopeia, which were discovered first, are, moreover, quite different types of objects. The source in Cygnus was in 1951 identified as a peculiar galaxy while the source in Cassiopeia (to which, soon after the discovery, the name "Cassiopeia A" was assigned) proved to be the remnant of a supernova outburst.

The overwhelming majority of the radio sources known at present are metagalactic objects which resemble more or less the source Cygnus A. At the same time a relatively small group of sources were identified as remnants of supernovae. Today we know more than fifteen such objects which belong to this group. It is a very important fact that, without a single exception, all known remnants of galactic supernovae are radio sources. These sources are remnants of supernovae of either type I or type II. At least three sources of this type were recently discovered in galaxies which are our nearest neighbours, namely the Magellanic Clouds.[88]

The discovery of the radio-frequency emission from the remnants of supernovae of both types is certainly the most important stage in the history of the research into these objects. The investigation of the radio-frequency emission is the most effective method of analyzing the physical conditions in their expanding shells which, in its turn, raises a series of problems which are directly connected with the very nature of the outbursts. In individual cases the distances of supernovae could be determined by means of purely radio-astronomical methods which was often quite impossible using the methods of optical astronomy. Finally, an analysis of the radio-frequency emission of the remnants of supernovae enables us to understand the nature of the interaction between their expanding shells and interstellar matter. In the present section we shall consider the radio emission of only the remnants of type II supernovae. The radio-frequency emission from the remnants of type I supernovae and, last of all, from the Crab nebula, will be dealt with in detail in Chapter III.

Let us first discuss the problem of the radio emission from the "youngest" remnant of a supernova of type II, Cassiopeia A. The most important characteristic of the radio-frequency emission of any source is its spectrum. In radio-astronomy the spectral flux density is usually determined by the following relation:

$$F_\nu = C\nu^{-\alpha} \qquad (6.1)$$

where α is called the spectral index. The spectral index is usually of the order of unity.

Modern radio-astronomical investigations cover a very broad interval in the spectrum which ranges from $\lambda = 10\text{--}20$ m to ~ 1 cm. Naturally, it will seldom be possible to describe the variation of F_ν in a very broad frequency range by means of a single value of the parameter. For example, there are many metagalactic sources whose spectral index in the decimetre and centimetre ranges is higher than in the metre range. Sometimes one may observe with such sources a smooth increase of α as the frequency increases. This is especially interesting as the radio sources which are remnants of supernovae, in particular Cassiopeia A, possess a spectral index which remains surprisingly constant as the frequency varies within wide limits. Figure 36 shows the spectrum of Cassiopeia A which has been obtained on the basis of all observational data available.[90] We see that in the entire frequency range $\nu > 15$ Mc the spectrum is characterized by a single value of $\alpha = 0.8$. The "overfilling" of the spectrum in the low-frequency range ($\nu < 15$ Mc) is explained by particular causes which will be discussed below.

An important characteristic feature of any cosmic radio source is its angular dimensions. The angular dimensions of Cassiopeia A were first measured in 1952 by Hanburry Brown, Jennisson and Das Gupta.[91] To solve this problem they used a two-antenna interferometer with a variable measuring base from 0.3 to 4 km in different azimuths. The measuring

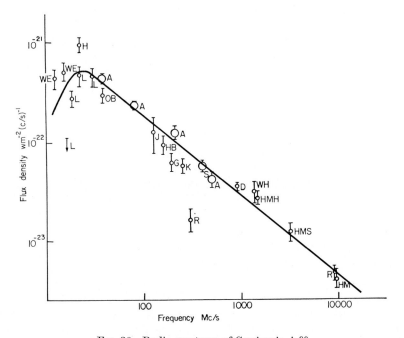

Fig. 36   Radio spectrum of Cassiopeia A.[90]

frequency was 120 Mc. Unlike the source Cygnus A, Cassiopeia A proved to be a more or less symmetrical (i.e., non-elongated) source with an equivalent angular diameter of about 4'. At almost the same time Smith,[92] in Cambridge, arrived at the same result; he used an analogous method and measured in the 1.4-m band.

The estimate of the angular dimensions obtained in this way is, however, a rather rough characteristic of the radio intensity distribution within the limits of the source. In the ideal case one should try to obtain a radio photograph of the source which displays a sufficiently high resolution.   Recently Ryle, Elsmore and Neville[93] used a very effective interference method.   The radio interferometer consisted of three elements: two fixed elements and one mobile element.   These elements were mirrors, somewhat more than nineteen metres in diameter; the

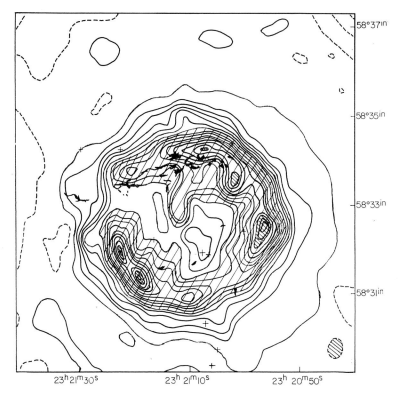

FIG. 37   Radio picture of Cassiopeia A on a wavelength of 21.3 cm.[93]

movable mirror could be rolled on rails.   The entire system was equivalent to two interferometers operating simultaneously.   The observations were made in the 21.3-cm band, the base length was equal to $\lambda\,7{,}000$.   The resolving power (for half the intensity) was $23''$ in right ascension and $23''$ cosec δ in declination.   An evaluation of the results of these observations made it possible to draw a "radio picture" of Cassiopeia A, which is

given in Figure 37.   In the same figure we see the position and form of the
brightest optical filaments of the nebula which we discussed in the previous
section.   The cross marks indicate the positions of the brightest stars in
the environment of Cassiopeia A.   The isophotes are drawn through
brightness temperature intervals of $\Delta T_b = 3,000°$.

The clearly marked shell structure of this source is a fundamental
characteristic feature of the radio intensity distribution of Cassiopeia A.
It should be noted that even before the observations of Ryle and his co-
workers, French radio astronomers had observed a (of course) blurry
shell structure of Cassiopeia A[94] (see Fig. 37a, b).   The observations made

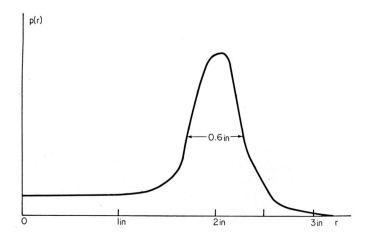

FIG. 37a   Linear intensity distribution in Cassiopeia A.[94]

in Cambridge showed that this shell has a very irregular structure.   It
contains about ten condensations, three of which are extremely bright.
However, in spite of the presence of these condensations, it may be
assumed that 90 per cent of the total radiation comes from a homogeneous
(as regards the volume luminosity) spherical shell, whose thickness amounts
to $\Delta r \sim 0.25r$.   Note that the thickness of the radio-emitting shell
exceeds considerably the thickness of the shell which contains the
optical filaments and the condensations (cf. § 5).   The increased intensity
in the central part of Cassiopeia A ($\alpha = 23^{\mathrm{h}}21^{\mathrm{m}}11^{\mathrm{s}}$, $\delta = 58°33'$) has its
most likely explanation in the effect of shell projection.   Moreover, there

are real "radio condensations" (e.g., at $\alpha = 23^h20^m55^s$, $\delta = 58°32'.6$, in which the "volume luminosity" is at least ten to twenty times higher than the mean volume luminosity of the shell.   It is interesting that these "radio condensations" in the shell, as a rule, do not coincide with the optical condensations.   A conspicuous feature is the marked "rupture" in the shell at $\alpha = 23^h21^m25^s$, $\delta = 58°33'$. This rupture is located opposite to the brightest "radio condensation" in this shell.

The brightness of the source Cassiopeia A is very high.   The volume luminosity of the shell is at least 10^8 times higher than that of the surrounding interstellar space.   The volume luminosity in the "radio condensations" is particularly high.

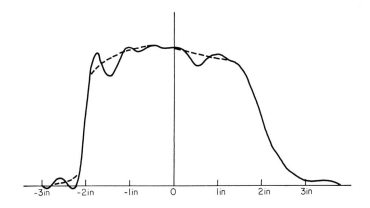

FIG. 37b   Schematic representation of the shell structure of Cassiopeia A.[94]

Let us now consider the radio-astronomical observations of Cassiopeia A.   The mechanism usually adopted to explain the radio-frequency emission of the overwhelming majority of both galactic and meta-galactic radio sources is the so-called "magneto-bremsstrahlung" or synchrotron radiation.   This type of radiation is produced when relativistic particles move into a magnetic field; it displays a series of interesting peculiarities. We do not intend to develop a complete theory of synchrotron radiation here, since this may be found in a series of textbooks (see, for example, [95]). We shall give only the fundamental formulas which will often be used in the following calculations.

The energy emitted by one relativistic particle per second in a unit interval of frequency is equal to

$$P(\nu, E) = \frac{16e^3 H}{mc^2}\, P\!\left(\frac{\omega}{\omega_m}\right) \tag{6.2}$$

where

$$\omega = 2\pi V, \qquad \omega_m = \frac{eH}{mc}\left(\frac{E}{mc^2}\right)^2$$

E is the energy of the relativistic particle and m is its mass. The function $P(\omega/\omega_m)$ has been tabulated in [96]. Its graph is shown in Figure 38.

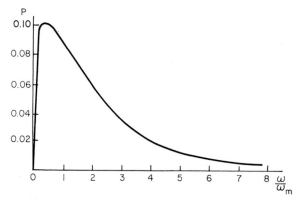

FIG. 38   P as a function of ω/ω_m.[96]

Let us give the limiting values of $P(\omega/\omega_m)$: if $\omega/\omega_m \ll 1$, $P(\omega/\omega_m) = 0.256(\omega/\omega_m)^{1/3}$ and if $\omega/\omega_m > 1$,

$$P\!\left(\frac{\omega}{\omega_m}\right) = \frac{1}{16}\left(\frac{\pi\omega}{\omega_m}\right)^{1/2} e^2\omega^3/\omega_m$$

The function $P(\omega/\omega_m)$ reaches its maximal value if $(\omega/\omega_m) \approx 0.5$. We therefore have at maximum

$$\nu_{\max} = 0.5\,\frac{\omega_m}{2\pi} = 1.4\cdot10^6 H_\perp\left(\frac{E}{mc^2}\right)^2 \text{c/s} \tag{6.3}$$

$$P(\nu_{\max}) = \frac{1.6e^3 H_\perp}{mc^2} = 2.15\cdot10^{-22}H_\perp \text{ erg/s·c/s} \tag{6.4}$$

where $H_\perp$ is the magnetic field component which is perpendicular to the velocity of the relativistic particle.

If the relativistic particles have an energy distribution which can be described by a power law

$$N(E) = KE^{-\gamma} \tag{6.5}$$

where $N(E)$ is the concentration of the relativistic particles whose energies are within the limits E and $E + \Delta E$, the power of the synchrotron radiation per unit volume, calculated per unit interval of frequency, will be equal to:

$$
\begin{aligned}
\varepsilon_\nu &= \int_{E > mc^2}^{\infty} P(\nu, E)N(E)\, dE \\
&= 12(2\pi)^{(1-\gamma)/2} \frac{e^3 H_\perp}{mc^2} \left[\frac{2eH}{m^3 c^5}\right]^{(\gamma-1)/2} U(\gamma)K\nu^{(1-\gamma)/2}
\end{aligned}
\tag{6.6}
$$

The function $U(\gamma)$ is equal to 0.37, 0.125, 0.087 and 0.153 with $\gamma = 1, 2, 3$ and 7, respectively.

If the relativistic particles are electrons or positrons we obtain the following numerical expression for the intensity of the synchrotron radiation

$$I_\nu = \frac{1}{4\pi} R\varepsilon_\nu = 1.3 \cdot 10^{22}(2.8 \cdot 10^8)^{(\gamma-1)/2} U(\gamma)KH^{(\gamma+1)/2} R\lambda^{(\gamma-1)/2} \tag{6.7}$$

where R is the extension area of the source along which the volume luminosity ε_ν is considered as constant.

From Equations (6.1) and (6.7) it follows that the spectral index α of the synchrotron radiation is only a function of the exponent in the energy spectrum of the relativistic particles,

$$\alpha = \frac{\gamma - 1}{2} \tag{6.8}$$

The fact that the spectra of cosmic radio sources can well be described by a power law of the form (6.1) is consistent with the well-known circumstance that the energy spectra of relativistic particles in cosmic rays are also governed by a power law. This alone provides a good argument in favour of the synchrotron theory of the radio emission of cosmic sources.

At present, however, we have much better proofs of the validity of the synchrotron theory at our disposal; they are, first of all, provided by polarization measurements (cf. § 10) and a series of observable consequences resulting from the synchrotron theory. Today the synchrotron theory of cosmic radio sources, which was mainly developed in the works of Soviet scientists, has won general recognition. When this theory was adopted in astronomy a fairly new element was introduced automatically: the non-thermal radiation. Previously the radiation from celestial bodies of all types considered in astronomy (stars, nebulae, galaxies, planets) has always been viewed as thermal. Its properties were described by the laws of Stefan–Boltzmann, Rayleigh–Jeans, Wien–Planck and the laws of light reflection and refraction. The production of the lines in emission and absorption spectra is another aspect of thermal radiation.

The discovery of non-thermal synchrotron radiation of relativistic particles afforded the astronomers a unique opportunity of studying cosmic radiation in the depths of the universe. Further investigations showed that cosmic radiation is by no means less important, for the evolution of the universe from matter, than gas and magnetic fields. Moreover, it was very soon proved that synchrotron radiation was not restricted solely to radio astronomy. For the problems we are interested in it is particularly important that such a "classic" remnant of a supernova as is the Crab nebula is a powerful source of optical and even Roentgen synchrotron radiations.

When the mechanism of radio emission of Cassiopeia A (just as that of other remnants of supernovae) is synchrotronic, this source must contain great quantities of relativistic electrons (or positrons). The problem will then be to calculate their number, energy and other characteristics on the basis of the synchrotron theory. The problem of the magnetic field in Cassiopeia A is inseparably connected with this.

The initial quantity for such a calculation will be the volume luminosity ε_ν which must be obtained empirically. The observed spectral flux density of Cassiopeia A, on the wave $\lambda = 21$ cm, is according to [93] equal to $F_\nu = 2.7 \cdot 10^{-23}$ W/m$^2 \cdot$c/s $= 2.7 \cdot 10^{-20}$ erg/cm$^2 \cdot$s$\cdot$c/s. If the distance to this source is taken as $R = 3.4$ kps $= 1.05 \cdot 10^{22}$ cm, we find that the radiant power at this frequency must be $L_\nu = 3.7 \cdot 10^{25}$ erg/s$\cdot$c/s. When the angular radius of the source is assumed equal to $2'.3$ (cf. Fig. 37) a linear radius of $r = 2.3$ psc of $7 \cdot 10^{18}$ cm is obtained. The volume of the radio-emitting spherical shell of the thickness $\Delta r = 0.25r$ is equal to $V = 8 \cdot 10^{56}$ cm^2. If 90 per cent of this radiation comes from this shell (see above) its mean volume luminosity must be $\bar{\varepsilon}_\nu = 4.1 \cdot 10^{-32}$ erg/cm$^3 \cdot$c/s. With $\alpha = 0.8$, $\gamma = 2.6$, we obtain $U(\gamma) = 0.1$. With these values Equation (6.7) yields

$$KH_\perp^{1.8} = 2.5 \cdot 10^{-18}$$

Let us impose yet another additional condition:

$$w_{\text{rel.part.}} = \int_{E_1}^{\infty} E dN(E) = K \int_{E_1}^{\infty} \frac{dE}{E^{\gamma-1}} = \frac{H^2}{8\pi} \qquad (6.9)$$

where, in the case of isotropy, $H_\perp^2 = 2H^2/3$. Equation (6.9) expresses that the energy density of the relativistic particles must be equal to the energy density of the magnetic field. If $H^2/8\pi > w_{\text{rel.part.}}$, the relativistic particles will not be trapped by the magnetic field. Of course, we cannot exclude the possibility that $H^2/8\pi < w_{\text{rel.part.}}$. Then, however, the total energy of the magnetic field and of the relativistic particles will be higher than in the case where condition (6.9) is fulfilled. Solving the system of equations (6.7) and (6.9) we find the value of the minimum energy of the relativistic particles plus the field. Our numerical results are the following:

$$K = 7.5 \cdot 10^{-12}, \qquad H = 2.5 \cdot 10^{-4} \ldots,$$

$$\frac{H^2}{8\pi} = w_{\text{rel.part.}} = 2.5 \cdot 10^{-9} \text{ erg/cm}^3 \qquad (6.10)$$

The lower limit of the relativistic electrons' energy was here chosen as equal to 10^7 eV; the value of E_1 is determined by the fact that the synchrotron spectrum of Cassiopeia A is maintained up to at least $\nu = 10$ Mc for which it is necessary that the energy spectrum of the relativistic electrons with $\gamma = 2.6$ ranges to at least $E \sim 30$ MeV (with $H \sim 2.5 \cdot 10^{-4}$). For a volume of the radio-emitting shell of $v = 8 \cdot 10^{56}$ cm^3 the total energy of the relativistic electrons (which, according to agreement, is equal to the total energy of the magnetic field) is given by $\varepsilon_{\text{r.r.}} = v \cdot w_{\text{rel.part.}} = 2 \cdot 10^{48}$ erg, a very high value which is of the order of the total energy emitted in the outburst of a type II supernova. We have so far assumed that the only relativistic particles present in the shell of the supernova are electrons (or positrons). It is quite a natural assumption that relativistic protons and heavy nuclei may also be present which do not manifest themselves by synchrotron radiation.

It is well known that the main component of solar-neighbourhood cosmic rays consists of relativistic protons and heavy particles. According to recent measurements the electron component amounts to about 1 per cent of the entire primary cosmic radiation (see § 16). It may be assumed that the relativistic particles in the shell of a supernova will also consist chiefly of protons and heavy nuclei, though this, of course, is not certain. If we assume that the energy density of the relativistic protons is k times that of the relativistic electrons, we shall, on the basis of the theory of synchrotron radiation, obtain the following expression[97]:

$$\left. \begin{array}{c} \mathscr{E}_{\text{rel.part.}} + \mathscr{E}_M \propto F_\nu^{4/7} r^{17/7} \varphi^{9/7} k^{3/7} \\[2mm] H \propto F_\nu^{2/7} r^{-2/7} \varphi^{-6/7} k^{3/14} \end{array} \right\} \qquad (6.11)$$

where r is the distance to the source and φ its angular dimension. This relationship is based upon the assumption that the magnetic energy in the source is equal to the energy of the relativistic particles. If, for example, $k = 10$, the total energy of the relativistic particles in Cassiopeia A is increased by a factor of 2.7 and the total energy of all relativistic elements is reduced by a factor of 3.7. In this case the magnetic field H has grown in intensity by a factor of 1.65, thus reaching a value of $\sim 4.1 \cdot 10^{-4}$. If $k = 100$ (as is the case in the neighbourhood of the sun), $\mathscr{E}_{\text{rel.part.}}$ rises to the 7.25-fold, reaching a value of $1.4 \cdot 10^{49}$ erg, whereas the total energy of the relativistic electrons drops to a fraction of almost $\frac{1}{14}$ and the magnetic field intensifies by a factor of 2.7, thus reaching a value of $\sim 7 \cdot 10^{-4}$ Oe. In any case, with all admissible assumptions on the value of k, the minimum value of the total energy of all relativistic particles plus the field in Cassiopeia A must be of the order of $5 \cdot 10^{48}$ to $3 \cdot 10^{49}$ erg.

Let us now consider the conditions in the radio-emitting condensations found in the shell of Cassiopeia A. If we assume the angular dimension of such a condensation as equal to about $20''$ (that is thirteen times smaller than the shell dimensions) and the flux as ~ 3 per cent of the total flux from this source, we find on the basis of Equation (6.7) that the energy contained in the condensation in the form of magnetic fields and relativistic particles is the 1/180th part of the energy contained in the whole shell and that the magnetic field strength is 3.4 times higher. It is, however, quite possible that the relative intensification of the field in the radio-emitting condensations is lower.

We shall, in fact, assume that the relativistic particles move in a magnetic field, under conservation of the adiabatic invariant

$$\frac{\sin^2 \theta}{H} = \text{constant} \qquad (6.12)$$

where θ is the angle between the directions of the velocity of the relativistic electron and the magnetic field. Let us further assume that, for some reason or other, the magnetic field in the region considered is intensified to its mth strength. Since the relativistic particles move on helical paths around the corresponding lines of force and cannot fly far away from them, the density of the relativistic particles will likewise increase to its m-fold value and, consequently, the value of k in their differential energy spectrum will grow by the same factor. Finally, according to Equation (6.12), $H_\perp$ will grow to the $m^{1/2}$-fold. When we take all this into consideration we find that the volume luminosity of the "radio condensations" in synchrotron radiation can be described by

$$\varepsilon_\nu \propto kH_\perp^{(\gamma+1)/2} \propto m^{(3\gamma+7)/4} \sim m^{3.7} \qquad (\gamma = 2.6) \qquad (6.13)$$

If, for example (as this is the case in Cassiopeia A), the volume luminosity in the radio-emitting condensations is twenty times higher than in the shell, $m = 2.24$ under the above conditions. In other words, a local intensification of about 100 per cent of the magnetic field is sufficient for a "radio condensation" to appear, since ε_ν is a very sensitive function of $H_\perp$.

It is difficult to understand both the shell structure and the presence of radio-emitting condensations, caused by local intensifications of the magnetic field to a multiple strength, unless the entire region of the shell is assumed to be filled with gas. The density of this gas may be estimated from magnetohydrodynamic considerations. First of all we must take into consideration that the field in the shell will in all probability be quite irregular and complex. Otherwise (in the case of low density of the ionized gas) the radiation would display linear polarization. In fact, however, the observations showed that the polarization of radiation must be below 1 per cent, even at highest frequencies.[98,99] Generally speaking, the cause of the absence of polarization might be the depolarizing influence of Faraday rotation. Let us estimate this effect. The angle of rotation of the plane of polarization in the propagation of an electromagnetic wave in the medium, where the magnetic field strength is equal to H and the free electron concentration is N_e, is determined by the expression

$$\Psi = \frac{10^6 H N_e l \sin \alpha}{\omega^2} \qquad (6.14)$$

where l is the length of the path travelled by the wave in the magnetoactive medium and α is the angle between the magnetic field vector and the direction in which the wave is propagated. If Faraday rotation is to cause an essential depolarization, Ψ must be > 10. Assuming that $\omega = 6 \cdot 10^{10}$ c/s ($\lambda = 3$ cm), $H = 3 \cdot 10^{-4}$ Oe, $l = 10^{18}$ cm, and $\cos \alpha = \frac{1}{2}$, we find that in this case $N_e > 200$ cm^{-3}. So that the total mass of the shell must exceed $200 M_\odot$. This value seems to be too high and can hardly be adopted.

If the absence of polarization in the radio-frequency emission of Cassiopeia A is explained by the existence of an irregular chaotic field, we are led to the idea of a magnetically turbulent medium for which the condition

$$\frac{\rho v^2}{2} \sim \frac{H^2}{8\pi} \qquad (6.15)$$

must be satisfied, where v is the velocity of vortices in this scale of the turbulent spectrum which may already "entwine" the magnetic lines of force. In any case v must be much lower than the fundamental velocity of expansion, $v_0 = 8 \cdot 10^8$ cm/s, with a scale of $\sim 10^{19}$ cm. If we adopt the conception of a locally isotropic turbulence (which, of course, cannot be proved as yet) and assume dimensions of the order of 10^{18} cm for the "radio condensations," we arrive, on the basis of Kolmogorov's formula $v_3/l = $ const, with the result that $v < 3 \cdot 10^8$ cm/s. From this and condition (6.15), with $v \sim 10^8$ cm/s and $H = 5 \cdot 10^{-4}$ Oe, we find that $\rho \sim 10^{-24}$ g/cm^3, which corresponds to a total mass of $\sim 0.5 M_\odot$; this is a very low value. Hence it follows that, under the conditions in the shell of Cassiopeia A, a turbulent motion of the ionized gas is able to "entwine" the field very strongly, even if the density is rather low. The dissipation energy of the gas which is in turbulent motion amounts to $\varepsilon = v_3/l$ per unit of mass. In our case $\varepsilon \sim 10^6$ erg/s·g, the total loss of energy of the turbulent shell is $5 \cdot 10^{38}$ erg/s and the time of energy dissipation will amount to $\sim 10^{10}$ s or ~ 300 years, which is obviously not contradictory to observation.

It can be expected that the individual radio-emitting condensations in the shell of Cassiopeia A must slowly change their positions relative to the nebula which must result in a characteristic change in the radio-picture with time. If we assume, for example, a velocity of $\sim 3 \cdot 10^8$ cm/s for the magnetohydrodynamic wave (which can be determined by Equation (6.15)), a value which may be a little too high, we find that the centre of gravity of the condensation is displaced by 5″ in ~ 30 years. It is possible that such an effect is discovered in future precision observations.

On the other hand it is impossible to exclude the possibility that the rates of change in the radio-emitting condensations are considerably higher than those resulting from the simple model of magneto-turbulent motions.

In the radio-spectrum of Cassiopeia A absorption has been observed in the 21-cm band.   Figure 39 shows the profiles of the absorption lines obtained with the help of a radio-telescope with a mirror diameter of 15 m.[100]   These lines are caused by the absorption of the radio waves of the source by clouds of interstellar neutral hydrogen.   The three deep minima observed in the spectrum of Cassiopeia A correspond to radiation velocities of absorbing clouds of -1.0, -38.4 and -48.6 km/s.

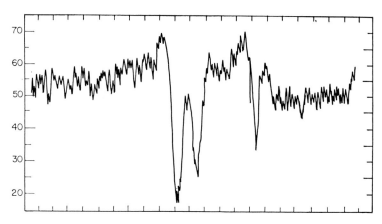

Fɪɢ. 39   21-cm absorption line profile in the radio spectrum of Cassiopeia A.[100]

According to [100] the contour of the 21-cm absorption line in the spectrum of Cassiopeia A is interpreted as follows: The minimum in the spectrum which corresponds to a radiation velocity of -100 km/s is explained by the absorption in a cloud in the "Orion" arm, nearest to the sun, of the galactic spiral structure, and the two other minima, which correspond to higher radiation velocities, are attributed to absorption in the more remote "Perseus" arm.   Since in the direction of the Cassiopeia A source the Perseus arm is at a distance of 3,000 psc away from the sun, the distance to Cassiopeia A must in any case exceed 3,000 psc (cf. Fig. 40). It should be noted that, when this work was finished, the distance to

5+s.

Cassiopeia A was assumed as equal to 500 psc, according to an estimate given by Baade and Minkowski.[77] Recently, however, Baade and Minkowski revised the interpretation of their optical observations of Cassiopeia A and obtained a distance of about 3,400 psc (cf. § 5). In this way both the radio method and the optical method of determining distances yield consistent results.

It must be pointed out that the source Cassiopeia A, owing to its high fluxes and low angular dimensions, is very well suited to study the weak interstellar radio-frequency lines. It can be shown that the depression in the line centre, given in terms of the antenna tempera-

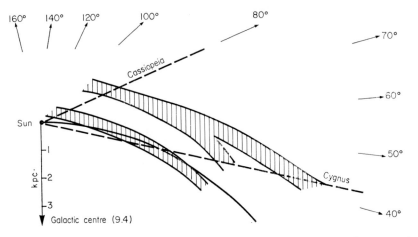

Fig. 40   Schematic representation of arrangement of the arms of the galactic spiral structure in the direction of Cassiopeia A.[100]

ture, is equal to $\Delta T = T_A \tau_\nu$, where $\tau_\nu \ll 1$ is the optical thickness in the centre of a weak radio line. Owing to the small angular size and the high value of the flux it is possible to use relatively large aerials and thus obtain very high values of T_A. If the dimensions of the radio-telescope are so large that the width of the main leaf is close to the angular dimensions of the source, $T_A = T_b$, where T_b is the brightness temperature. The modern technique of radio-astronomical investigations permits the measurement of $\Delta T_A \sim 0°.1$ and even less. At the end of 1963 this method first made it possible to discover the absorption line of interstellar hydroxyl OH in the radio-spectrum of Cassiopeia A[101]; its wave-

length is 18.3 cm; the existence of this line was predicted by the author of
the present book as early as 1953.[102]   It must be noted that the dimensions of the aerial used were considerably smaller than the optimum for
which $T_A = T_b$.

It may be expected that in the future also other weak absorption
lines will be discovered in the radio-spectrum of Cassiopeia A; for example,
the lines due to the interstellar molecules CH, SiH and nitrogen atoms.
The wavelengths of the latter lie in the 10-m band (cf. [103]).

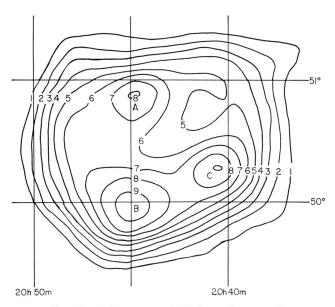

FIG. 41   Radio picture of HB 21 on λ 169 cm.[105]

We considered in detail the structure and the physical conditions in
the radio source Cassiopeia A, which is a "young" object that owes its
existence to the "recent" explosion of a supernova of type II.   We may
now inquire into the characteristics of radio sources connected with "old"
remnants of supernovae of this type.   In the past years a series of interesting investigations into these objects was carried out.   We must remark
that the angular dimensions of these "old" objects in some cases reach
3 to 4°, which enables us to study the brightness distribution, sometimes

even without applying an interference method.   In addition to this the
surface brightness of these objects is relatively low.

In 1960 Lesley came to the conclusion that the source 3C–392, which
has been identified with the remnant of a supernova of type II, has a shell
structure.[104a]   Since then a series of investigations have been published
which show also that other sources of this type have shell characteristics.
Let us consider, for example, the brightness distribution in the source
HB 21.   The observations of Boischot in the 21-cm band[104] and Crowther
in the 169-cm band,[105] carried out with radio-telescopes of similar
fairly high resolving powers ($\sim 30' \times 20'$), yielded almost identical
intensity distributions.

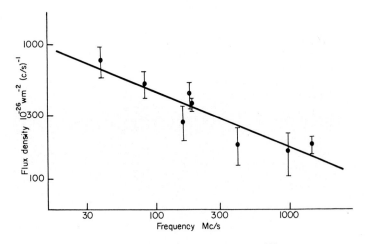

FIG. 42   Radio spectrum of HB 21.[105]

Figure 42 shows a radio-photograph of this source, taken on the
169-cm wave.

A comparison of all observations of the radio-frequency radiation
flux from this source (cf. Fig. 43) makes it possible to determine its spectral
index; in this way we obtain a value of $d = 0.4 \pm 0.1$.   In Figures 41 and
42 we see the secondary maxima of the isophotes which are marked by the
letters A, B, C, in analogy to the "radio condensations" in Cassiopeia A.
Interferometrical measurements with constant base, on the wavelength,
$\lambda = 169$ cm, showed that the condensations A and B have angular dimensions $> 6'$ whereas the condensation C has smaller angular dimensions.

The best model which satisfies the intensity distribution observed is an ellipsoidal shell with a ratio of the axes of 1.2 : 1 and a ratio of the inner to the outer diameters equal to $\rho = 0.4$.   The dots in Figure 44 represent the variations in brightness temperature of the source with the distance from its centre.   The curves give the theoretical intensity distribution, calculated for different values of ρ.

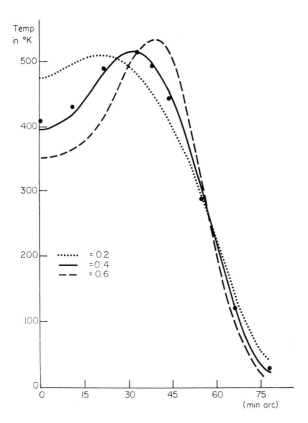

FIG. 43   Model of the source HB 21.[105]

The extended radio source, connected with the well-known system of filamentary nebulae in the constellation Cygnus, is undoubtedly the remnant of a supernova of type II; it was often investigated at various frequencies, but only in a few cases was the resolving power sufficiently high.   The observations by Mathewson and colleagues[106] on $\lambda = 74$ cm, Harris[107] on $\lambda = 31$ cm and Kenderline[108] on $\lambda = 7.9$ cm belong to the latter.   The observations made on the longest wavelength are particularly valuable as they permit a reliable determination of the spectral index of

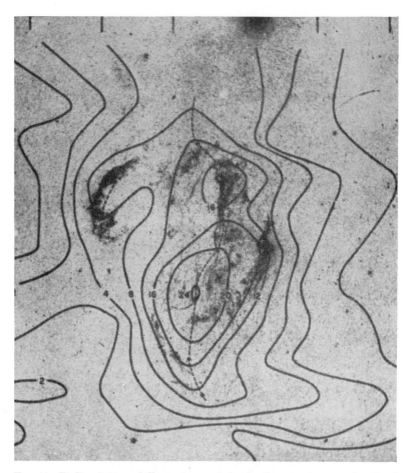

FIG. 44   Radio picture of filamentary nebulae in Cygnus at a wavelength of 31 cm.[107]

this source.   The brightness distribution of the source possesses three clearly marked maxima, denoted as A, B and C.   The brightest maximum A corresponds to a site at which there is almost no optical radiation.

The northern continuation of this maximum, marked by letter B, coincides in its position with a group of fairly bright filaments (optically bright fibres). Finally, the C peak coincides with the brightest fibre of the system, which has become known as the nebula NGC 6992–5. A comparison of the radio-frequency radiation fluxes from the system of filamentary nebulae obtained at different frequencies (for an extended

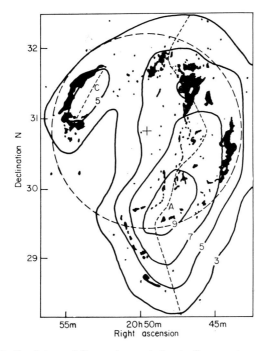

F$_{IG}$. 45   Radio picture of filamentary nebulae in Cygnus at a wavelength of 75 cm.[106]

source of complex structure, this problem is far from being simple) permits us to determine both the "mean" spectral index and the spectral indices of the individual maxima (cf. Figs. 45 to 46). According to a quite reliable determination in [108] (see Fig. 47a) the mean spectral index is equal to $\alpha = 0.47 \pm 0.10$; in [107], however, a considerably smaller value has been obtained. For the regions A and B, $\alpha = 0.54 \pm 0.10$ and 0.48 ± 0.10, respectively (cf. Fig. 47b). Region C has a characteristic curved spectrum and its spectral index is low for lower frequencies.   This suggests the question whether the radio-frequency radiation observed in this region was not simply a thermal radio emission from the nebula NGC 6992–5.   Since the brightness temperature of region C on $\lambda = 7.9$ m

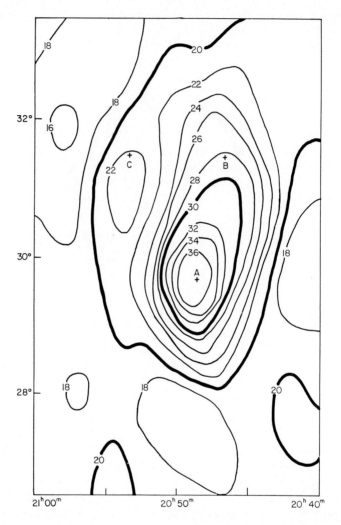

FIG. 46   Radio picture of filamentary nebulae in Cygnus at a wavelength of 7.9 m.[108]

is equal to $T_b = 20,000°$, the filament must be assumed to be optically thick on this wavelength (as for thermal radio emission, $T_b = T_e(1 - e^{-\tau_\nu})$, where T_e is the electron temperature ($\sim 20,000°$, see § 5) and τ_ν is the optical thickness). According to spectro-photometrical observations $N_e \sim 500 \text{ cm}^{-3}$ in bright filaments, from which we may conclude that the optical thickness of each filament (taking its visual thickness into account) will be as small as 0.05. Since the filaments do not exert a noticeable screening effect on one another their thermal radio emission cannot contribute more than 5 per cent to the observable flux.

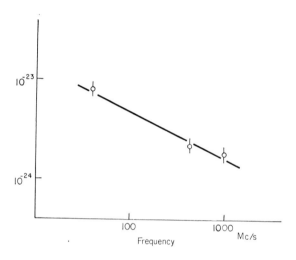

Fig. 47a   "Averaged" radio spectrum of filamentary nebulae in Cygnus.[108]

The complex structure of the radio-frequency emitting regions of such an "old" object as the filamentary nebula in Cygnus does not provide such clear indications as to the presence of a shell as the comparatively younger object HB–21, not to mention Cassiopeia A. It is obvious that in the presence of a source in Cygnus a shell must have been strongly deformed and even lost its "compactness."

Let us now consider the characteristics of the relativistic particles responsible for the synchrotron radio-frequency radiation of a source in filamentary nebulae. We shall begin with region A. The angular dimensions of this region (referred to half the brightness) may be assumed as

5*

$2° \times 1°.5$ (see Fig. 46).   Since the distance to the source is $r = 770$ psc, the linear dimensions of region A are 27×20 psc and the volume $\sim 2 \cdot 10^{59} \, \mathrm{cm}^3$. According to [108] about 65 per cent of the total radio radiation flux comes from region A.   According to [106] the total flux at a frequency of 408 Mc is equal to $2.3 \cdot 10^{-24}$.   From these data we can obtain the mean

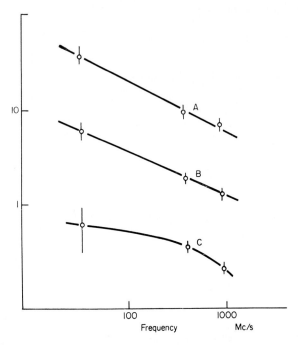

FIG. 47b   Radio spectrum of individual details of filamentary nebulae.[108]

volume luminosity in region A: $\bar{\varepsilon}_\nu = 5.2 \cdot 10^{-37} \, \mathrm{erg/cm}^3 \cdot \mathrm{s} \cdot \mathrm{c/s}$.   Substituting $\alpha = 0.5$, $\gamma = 1 + 2\alpha = 2$ and $U(\gamma) = 0.125$ in (6.7) we obtain

$$KH_\perp^{1.5} = 1.1 \cdot 10^{-20}$$

On the usual assumption that the energy density of relativistic particles is equal to the magnetic energy density, and considering the contribution of relativistic protons as insignificant, we find that $H = 1.6 \cdot 10^{-5}$, $K = 1.6 \cdot 10^{-12}$ if the limits of integration for relativistic electrons are $E_1 = 10^7$ eV and $E_2 = 10^{10}$ eV.   Their energy density (equal to the magnetic energy density) will be $\mathscr{E}_{\text{rel.part.}} = 1.2 \cdot 10^{11}$ erg/cm^3 and the total energy of the relativistic electrons contained in region A will be equal to $2.5 \cdot 10^{48}$ erg, i.e., it is only a little lower than in Cassiopeia A.

If, as in the case of Cassiopeia A, we take the relativistic protons into account, we find, with $k = 10$, a value of $\mathscr{E}_{\text{rel.part.}} \sim 6.2 \cdot 10^{48}$ erg for the total energy of the relativistic protons and a value of $H \sim 2.5 \cdot 10^{-5}$ Oe for the magnetic field. With $k = 100$ the corresponding values are $1.7 \cdot 10^{49}$ erg and $4 \cdot 10^{-5}$ Oe.

However low the volume luminosity of radio emission is in the region of the filamentary nebulae, it is about a thousand times higher than in the "non-perturbed" interstellar medium in the region of spiral arms where, as a rule, we may observe objects similar to the filamentary nebulae. If we regard the magnetic field in the region of filamentary nebulae as an intensified interstellar magnetic field and apply Equation (6.13) we obtain $m = 10$, i.e., the interstellar magnetic field in the spiral arms must be $\sim 2 \cdot 10^{-6}$ Oe. It is, however, more likely that the magnetic field in the spiral arms is several times higher (see [109]) so that the relativistic particles in the region of filamentary nebulae are not of interstellar origin but have been produced in an outburst.

An object which, as to its characteristic features, is analogous to the system of filamentary nebulae in Cygnus, is the nebula IC 443. Figure 48a shows us the isophotes of radio-frequency radiation from a source connected with this nebula, as they were obtained by Hogg on the 21.4-cm wave.[110] The observations were carried out at the large radio-telescope of the National Radio-astronomical Observatory with a mirror diameter of about 96 m. The radio photographs of this source were obtained in a resolution of $\sim 10'$, that is about one-fifth of the source diameter. Moreover, the isophotes of this source were determined for the 40-cm and the 10-cm wavelengths (see Figs. 48b and 48c).

A characteristic peculiarity of the radio photograph of IC 443 is the presence of a maximum in the north-western part of the nebula where the emission of the filaments observed in the optical range is centred, while the maximum of radio emission does not coincide at all with the maximum of optical emission from the nebula, but is shifted somewhat towards its centre.

The spectral index of the source, whose structure is comparatively simple, is according to [110] equal to 0.41 ± 0.04. It might be expected that the thermal radiation of ionized gas in rather bright filaments would make a definite contribution to the radio emission of IC 443. The

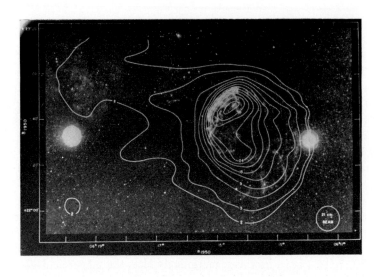

(a)

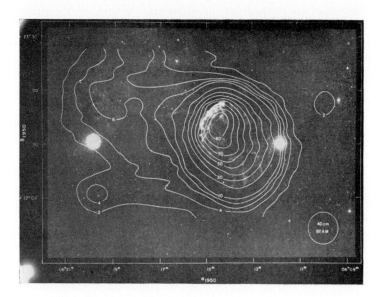

(b)

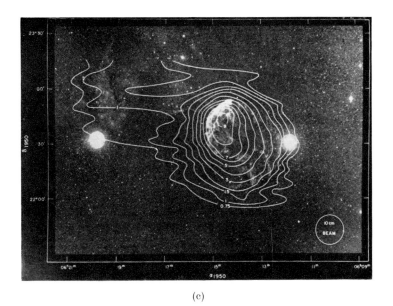

(c)

FIG. 48a, b, c   Radio picture of IC 443 at the wavelengths 21.3 cm, 40 cm and 10 cm.[110]

luminescence of these filaments must be excited by electron impacts, just as in the filaments of the nebula in Cygnus (see § 5). With this mechanism of excitation and $T_e = 10^4$, the volume luminosity in the Hα line is $\varepsilon_{H\alpha} = 5 \cdot 10^{-24} N_e n_p$ erg/cm$^3 \cdot$s, while the volume luminosity in the 21-cm radio band, calculated per unit interval of frequency, is equal to $\varepsilon_\nu = 3.9 \cdot 10^{-39} N_e n_p$ erg/cm$^3 \cdot$s$\cdot$c/s. Therefore

$$\varepsilon_\nu = 0.8 \cdot 10^{-15} \varepsilon_{H\alpha}$$

According to [110] the total flux from IC 443 in the Hα line, corrected for interstellar absorption, is equal to $F_{H\alpha} = 1.3 \cdot 10^{-8}$ erg/cm$^2 \cdot$s; hence we obtain for the corresponding radio-frequency radiation flux

$$F_\nu = 1.1 \cdot 10^{-23} \text{ erg/cm}^2 \cdot \text{s} \cdot \text{c/s} = 1 \cdot 10^{-26} \text{ watt/m}^2 \cdot \text{c/s}$$

which is less than 1 per cent of the observed radio-frequency radiation flux.†

† Recently Morrison (in a private communication) suggested a quite new interpretation of the spectra of supernovae of type I. According to his hypothesis, the emission bands characterizing these spectra are due to a fluorescence of He$^+$ ions in interstellar matter surrounding the supernova. This fluorescence is assumed to be excited by power-

It is very probable that this source has also a shell structure but the main part of the radiation emerges from the north-western "sector" of this shell. The calculation of the relativistic particles and the magnetic fields in this source can be carried out in the usual manner. However, unlike Cassiopeia A and the filamentary nebulae in Cygnus, the exact distance to IC 443 is not known. In § 7 we shall develop a new method of determining the distances to such sources, which is based only on radio-astronomical observations. An application of this method to IC 443

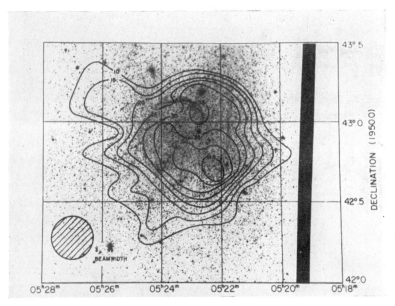

Fig. 49   Radio picture of source in Auriga.[110a]

yields a distance of $r = 1,900$ psc. When we use the same method of calculation as in the case of the filamentary nebulae in Cygnus (the spectral indices of the two sources are very similar) we obtain with $k = 1$ (i.e., without taking relativistic protons into account), $\mathscr{E}_{\text{rel.part.}} = 1.3 \cdot 10^{48}$ erg, $H = 3 \cdot 10^{-5}$ Oe. With $k = 100$, $\mathscr{E}_{\text{rel.part.}} = 10^{49}$ erg and $H = 7 \cdot 10^{-5}$ Oe.

---

ful ultraviolet and X-ray emission from the exploded star. It is, however, easy to show that the interstellar helium around a supernova, under these conditions, would be virtually promptly ionized by losing both electrons so that fluorescence is impossible.

As already mentioned above, so far we know a total of about fifteen extended galactic sources which have been identified with the remnants of supernovae of the type II. Radio pictures were, however, obtained for only a relatively small number of such objects. Recently, for example, a radio picture of a source has been obtained which, in its co-ordinates, coincides with the system of fine-fibred nebulae observed in the constellation Auriga.[110a] The centre of gravity of this source has the co-ordinates $\alpha = 5^\mathrm{h}31^\mathrm{m}$, $\delta = 42.8$ (1950). The observations were made at a velocity of 610 Mc. The spectral flux density at this frequency was equal to $F\nu = (7.5 \pm 1) \cdot 10^{-26}$ W/m$^2 \cdot$c/s. Figure 49 shows a radio photograph of this source, copied from a photograph of the system of filamentary nebulae with which this system was identified. It is clearly seen that two maxima of the radio-frequency radiation lie in the region where the nebular filaments are particularly bright. An analogous situation is observed in IC 443 (see Fig. 48). The effective angular dimensions of the source IC 443 amount to about 1°. The spectral index is not yet known but, judging from the fact that this source is not observable at higher frequencies, its spectrum must be rather steep.

As already indicated in the previous section, the remnants of the supernovae of type II which were recently discovered in the Large Magellanic Cloud are of particular interest. We have already discussed their optical characteristics in § 5. The characteristics of their radio-frequency radiation are given in Table 12.

TABLE 12

	N 49	N 63A	N 132D
Co-ordinates:			
α (1950)	$05^\mathrm{h}26^\mathrm{m}00^\mathrm{s}$	$05^\mathrm{h}35^\mathrm{m}39^\mathrm{s}$	$05^\mathrm{h}25^\mathrm{m}32^\mathrm{s}$
δ (1950)	$-66°08$	$-66°03.5$	$-69°41.0$
$F\nu$ ($\lambda = 11$ cm)	1.3	1.2	2.8
$\lambda = 20$ cm	2.5	1.5	4.0
$\lambda = 50$ cm	6	2.5	—
$\lambda = 75$ cm	9	3	(7)
$\lambda = 350$ cm	34	—	—
α	-1.0	-0.5	-0.5
$2R$	18 psc	7 psc	6 psc

The first row gives the number of the source according to Henize's Catalogue.[111] In the second and third rows the co-ordinates of the source are given as measured with the 66-m radio-telescope in observations on the 11-cm wavelength, where the width of the principal leaf in the radiation pattern was $7'.5$. The accuracy of co-ordinate determination is $0'.5$, within which limits the sources coincide with the corresponding nebulae whose angular dimensions are $\sim 0'.5-1'.0$. The fluxes were measured at four frequencies with the help of the 66-m radio-telescope in Parks. The value of the spectral flux density of N 49 on $\lambda = 350$ cm has been taken from the catalogue by Mills, Slee and Hill.[112] The row before the last gives the spectral indices obtained from these observations and the last row contains the diameters of the optical nebulae with which these sources have been identified.

When we know the distance to the Large Magellanic Cloud, the fluxes, the spectral indices and the angular dimensions of the sources, we can use the procedure described above to calculate for all objects the total energy of the relativistic particles and the magnetic field intensity, on the supposition of equal magnetic-energy densities of the cosmic-ray particles. The corresponding data are given in Table 13.

TABLE 13

No.	$\varepsilon_\nu = 400$ megacycles	$\varepsilon\ (\kappa = 1)$ ergs	$\varepsilon\ (\kappa = 100)$ ergs	$\mathbf{H}\ (\kappa = 1)$	$\mathbf{H}\ (\kappa = 100)$
N 49	$1.6 \cdot 10^{-33}$	$4.5 \cdot 10^{48}$	$3.2 \cdot 10^{49}$	$1.1 \cdot 10^{-4}$	$2.5 \cdot 10^{-4}$
N 63A	$1.0 \cdot 10^{-32}$	$9.0 \cdot 10^{47}$	$6.3 \cdot 10^{48}$	$1.5 \cdot 10^{-4}$	$3.7 \cdot 10^{-4}$
N 132D	$3.4 \cdot 10^{-32}$	$1.3 \cdot 10^{48}$	$9 \cdot 10^{48}$	$2.2 \cdot 10^{-4}$	$5.5 \cdot 10^{-4}$

These different examples show that the various sources in our own galaxy display quite a similar content of relativistic particles as the sources in the Magellanic Clouds. In this respect the remnants of supernovae of type II constitute therefore a relatively homogeneous group of objects. The powers of their radio-frequency radiations, however, vary within very wide limits. This problem will be discussed later.

§ 7 Secular decrease in flux and intensity of radio-frequency radiation from remnants of supernovae

By way of several concrete examples we have already considered the synchrotron theory of radio sources connected with the remnants of supernovae of type II. In particular, the emission spectra of these sources can be freely explained by the peculiarities of the energy spectrum of the relativistic electrons responsible for the emission of radio waves. But any theory can be viewed as correct only when, based on it, a quite new effect can be predicted which is then observed. The most important landmark in the history of radio-astronomy was the discovery of the strong polarization of the optical radiation from the Crab nebula; this synchrotron radiation had been predicted by theory. We shall discuss it later on. Here we will consider another important consequence of the synchrotron theory which permitted an important prediction which was thereafter verified by observations.

The remnants of supernovae present themselves first of all as expanding systems. We can observe the various stages of this expansion process. The nebula Cassiopeia A which we discussed in detail in the foregoing sections is, as already stressed previously, a comparatively young object. The shell ejected in the explosion of a supernova has not yet quite been slowed down by interstellar matter and its expansion velocity ($\sim 7,000$–$8,000$ km/s) is virtually equal to the initial velocity of the gases ejected during the explosion. On the other hand, such objects as the system of filamentary nebulae in Cygnus and IC 443 are rather old objects. Their linear dimensions are five to ten times the dimensions of Cassiopeia A. The speed of expansion has dropped considerably. Finally, the power of the radiation and the surface brightness in the radio-frequency range have decreased most.

The source connected with the very faint filamentary nebulae S 147 represents a still earlier stage of evolution of these objects. Its brightness temperature is much lower than the brightness temperature of the background. This object has almost "dissolved" itself in the surrounding interstellar medium. Thus even a superficial analysis of the observational results permits the conclusion that the remnants of supernovae of type II constitute a clearly marked evolutional sequence. Their fundamental characteristics must display a regular variation with time.

In this connection the following question arises: which is the law that governs the variation in radio-emission intensity and surface brightness of these sources? As the nebular remnant expands, the intensity of the magnetic field connected with it will drop. This process must be expected, accompanied by an energy loss of the relativistic particles in this nebula (see below). If we assume that the process of formation of relativistic particles ceased in a certain relatively early stage of nebular expansion, it is then obvious that, as the nebula expands further and the magnetic field strength and the energy of relativistic electrons decrease, the radio-frequency radiation flux will decrease continuously. The surface brightness of the source will decrease still more rapidly. Let us estimate this effect quantitatively.

The spectral radiation flux density from a source whose radiation is of synchrotron origin is determined by the relation

$$F_\nu \propto R^3 k H_\perp^{(\gamma+1)/2} V^{(1-\gamma)/2} (2.8 \cdot 10^8)^{(\gamma-1)/2} \tag{7.1}$$

According to [113] the statistical mechanism of Fermi acceleration in an expanding nebula can be described by

$$\frac{dE}{dt} = \left[u^2 - \frac{acVl}{R} \right] \frac{1}{lc} \cdot E \tag{7.2}$$

where $a \sim 1$ and l is a region within which the magnetic field may be considered as more or less homogeneous, V is the velocity of expansion of the nebula, R is its radius and u the characteristic turbulent velocity in it. With the exception of a very early stage of expansion of the nebula (in which here we are not interested) the second term in the brackets is always greater than the first. Consequently, the relativistic particles present in the expanding nebula will continuously lose energy. This process is equivalent to adiabatic cooling of an expanding gas. Since

$$u^2 \ll \frac{acVl}{R}$$

$$\frac{dE}{dt} = -\frac{V}{R} E \tag{7.3}$$

and therefore

$$E = E_0 \left(\frac{R_0}{R} \right) \tag{7.4}$$

It is essential that all relativistic particles will lose energy proportionally so that the energy spectrum remains unchanged. If with $R = R_0$ the energy spectrum has the form of

$$dN(E) = k_0 E^{-\gamma} \, dE \tag{7.5}$$

and in the following γ = constant and the quantity k will vary according to the law,

$$k = k_0 \left(\frac{R_0}{R} \right)^{\gamma-1} \left(\frac{R_0}{R} \right)^3 \tag{7.6}$$

This results from the condition

$$R_0 k_0 \int_{E_1}^{E_2} E^{-\gamma} \, dE = R^3 k \int_{E_1(R_0/R)}^{E_2(R_0/R)} E^{-\gamma} \, dE \qquad (7.7)$$

The law according to which the magnetic field strength decreases as the nebula expands cannot yet be determined accurately. But in a first approximation we may assume that during the expansion of the nebula the general structure of its magnetic field remains more or less unchanged ("similarity" expansion). In this case the magnetic flux must remain constant. We therefore have

$$H = H_0 \left(\frac{R_0}{R}\right)^2 \qquad (7.8)$$

With this law governing the decrease of $H(R)$ the volume density of the magnetic energy must drop according to the law $\varepsilon_M \propto R^{-4}$. The same law of energy density decrease is also obtained for the relativistic particles contained in the expanding nebula. Thus, if at some definite instant of time the energy density of cosmic radiation in the expanding nebula was equal to the energy density of the magnetic field, this equality will not be violated in the following.

We have good cause to assume that in "old" nebulae, which are remnants of supernovae of type II whose characteristics were discussed in detail in the previous two sections, the condition of equality between magnetic energy density and energy density of cosmic rays is approximately satisfied. This is an argument in favour of the validity of the law adopted above which describes the variation of the magnetic field with expansion of the nebula (Eq. 7.8).

We must also note that as the nebula expands $H_\perp$ will vary with R in the same way as H. This becomes obvious from the expression for the adiabatic invariant

$$\frac{P_\perp^2}{H} = \frac{P^2 \sin^2 \theta}{H} = \text{const} \qquad (7.9)$$

Since for relativistic particles the momentum $P \propto E$, with $H \propto r^{-2}$ and $E \sim R^{-1}$, $P^2 \sim H$. Therefore $\sin \theta = \text{const}$ and $H_\perp = H \sin \theta \propto R^{-2}$.

From the relations given above it follows that the spectral flux density will depend on R in the following way:

$$F_\nu \propto R_0^\beta R^{-\beta} k_0 H_{0\perp}^{(\gamma+1)/2} \propto R^{-\beta} \qquad (7.10)$$

where

$$\beta = 2\gamma \qquad (7.11)$$

The mean intensity given in terms of R will read as follows:

$$I_\nu \propto T_b \propto R_0^\beta R^{-(\beta+2)} k_0 H_{0\perp}^{(\gamma+1)/2} \propto R^{-(\beta+2)} \qquad (7.12)$$

In an early stage of expansion of the nebula, when it has not yet been slowed down by interstellar matter, $R \propto t$ where t is the age of the nebula. It is therefore possible to replace R by t in Equations (7.10) and (7.12).

The validity of our conclusion on the regular changes of flux and brightness of expanding nebulae may be illustrated by way of the following example. If the systems of filamentary nebulae in Cygnus and Cassiopeia A are objects which are more or less similar in nature but different in age, and the age is proportional to the expansion phase, their fluxes and surface brightnesses must be in a certain proportion which is determined by the ratio of their radii. According to optical and radio-astronomical observations (see §§ 5 and 6), the distance to Cassiopeia A is $r = 3{,}400$ psc from which it follows that with an angular radius of the source of $2'.3$ the linear radius is $R = 2.3$ psc. The spectral index of Cassiopeia A is $\alpha = 0.80$, hence it follows that $\beta = 2(2\alpha + 1) = 5.2$. The spectral flux density from Cassiopeia A at a frequency of 100 Mc is $F_\nu = 1.8 \cdot 10^{-22}$ W/m²·c/s from which the mean brightness temperature is obtained as $T_b = 4.3 \cdot 10^7$.

On the other hand, the distance to the filamentary nebulae in Cygnus is equal to 770 psc, the angular dimensions $\sim 3°$ and the linear radius is ~ 20 psc (we digress from the structure of the sources in Cygnus and Cassiopeia, which was discussed in § 6). The radio-frequency radiation flux at the frequency $\nu = 100$ Mc is given by $F_\nu = 4 \cdot 10^{-24}$ W/m²·c/s and the brightness temperature at this frequency is $T_b = 4 \cdot 10^2$.

Observations have thus shown that at 100 Mc the power of radio emission from Cassiopeia A is one thousand times higher than that from the filamentary nebulae in Cygnus and the surface brightness exceeds that of the source in Cygnus by a factor of almost 100,000.

The spectral index of the filamentary nebulae in Cygnus is much smaller than with Cassiopeia A; it is equal to 0.47, therefore $\beta = 3.9$. In the past, when the dimensions of the system of filamentary nebulae in Cygnus were 8.7 times smaller than at present, i.e., when they were equal to the present dimensions of Cassiopeia A, the intensity of their radio emission, according to Equation (7.10), must have been about five thousand times higher than today and the surface brightness was about 370,000 times the present one.   As to its fundamental characteristics this source is quite similar to Cassiopeia A but exceeding it somewhat in power and surface brightness.   This reveals immediately the genetic connections between the sources which resemble the filamentary nebulae in Cygnus and the powerful and young sources like Cassiopeia A.†

The decrease in power and surface brightness of the sources accompanying the expansion of the nebulae connected with them depends sensitively on their spectral index.   This effect must be particularly remarkable when α is relatively high.   For example, when Cassiopeia A expands up to the present dimensions of the filamentary nebulae in Cygnus, its flux drops to a fraction of 10^{-5}, becoming equal to $\sim 10^{-27}$ $W/m^2 \cdot c/s$ in the meter range, and the brightness temperature in this range will be $\sim 5°$.   The modern means of observation are insufficient to discover such a weak source.   Cassiopeia A will remain observable down to a radius of about 13 psc.

From this we may in particular draw the important conclusion that among the fairly "old" remnants of supernovae there are no objects with high spectral indices, e.g., $\alpha = 0.8$–1.0.   In their evolution process such objects can be observed for a relatively short time.   In other words, the evolution process is accompanied by a peculiar "selection" of the sources with respect to their spectral indices.   In the previous section we have seen that all sources connected with old remnants of supernovae of type II have relatively "sloping" radio spectra with spectral indices between the limits of 0.4 and 0.5.   This fact is easy to explain by the above theory of evolution of such sources.   This theory is in principle also suitable for an analysis of the evolution of sources connected with outbursts of supernovae of type I.   On the grounds of these theoretical concepts one may also understand the remarkable fact that the present Crab nebula is an exceptionally powerful radio source, whereas the much "younger" sources, which have been identified with the remnants of the supernovae of 1572 and 1604, are considerably weaker.   The fact is that the Crab nebula has an anomalously low spectral index of $\alpha = 0.28$, and therefore $\beta = 3.1$. The younger remnants of the supernovae of 1572 and 1604 have an index of $\alpha \sim 0.6$ and they "die out" considerably faster.   Details of this problem will be discussed in Chapter III.

---

† Owing to the relative proximity of the filamentary nebulae which, if they are "young" (about 50,000 years, see next section, § 8), emit a flux which is a hundred times the flux from present Cassiopeia A.

These considerations provide a natural explanation of the interesting peculiarity of the non-thermal radio sources discovered by Whitfield[90] and verified by Kellerman[115] with the help of modern statistical material. It proved that, on the average, the spectral index of galactic sources of non-thermal radio-frequency radiation is much smaller than that of extragalactic sources.   Since a great part of the galactic non-thermal radio sources with known α are comparatively "old" remnants of supernovae of type II, only those objects among them can "survive" which have a comparatively low spectral index.   If we had known the spectral indices of other sources of this type (today we know about fifteen of them), the mean spectral index of the galactic sources would have been still smaller.

The "youngest" of the known radio sources identified with supernova remnants is Cassiopeia A.   Its age was estimated as 270 ± 14 years (see § 5).   Therefore, if we also take the exceedingly high radio flux from this force into account, we might expect that precision observations made at relatively short intervals would reveal the effect of the secular decrease in flux.   According to Equation (7.11) $\beta = 5.2$ if $\alpha = 0.80$.   If the expansion is a steady process occurring at a constant rate, the relative decrease in flux from Cassiopeia A will be

$$\Delta F_\nu / F_\nu = \beta/270 = 1.9 \text{ per cent per year}$$

On the basis of the above calculation the author of the present book predicted in 1960 that the secular decrease in radio flux from Cassiopeia A may be observed with the modern means of radio-astronomy.[116] Before we pass over to a consideration of the results of observations which especially furnish a verification of the predictions of theory, it is convenient once again to discuss the basic premises of the theory from which this conclusion results.   These premises are the following:

(1) The synchrotron mechanism of radio emission.
(2) The radio source expands with a rate that can be determined by optical observations of the nebula.
(3) The magnetic field strength decreases during the process of nebular expansion according to a certain power law.
(4) The number of relativistic electrons does not grow in the process of expansion of the nebula.

The premises (1) and (2) can be regarded as well established.   The third premise is also quite natural though, of course, it cannot be excluded that in individual stages of nebular expansion local fluctuations of the field may occur because of interactions with the non-uniform interstellar medium surrounding the nebula.

This is particularly clearly marked in the radio pictures of Cassiopeia A, where we can see a great number of "radio condensations" which, in all probability, are connected with local intensifications of the magnetic field. The total flux from these condensations, however, does not exceed 10 per cent of the total flux (see § 6) and when their lifetime is at least thirty years they cannot contribute considerably to the expected amount of the annual change in flux. As regards the last premise, it can hardly be expected that the number of relativistic electrons in Cassiopeia A increases with time, compensating the effect of the decrease of field strength during the expansion of the nebula. For this it would be necessary to assume that the generation of relativistic electrons increases with time according to a certain power law, an assumption which can hardly be accepted. Could there exist any mechanisms in an expanding nebula preventing the relativistic electrons from being slowed down or even accelerating them? If this were so, in earlier stages of expansion the pressure of the relativistic particles would have exceeded the magnetic pressure and they would have "escaped" from the nebula. But in this case we had never observed such "old" objects of the type of IC 443, the filamentary nebulae in Cygnus and the like. Note that in the Crab nebula relativistic electrons are still injected, even at present. This will be discussed in Chapter III. The shell structure of the radio sources which have been identified with the remnants of supernovae of type II, however, seems to contradict the possibility of continuous injection of relativistic particles. The Crab nebula displays no shell structure and in its central part a singularity can be observed.

The expected effect of a secular decrease in flux and brightness of Cassiopeia A is thus a natural consequence of the present ideas on the nature of the radio emission from the remnants of supernovae. It is specific of the source Cassiopeia A that this process may be observed for a relatively short period.

After this prediction on the secular reduction of the radio flux from Cassiopeia A several observations were made with the aim of verifying this consequence of the theory. The method of experimental verification has been suggested by us in [116]; it consists of the following: Since the error in absolute radio-astronomical observations is at present still rather high, it is expedient to study the flux ratio from Cassiopeia A and some suitable source of well-known constant flux. It proved convenient to choose

Cygnus A as this source; its flux is comparable with that of Cassiopeia A and its intergalactic nature virtually excludes the possibility of flux variations.

The first observations were made in 1961 by Högbom and Shakeshaft[117] who repeated the flux ratio measurements of Cassiopeia A and Cygnus on $\lambda = 3.7$ m, using the same radio-telescope as in the fifties. The results of their measurements are shown in Figure 50. They obtained a value of 1.06 ± 0.14 per cent for the mean annual rate of decrease in flux. However, it must be noted that (as we see from Figure 50) the change in flux per year, as obtained from an analysis of later and probably more accurate measurements, yields a value of about 1.7 per cent for the annual decrement of flux. Soon after this Heeshen and Meredith, on the

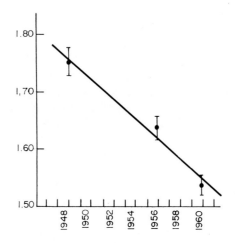

FIG. 50   Secular decrease of radio flux from Cassiopeia A at a wavelength of 3.7 m.[117]

21-cm wavelength, verified the results of the English researchers, which were obtained at lower frequencies.[118]   Recently Meyer, McCullough and Sloanaker accomplished new observations with the 16-m radio-telescope of a naval laboratory, on $\lambda = 9.4$ cm.[119]   Comparing their results with those of the old observations of 1953 they found that the ratio of the fluxes from Cassiopeia A and Cygnus A which, in 1953, had been equal to 2.247 ± 0.045, was in 1962 equal to 2.032 ± 0.024; this corresponds to a decrement of 10 per cent.   A recalculation yields a value of 1.14 ± 0.26

per cent per year for the mean decrease of the flux from Cassiopeia A. In Figure 51 the results of flux ratio measurements for several sources, referred to the flux from Cygnus A, are compiled for the period 1953 to 1962. Compared with other ratios, this great difference in the behaviour of the Cassiopeia/Cygnus flux ratio is quite striking. Only the Crab nebula, the source Taurus A, alludes to the effect of secular reduction of

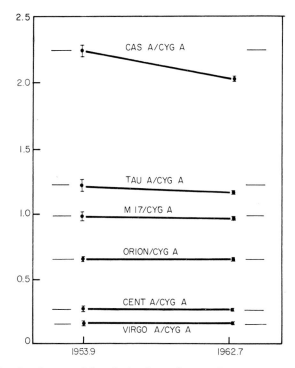

FIG. 51   Secular changes of the relative fluxes from various sources at a wavelength of 9.4 cm.[119]

flux, which here amounts to 0.53 ± 0.40 per cent per year. Note that with a spectral index of $\alpha = 0.28$ and an age of 910 years the expected annual decrease of the flux from Crab nebula, according to Equation (7.10), must amount to about 0.3 per cent per year.

Apart from the relative measurements, absolute measurements were also carried out in order to verify the conclusion as to the secular decrease of the flux from Cassiopeia A. In 1964 Lastochkin and Stankevich,[120] comparing the results of their absolute measurements on $\lambda=3.2$ cm, carried out in 1962 and 1964, obtained a decrement of 1.7 per cent per year for the flux from Cassiopeia A. Finally, in 1965 Findlay, Hvatum and Waltman, who made absolute measurements at a wavelength of about 21 cm with the help of a large horn antenna at the National Radio-astronomical Observatory in Green Bank, obtained a value of 1.75 ± 0.52 per cent per year for the flux decrement (see Fig. 52).[121]

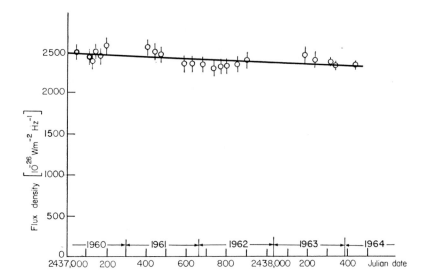

FIG. 52   Absolute measurements of secular decrease of the flux from Cassiopeia A at a wavelength of 21 cm.[121]

It can thus be considered as proved that the radio flux from Cassiopeia A decreases continuously. Though we cannot yet draw any final conclusions as to the exact value of this decrease, we may now stress two facts:

(i) The annual decrease in flux is independent of the frequency. Within the limits of error, the same results are obtained from observations at $\lambda = 3.7$ m and $\lambda = 9.4$ m, as was to be expected from the theory discussed above.

(ii) The annual decrease in flux is likely to be somewhat smaller than that predicted on the grounds of the simple theory.   It was found within the limits of 1.1 and 1.75 per cent, whereas the theoretical value was between 1.9 and 2 per cent.   These results require an explanation.

First, however, let us consider the following fact.   If we base our considerations on the existing observations of the actual annual diminution of the radio flux from Cassiopeia A of 1.5 per cent, the relative change in flux of this source may be represented in the following table.

TABLE 14

Date	F_ν (relative)
1800	5,500
1850	1,050
1900	325
1965	100
1995	65
2195	8

The flux obtained in 1956 was taken as the reference value 100.   We see from this table that within 30 years the radio flux from Cassiopeia decreased to $\frac{2}{3}$ and within 230 years to a fraction of $\frac{1}{12}$.   Previously, before the era of radio-astronomy, the flux was much more intense.   In 1900, for example, it was more than three times stronger than the present flux.

There arises the quite natural question, how far back we may extrapolate the secular decrease in the flux observed.   The "future" extrapolation does not present any particular difficulties.   We must take into account only the inevitable deceleration of the shell by the interstellar medium and continue the function $F(R)$ with $R = R(t)$ according to Equation (7.10).   The form of the function $R(t)$ will be discussed in § 8. As regards the extrapolation "to the past" a limitation will arise.   The fact is that, when deriving Equations (7.10) and (7.12), we assumed the nebula transparent for its own radio emission.   But in some comparatively early stages of expansion, when the density of the ionized gas in it was high, this condition will not have been satisfied.   It is obvious that the earlier this limitation arises, the lower the frequency.   Here we shall give quite a rough estimate of this effect.

Let us start from a simple model, assuming that the density N_e of the ionized gas and the magnetic field strength H are constant throughout the nebula. Let us further assume that opaqueness sets in when the optical thickness $\tau_\nu = 1$. In other words,

$$\tau_\nu \propto N_e^2 R/\nu^2 T_e^{3/2}$$

The frequency for which $\tau_\nu = 1$ is therefore determined by the condition

$$\nu_{\tau_\nu = 1} \propto N_e R^{1/2} T_e^{-3/4} \qquad (7.13)$$

In our rough estimate we shall not care for the T_e-dependence of $\nu_{\tau_\nu = 1}$, which may also be inadmissible. From the condition of uniformity of expansion we shall have

$$\nu_{\tau_\nu = 1} \sim R^{-5/2} \qquad (7.14)$$

In the case of a great optical thickness a thin layer of thickness d will be emitted, on the periphery of the nebula; its optical thickness will be ~ 1. The volume of the region from which the radio-frequency radiation of the nebula will emerge "without hindrance" will be equal to $R^2 d$. For a fixed frequency the condition that the optical thickness of the layer must be equal to unity yields

$$d \propto \frac{\nu^2}{N_e^2} \propto R^6 \qquad (7.15)$$

For an optically thick nebula the intensity of radio emission (and the flux) will then vary according to the law

$$L_\nu \propto F_\nu \propto R^{5 - \beta} \qquad (7.16)$$

If for a certain source $\beta < 5$, during the evolution of the nebula the flux at a definite frequency will first increase relatively slowly, then reach a sloping maximum (at $\tau_\nu \sim 1$) and then it will drop quite rapidly, according to Equation (7.10). With higher frequencies the flux maximum will obviously be reached earlier. For an optically thick nebula the radio spectrum takes the form

$$F_\nu \propto \nu^{2 - \alpha} \qquad (7.17)$$

In most cases $\alpha < 1$ and F_ν will be a growing function of the frequency. We know that in the case of Cassiopeia A the spectrum is "heaped up" at $\nu < 16.5$ Mc (see § 6).   If we assume that this steep slope is caused by an absorption of ionized gas present in this nebula, we may reach the interesting conclusion that about a hundred years ago this "heap" in the spectrum must have been at $\nu < 60$ Mc and after a further hundred years it will be at $\nu < 8$ Mc.   With $\beta > 5$ and an optically thick nebula F_ν will drop relatively slowly as R increases until τ_ν has reached unity; then it begins to fall rapidly as this is described by Equation (7.10).

Our calculations are of course very rough; apart from having ignored that T_e depends on R we did not take into account the fine structure in the distribution of the ionized gas in the nebula which is clearly observed in Cassiopeia A.   This fact may exert an essential influence on the estimate of the optical thickness of the expanding nebula.

However, in spite of the roughness of this approximation, some essential features of the effects accompanying the evolution of such an expanding nebula could be described.   Let us try to obtain a roughly approximate quantitative estimate of the effect of absorption by ionized gas in the expanding nebula.   In the case of supernovae of type II we may expect that the mass of ejected ionized gases may be $\sim 10 M_\odot$ or $2 \cdot 10^{34}$ g which corresponds to $\sim 10^{58}$ pairs of ions.   With a radius of $\sim 10^{17}$ cm of the expanding nebula the mean concentration is $\bar{N}_e \sim 2.5 \cdot 10^6$ cm^{-3}, the measure of emission $ME \sim N_e^2 R \sim 10^{10}$ cm$^{-6} \cdot$ psc, and even with $T_e \sim 10^5$ to 10^6 the nebula will be opaque up to the highest radio frequencies.   With $R = 10^{18}$ the measure of emission $ME \sim 10^6$ and the nebula will now be opaque for waves of the metre band (of course, provided that T_e is not extremely high and the degree of inhomogeneity is not too high).   Only if $R \sim 1$ psc (a value which is only about one-third of the present dimensions of Cassiopeia A) the measure of emission $ME \sim 10^4$ and with $T_e \gg 10^4$ the nebula becomes transparent for meter waves.

We may therefore draw the conclusion that for nebulae which are remnants of supernovae of type II, Equation (7.10) may be extrapolated "into the past" down to $R \sim 1$ psc.   In the case of Cassiopeia A this corresponds to an epoch in which it was about a hundred years old, which proves the above extrapolation.

There also exists another specific effect of re-absorption in an expanding nebula which we shall discuss here.   This is the re-absorption of the synchrotron radio emission by the relativistic electrons themselves which are present in the nebula.   A general theory of this effect has been developed by V. I. Slish[122] and we shall keep to his way of calculation. Owing to the re-absorption by the relativistic electrons present in the nebula, the primary synchrotron spectrum is "overfilled" for frequencies $\nu < \nu_{max}$, with $F_{\nu < \nu_{max}} \sim \nu^{2.5}$. Let us now find the frequency of the "heap" in the spectrum as a function of R.

According to [121]

$$\nu_{max} = 1.2 \left[\frac{F(\nu_2)}{\theta^2} \cdot \nu_2^{\alpha} \cdot 10^{33} \right]^{1/(\alpha + 2.5)} H^{1/(2\alpha + 5)} \qquad (7.18)$$

where $\theta = 2R/r$ is the angular diameter of the source, $\nu_2 > \nu_1$ and H is the magnetic field strength. Assuming that $F(\nu_2) \propto R^{-\beta}$ we find

$$\nu_{max} \propto R^{-(\beta + 3)/(\alpha + 2.5)} \qquad (7.19)$$

For Cassiopeia A, $\nu_{max} \propto R^{-2.5}$.

At present, according to Equation (7.19), $\nu_m \sim 3$ Mc for Cassiopeia A. Therefore, even if $R = 1/10 R_0$, $\nu_{max} \sim 10^3$ Mc, the decimeter waves from Cassiopeia A will be free from self-absorption by the relativistic electrons, although Cassiopeia A was then only about twenty-seven years old. Thus we see that in the remnants of supernovae of type II the self-absorption by the ionized gas is more effective than that by the relativistic electrons.

We shall now discuss the results of observations of the secular decrease in flux of the radio-frequency radiation from Cassiopeia A. As already mentioned above, the observations in general verify the predictions of the theory but yield somewhat lower values for the quantity $\Delta F_\nu / F_\nu$. This can be explained in several ways. First, Cassiopeia A may be a little older than calculated by Minkowski. Thus, for example, if we assume $T \sim 300$ years (this, of course, is quite possible) we obtain $\Delta F_\nu / F_\nu \approx -1.75$ per cent, a value which is in good agreement with some observations but, very likely, is somewhat higher than the true value.

Another possible explanation presents itself by taking into account that the expanding nebula Cassiopeia A has already begun to be slowed down by interstellar matter. According to [81] the outermost layer of the expanding shell has already begun to be slowed down, a fact that follows from the noticeable differences in the radiation velocities of the approaching and the removing parts of the shell (see § 5). By virtue of the strong dependence of F_ν on R this fact can be taken into account schematically, in the following way. The half of the nebula which faces the observer does not change its flux with time in a noticeable manner, whereas the opposite half expands as if there were no decelerating effect at all. This simple scheme is based on the fact that with a speed ratio of $7,400/6,000 = 1.23$ for the front and rear surfaces of expansion, the value of the annual decrease in flux of the front half of the nebula will be smaller by a factor of $(1.23)^{5.2} \sim 4$ than that of the rear part. If at a given instant each of these halves emits 50 per cent of the power, the annual flux decrement of the whole source will be

$$\frac{\Delta F_\nu}{F_\nu} = 0.5 \cdot 2 \text{ per cent} + 0.5 \cdot 0.5 \text{ per cent} = 1.25 \text{ per cent per year}$$

(7.20)

a result which is in good agreement with the results of relative measurements of the secular decrease in flux from Cassiopeia A which were discussed above.

Lequeux[94] tried to generalize Equation (7.10) which we obtained for a homogeneous expanding nebula to the case of a shell structure. According to observations the source Cassiopeia A is not a homogeneous object but displays a shell structure so that the Lequeux attempt was quite justified.

Let us denote by v the velocity of shell expansion, by R its radius and by l its thickness. We assume that the density ρ of the ionized gas and the magnetic field strength H in the shell are much higher than the corresponding values in the surrounding interstellar medium. Lequeux makes the natural supposition that the thickness of the shell increases twice as fast as the Alfvén waves are propagated, their velocity being equal to $a = H/\sqrt{4\pi\rho}$. We will further assume that the total velocity of expansion of the source, given by $V = dR/dt$, is constant. We therefore consider supernova remnants which are not yet decelerated; this is more or less admissible in the case of Cassiopeia A. On the other hand, however, the rate of expansion of the shell varies with time. From the condition of conservation of magnetic flux it follows that

$$H \sim (lR)^{-1}$$

(7.21)

and, on the other hand, the gas density in the shell is

$$\rho = (lR^2)^{-1}$$

(7.22)

from which it follows that

$$v = \frac{dl}{dt} = (lR)^{-1}(lR^2)^{\frac{1}{2}} \sim l^{-\frac{1}{2}}$$

(7.23)

The solution to Equation (7.23) has the form $1 \propto t^{2/3}$ so that

$$v = \frac{dl}{dt} = \frac{2l_0}{3t_0^{2/3}} t^{1/3} \tag{7.24}$$

where t_0 is the present age of the nebula (270 years) and l_0 is its present thickness (0.6 psc). At present

$$v_0 = \frac{2}{3} \frac{l_0}{t_0}$$

1,500 km/sec $= 2a$, so that $\rho = 4.9 \cdot 10^{-24}$ g/cm^3 and the total mass of the gas in the shell is equal to $4.5 \cdot 10^{33}$ g or $2.3 M_\odot$ which is not a contradiction of the estimates of § 5.

The adiabatic expansion of the nebula results in a continuous loss of energy of each particle, according to the law

$$\frac{dE}{dt} = -\frac{v}{R} E$$

Using Equation (7.24) we obtain

$$\frac{dE}{dt} = -\frac{2l_0}{3t_0^{2/3}} t^{1/3} \frac{t_0}{R_0 t} E \tag{7.25}$$

and accordingly

$$E = E_0 \exp\left\{ \frac{2l_0}{R_0} \left[\left(\frac{t_0}{t}\right)^{1/3} - 1 \right] \right\} \tag{7.26}$$

When the differential energy spectrum of the relativistic electrons has the general form $dN(E) = KE^{-\gamma}$ we obtain

$$K = K_0 \left(\frac{R_0}{l}\right)^2 \left(\frac{l_0}{R}\right) \left(\frac{E}{E_0}\right)^{\gamma-1}$$

$$= K_0 \left(\frac{t_0}{t}\right)^{8/3} \exp\left\{ \left(\frac{2l_0}{R_0}\right) (\gamma - 1) \left[\left(\frac{t_0}{t}\right)^{1/3} - 1 \right] \right\} \tag{7.27}$$

Thus the energy flux at the frequency ν will be

$$F_\nu \propto 4\pi R^2 l K H_\perp^{(\gamma+1)/2} \tag{7.28}$$

Using the expression for the adiabatic invariant, from which it follows that $H_\perp \sim H^{3/2}E^{-1}$, we obtain the following relation for F_ν:

$$F_\nu \sim t^{-5(\gamma+1)/4} \exp\left\{\frac{2l_0}{R_0}\left(\frac{t_0}{t}\right)^{\frac{1}{3}(\gamma-3)/2}\right\} \qquad (7.29)$$

When we apply Equation (7.29) to Cassiopeia A for which $\gamma = 2.7$, $t_0 = 270$ years and $l_0/R_0 = 0.3$, we obtain

$$\frac{\Delta F_\nu}{F_\nu} = -1.7 \text{ per cent per year} \qquad (7.30)$$

which is only 10 per cent below the value obtained from the simple theory described above.

In any case, the three factors which have not been taken into account on deriving Equation (7.10) (that is the revision of the age T of the nebula, the non-uniformity of expansion and the shell structure) may altogether fully explain the slight deviation between theory and observation. It is well founded now to say that the theoretical prediction of the secular diminution of the radio-frequency radiation flux from Cassiopeia A is of great significance for the understanding of the nature of the expanding shells of supernovae of type II, as it

   (i) verifies the correctness of the synchrotron mechanism,
   (ii) substantiates the hypothesis that the magnetic flux is conserved during the expansion of the nebula and
   (iii) proves the validity of Equation (7.10), according to which $F_\nu \propto L_\nu \propto R^{-2\gamma}$.

The latter relationship is particularly important since we may use it as a base for building up a system of the distances to galactic radio sources which are remnants of supernovae of type II. It is therefore desirable to obtain an independent verification of its validity. For this purpose we use the characteristics of the remnants of type II supernovae in the Magellanic Clouds (see § 6) and plot an empiric graph of $L_\nu = \lambda_\nu(R)$ in a logarithmic scale (see Fig. 53).

From Figure 53 we see that the four objects: Cassiopeia A, N 132D, N 63A and the filamentary nebulae in Cygnus fit quite well to the straight line

$$\frac{\log R}{4.1} + \frac{\log F_\nu}{1.4} = 1 \qquad (7.31)$$

6 + s.

Hence it follows

$$F_\nu \propto R^{-2.9} = R^{-\beta_1} \qquad (7.32)$$

The power law governing $F_\nu(R)$ agrees with the theoretical expression
(7.10). However, β_1 is much smaller than $2\gamma = 2(2\alpha + 1)$, even if
$\alpha = 0.5$. But it must be kept in mind that the explosions which lead to
the observed radio sources are of course dissimilar in power. Three of
these four objects (namely N 63A, N 132D and the filamentary nebulae in
Cygnus) possess similar spectral indices which are equal to ~ 0.5. This
permits a more detailed comparison. If these three objects exploded with
the same power, they would lie in a straight line with an inclination of
-4.0 instead of -2.6. Hence we may estimate the relative powers of the
explosions which caused the formation of these radio sources. For this
purpose we shall extrapolate their observable luminosity back to the
instant of time when the radius of the source had been equal to a standard
value. Our extrapolation will be based on the theoretical law $L_\nu \propto
R^{-28} = R^{-4.0}$, and as the standard radius we choose a value of 20 psc,
the radius of the filamentary nebulae in Cygnus. The luminosities of
N 63A and N 132D proved to be equal to one another and each was one-
twentieth of the present luminosity of the filamentary nebulae in Cygnus.
This result is very interesting. It shows that the power of the explosion
and the number of relativistic particles, and the magnetic field connected
with this power, may be quite different with different objects. This results
also from estimates of k and N of the three sources carried out in the
previous paragraph. If the values of $\mathscr{E}$ and H are extrapolated according
to the theoretical laws $\mathscr{E} \sim 1/R, H \sim 1/R^2$ to $R = 20$ psc we obtain values
which differ considerably from the corresponding characteristics of the
filamentary nebulae in Cygnus ($\mathscr{E}$, for example, will be seven to eight times
smaller). We may hence draw the conclusion that the mass of the gas
ejected in the explosion of the type II supernova, as the result of which
we may now observe the system of filamentary nebulae in Cygnus and the
radio source connected with it, was about order of magnitude smaller
than in the case of the outbursts in the Large Magellanic Cloud which
created the objects N 63A and N 132D, because the velocity of ejection
in the shells of type II supernovae varies within relatively narrow limits
(5,000–8,000 km/s). If N 63A and N 132D represent typical remnants of
type II supernovae, the filamentary nebulae in Cygnus must have been
produced as the result of a particularly strong explosion.

In Figure 53 the point corresponding to the source N 49 does not
lie on the common straight line which is in direct connection with the

analogous characteristics of this object.   In § 6 we have already pointed out that the total energy of all relativistic particles in N 49 is twice as high as in Cassiopeia A, although the dimensions of the source in the Magellanic Clouds are four times larger.   It is beyond any doubt that in this

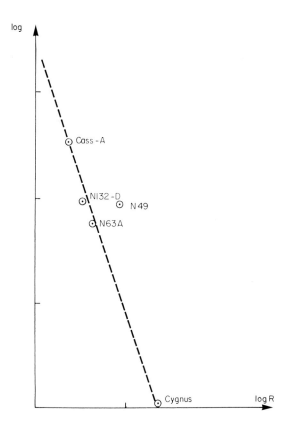

FIG. 53   Dependence of the radio-frequency emissivity of remnants of type II supernovae on their radii.

case the explosion was much more powerful than in the cases of Cassiopeia A, N 132D and N 63A.   We may therefore draw the conclusion that the mass of gas ejected in the case of N 49 was considerably greater than in other cases (with the exception of the filamentary nebula in Cygnus).

The spectral index of N 49 (with $\alpha = 1$) is high enough. Its luminosity must therefore drop particularly rapidly as the nebula expands (cf. Eq. (7.10)). It is interesting to compare N 49 with Cassiopeia A which has a similar spectral index of $\alpha = 0.80$. If the dimensions of the source in the Magellanic Clouds were the same as in Cassiopeia A, its luminosity, extrapolated according to the law $L_\nu \sim R^{-2\gamma}$, must have been about five hundred times that of Cassiopeia A at present.† The energy of the relativistic particles in this source then exceeded the energy of these particles in Cassiopeia A by about twentyfold and the magnetic field by fourfold. It is quite natural to assume that the mass of the ejected shell of N 49 was twenty times the mass ejected in Cassiopeia A.

Thus, N 49 assumed relative to Cassiopeia A the same position as the filamentary nebulae in Cygnus relative to N 63 and N 132D. If the mass ejected in the explosion in Cassiopeia A was of the order of several solar masses (see § 5), the mass ejected in the explosion of N 49 must have been of the order of $30M_\odot$.

In spite of the presence of extremely different initial conditions we shall assume that the function $L_\nu \sim R^{-\beta_1}$ applies to most of the objects observed. The graph shown in Figure 53 supports this assumption. In the following we shall assume that $\beta_1 = 3$, though in the case of galactic sources with which we are concerned β_1 may also assume another value. But we shall see from the following considerations that the final results obtained from this assumption will depend only slightly on the β_1 value adopted.

Today we know already a fairly high number of extended galactic radio sources which, obviously, are connected with the remnants of supernovae of type II. The extremely wide range within which the surface brightnesses of these objects vary indicates clearly that the various objects observed are in different stages of evolution. To study the nature of these objects it is, first of all, necessary to know their distances. At present, however, it is only Cassiopeia A and the filamentary nebulae in Cygnus whose distances we know sufficiently reliably (disregarding the three objects in the Large Magellanic Cloud; see above). As regards the other galactic radio sources of this type, their distances are virtually unknown.

To solve this primary problem the author of the present book suggested a statistical method in 1960.[61] This method is quite analogous to

---

† This indicates that at the same time the flux from this object towards the earth was twice as high as that from Cassiopeia A.

the method of determining the distance to the optically thin planetary nebulae, developed by the author in 1956,[123,124] which, at present, is generally accepted.

Let us briefly discuss the contents of this method.   If M is the mass of the optically thin planetary nebula and R is its radius, L_H is the luminosity in the Balmer lines, ε_H the emissivity per unit volume in these lines, I_H the surface brightness, N_e the electron concentration and r the distance of the planetary nebula, the following simple relationships will hold:

$$\varepsilon_H \sim N_e^2 \sim M^2 R^{-6}; \qquad L \propto N_e^2 R^3 \propto M^2 R^{-3}$$

$$I \propto \frac{L}{R^2} \propto M^2 R^{-5} \tag{7.33}$$

Moreover, we have

$$R = r\varphi \tag{7.34}$$

where φ denotes the angular dimensions of the nebula.

Since $R \propto M^{2/5} I^{1/5}$

$$r \propto M^{2/5} I^{1/5} \varphi^{-1} \tag{7.35}$$

where the values of I and φ are obtained from direct observations; these quantities are independent from the sought distance to the nebula.   Let us further assume that the mass dispersion of the planetary nebulae is insignificant.   Note, by the way, that the quantity enters Equation (7.35) in a power of $\frac{2}{5}$ so that the final result depends only slightly on the suppositions made.   If we admit that the distance of certain planetary nebulae was determined by some other methods, we shall have a zero for the relation (7.35) which must also be used in the determination of the distances to the planetary nebulae.

It is essential that the optically thin planetary nebulae may be considered as a homogeneous group of expanding objects where in the expansion process, thanks to the specific mechanism of emission (the strong dependence of L on R), the surface brightness, which is an immediately observable quantity, is also a strong function of the nebula's radius. The surface brightness of the individual planetary nebulae will therefore differ by factors of 1,000 and even 100,000.   Under these conditions the linear dimensions of the planetary nebulae will differ by relatively small amounts.   This is the reason for the very strong dependence of r on the angular dimensions φ.   Although I enters the relation (7.35) only in a power of $\frac{1}{5}$, its dependence on the surface brightness cannot be ignored since it varies within very wide limits.

The situation encountered in the case of the expanding remnants of supernovae of type II is quite analogous. Here, too, the surface brightness drops very rapidly as the radius increases, which results in a small dispersion of the linear dimensions of these objects. An analysis of the data given in the previous section (particularly as regards the objects in the Magellanic Clouds) actually shows that the linear dimensions hardly differ, whereas the surface brightness changes by a factor of 100,000.

As regards our problem, we can now write a system of equations quite analogous to Equations (7.33) and (7.35). According to Equation (7.10) the surface "radio-brightness" of the source connected with an expanding nebula will be given by

$$I_\nu \propto R_0^\beta H_{0\perp}^{(\gamma+1)/2} K_0 R^{-(\beta+2)} \qquad (7.36)$$

where the subscript 0 of R, $H_\perp$ and K refers to some initial stage of nebular evolution in which the production of relativistic particles in it was finished and the nebula became an object optically thin for radiation of a given radio frequency. If we denote the distance of the radio source by r and its angular radius by φ so that $R = r\varphi$ we obtain from Equation (7.36)

$$r \propto R_0^{\beta/(\beta+2)} H_{0\perp}^{(\gamma+1)/2(\beta+2)} K_0^{1/(\beta+2)} I_\nu^{-1/(\beta+2)} \varphi^{-1} \qquad (7.37)$$

This formula is quite analogous to Equation (7.35) which was used to determine the distance of the planetary nebulae. It may be assumed that $R_0^3 H_{0\perp}^2 \propto W$ where W is the power of the explosion. Relation (7.37) may then be rewritten in the form

$$r \propto W^{\beta/3(\beta+2)} H_{0\perp}^{(6-5\beta)/12(\beta+2)} I_\nu^{-1/(\beta+2)} \varphi^{-1} \qquad (7.38)$$

With $\beta = 3$, an assumption which is in agreement with empirical relationships (see Fig. 53), we find

$$r \propto W^{0.20} H_{0\perp}^{-0.15} I_\nu^{-0.20} \varphi^{-1} \qquad (7.39)$$

Note that this is a very weak function of the value accepted for β. If, for example, $\beta = 5$ (which is obviously too high),

$$r \propto W^{0.23} H_{0T}^{-0.22} I^{-0.14} \varphi^{-1}$$

The fact that r depends on W and $H_{0\perp}$ may be neglected in a first approximation. For example, in the previous section we saw that the numbers of relativistic particles contained in the sources differ from one another by at most ± 500 per cent. So the error of r, on the supposition that $W = \text{const}$, will then amount to 30 per cent which is sufficiently accurate for our purposes. The dispersion of the magnetic fields of the sources is much lower than that of W so that the error, due to the assumption that $H_{0\perp} = \text{const}$, will be even smaller.

In a quite analogous way we neglected in a first approximation that r depends on the mass M, when determining the distance to optically thin planetary nebulae from relation (7.37).

We shall demonstrate the effectiveness of this method by way of the following example. Assume that we do not know anything about the distance of the Large Magellanic Cloud and want to determine the distances of the sources N 63A and N 132D in this cloud with nothing else at our disposal other than the results of radio-astronomical observations. The angular dimensions of these sources are equal to $27''$ and $22''$, respectively (these data have been obtained from optical observations but this is insignificant as they can also be obtained in principle from radio-astronomical observations). In addition to that we know the fluxes and the spectral indices. From this we may calculate the surface brightnesses which are proportional to the brightness temperatures T_b. As the result of these calculations we find that at a frequency of 100 Mc T_b is equal to $1.5 \cdot 10^6$ and $3.7 \cdot 10^6 \, °\text{K}$, respectively, for these sources. On the other hand, the angular dimensions of a galactic source in the filamentary nebulae in Cygnus 170 are equal to $T_b = 6 \cdot 10^2$ (at the same frequency). With the help of these data and Equation (7.37), assuming that W and $H_{0\perp}$ are constant, we find that the distance of N 63A is seventy-nine, and that of N 132D is sixty-two, times that of the filamentary nebulae in Cygnus. Since the distance of the latter is, according to independent optical observations, equal to 770 psc, the distances of N 63A and N 132D are obtained as 61,000 psc and 48,000 psc, respectively. It is an interesting fact that the arithmetical mean of the distances obtained is equal to 54,500 psc, a value which is only 1 per cent below the true distance to the Large Magellanic Cloud! In any case the deviation of the distances to the two sources from the true distance amounted to only 10 per cent when the determinations were made with the help of radio-astronomical observations. And this deviation is so small in spite of the fact that W of the filamentary nebulae is about an order of magnitude higher than in the case of the objects in the Magellanic Clouds (see above). This justifies the assumption that Equation (7.37) can be used to establish a system for calculating the distances to the radio-emitting remnants of supernovae of type II.

To plot a distance scale for the radio sources connected with remnants of type II supernovae it is necessary to have a zero.   We now have good cause to choose as this reference point the distances to the filamentary nebulae in Cygnus and to N 63A and N 132D, which have been obtained from independent astronomical observations.

TABLE 15

No.	Name of Source	l^{II}	b^{II}	2φ	$T_b\ °K$	r psc	R psc	Z psc
1.	3C–392	34.3	−1.0	30	$4.3\cdot10^4$	2,600	11.6	−44
2.	NGC 6960–6992/5	74.2	−6.6	170	$3\cdot10^2$	770	20	−89
3.	BH, No. 21	88.9	+5.4	90	$1.4\cdot10^3$	1,260	16	120
4.	Cassiopeia A	112.3	−1.6	4	$5.5\cdot10^7$	3,400	2.7	−95
5.	BH, No. 3	132.8	+1.0	120	$3.2\cdot10^2$	1,100	19	19
6.	BH, No. 7	144.1	−1.8	120	$2.5\cdot10^2$	1,150	20	−37
7.	BH, No. 8	153.2	−3.5	120	$2.0\cdot10^2$	1,200	21	−73
8.	BH, No. 9	160.6	+1.6	90	$5.6\cdot10^2$	1,350	17	38
9.	S 147	177.3	−3.4	180	25	900	25	−53
10.	IC 443	188.3	+1.5	50	$7.5\cdot10^3$	1,900	13	49
11.	Auriga	166.3	+4.5	60	25	2,700	25	213
12.	Puppis A	260.4	−3.2	50	$4.7\cdot10^3$	2,000	14	−110
13.	Vela Y	263.3	−0.7	100	$1.6\cdot10^3$	1,150	17	−14
14.	Vela X	263.9	−3.2	90	$3.7\cdot10^3$	1,160	15	−64
15.	Vela Z	265.3	−1.1	90	$1.6\cdot10^3$	1,150	17	−23
16.	Centaur B	309.7	+2.5	75	$7.3\cdot10^3$	1,300	13	57

In Table 15 we find the fundamental characteristic features of some objects of interesting types.   We have chosen only such objects whose angular dimensions were known so that their brightness temperatures could be determined from the radio flux measured.   In the second column the names of the radio sources are listed.   The data for the sources Vela Y, X and Z and Puppis A were obtained from observations at a frequency of 85 Mc.[125]   The data of the sources Nos. 3, 5, 6, 7 and 8 stem from observations at a frequency of 158 Mc.[126]   For source No. 11 we used the results of observations at a frequency of 610 Mc (see Fig. 49). Unfortunately these data cannot be viewed as sufficiently accurate.

Source No. 9 is associated with the system of filamentary nebulae S 147 discovered by G. A. Shayn and V. F. Gaze.[74]   The data on the rather bright source No. 16 were derived from the isophotes published in [127]. The third and fourth columns of Table 15 give the galactic longitude and latitude (in the old system).   The fifth column contains the angular dimensions of the sources.   In those cases where the source has a lenticular shape we took the arithmetical mean of the largest and smallest angular dimensions.   The sixth column gives the mean brightness temperatures of the sources at a frequency of 100 Mc.   In those cases where no observations were made at a frequency of 100 Mc we extrapolated the value of F_ν obtained for other frequencies, using the spectral index $\alpha = 0.50$.   In the seventh column we find the distances of the sources calculated from Equation (7.37) with the help of the reference point determined above. In the cases of Cassiopeia A and the filamentary nebulae in Cygnus distances are given which were obtained by direct methods.   In the eighth column the nebular radii are compiled and in the last column the co-ordinates of the sources relative to the galactic plane.

   The mean value $|z|$ of the galactic sources listed in Table 15 is approximately equal to 60 psc, which is a very small value.   The spatial distribution of the radio sources of this type may alone give us valuable indications as to the nature of the exploding stars.   They form an extremely flat system, analogous to the system of the young and hot stars of the spectral classes O and B.   The analogy becomes an identity if we also take into account the statistical results obtained by Mills.[127]   According to [127] the galactic non-thermal radio sources (in the overwhelming majority remnants of supernovae of type II) are mainly concentrated in the spiral arms while their occurrence in the centre of the galaxy is insignificant.   We know that this is precisely the spatial distribution characterizing the early-type stars.   It is essential that the masses of the stars which explode as supernovae of the type II must be great, in any case much greater than the solar mass.   For example, from an analysis of the synchrotron radio emission of the source associated with the filamentary nebulae in Cygnus and the source N 49 in the Large Magellanic Cloud, it follows that the mass of the ejected shells must amount to at least $10 M_\odot$. The "sling effect," discussed in detail in § 4, leads quite independently to the conclusion that the exploding stars are massive and therefore very young.   In this way the data on the spatial distribution of the remnants of type II supernovae verifies perfectly the independently obtained conclusion that this type of supernovae pertains to the population I.
   6*

This conclusion may be defined more precisely: the exploding stars belong to the spectral class O or to the early subclass B.

There is, however, another very important problem which remains unsolved, namely the stage of evolution in which these stars explode. This might be a rather early stage of gravitational collapse (the mass distribution of the "runaway stars" would substantiate this conclusion, see § 4), but it is also possible that the outburst takes place in a later stage of evolution.

An analysis of Table 15 enables us to estimate the number of "old" remnants of supernovae of type II in our own stellar system. It follows from this table that there are, for example, ten objects with a distance shorter than 1,200 psc. Objects with a low brightness temperature T_b are hardly ever found at greater distances because of their relatively small angular dimensions (since the fluxes from them are too small). A considerable number of these objects were therefore not entered in Table 1. Here we have the same observational selection as in the case of the planetary nebulae: the observable objects of low surface brightness lie relatively near to us.[124] If we take into account the spatial distribution of the sources which have been identified with the remnants of type II supernovae (a flat system without any noticeable concentration towards the galactic centre), we may draw the conclusion that the number of these objects in the galaxy which display a brightness temperature higher than that of the filamentary nebulae in Cygnus must amount to between 500 and 700. On the other hand, the age of the filamentary nebulae may be estimated as 70,000 years (see § 8). Hence it follows that the frequency of supernova outbursts in the galaxy must be about 1 per 100 years. This estimate, which is based on radio-astronomical observations, is in close agreement with other estimates (see §§ 1 and 4).

In our galaxy the number of stars of the spectral class O is of the order of 10^4.[128] Let us assume that a supernova explosion occurred after the star had already travelled a great part of its evolutionary track on the main sequence. The period within which massive stars remain on the main sequence will be of the order of $3-10 \cdot 10^6$ years.[129] Hence it follows that about once in a hundred years such a star will be generated (and, consequently, disappear) in the galaxy. This would mean that the outburst frequency of supernovae of the type II should be three times as high as the frequency of formation of hot stars of the spectral class O. Therefore only part of the outbursts of type II supernovae may be explained as explosions of O-type stars. It is, however, quite admissible to assume that a considerable number of stars of the spectral class O "end their existence" as supernovae of type II. This may also be inferred from an analysis of the "sling effect" (see § 4). It is obvious that a great part of the supernovae of type II must be stars of the spectral class B.

§ 8   Shock waves in interstellar medium caused by outbursts of supernovae of the type II

Outbursts of type II supernovae are accompanied by an enormous release of energies. If the absolute photographic magnitude at maximum is $M_{ph} = -18$ (see § 1) then, in the case of a very high colour temperature ($\sim 40,000°$), the bolometric correction will exceed 3.5 magnitudes. If the effective time of radiation at the brightness maximum is assumed to be ~ 30 days, we find a value of $\sim 3 \cdot 10^{49}$ erg for the amount of energy emitted. The value may be even higher, since the amount of energy emitted in the high-frequency range of the spectrum cannot be estimated accurately. Still higher is the mechanical energy of the gases ejected during the explosion. If we assume that the gas mass is equal to $1 M_{\odot}$ (it may also be $10 M_{\odot}$, cf. § 2) and the speed of ejection is $\sim 7 \cdot 10^8$ cm/s, we find that the kinetic energy of the shell must be $> 5 \cdot 10^{50}$ erg.

In the present section we shall discuss the problem of the conversions of the kinetic energy of the gas ejected during the explosion. But first of all we shall consider the decelerating effect of interstellar matter exerted on the gas shell ejected. Twenty years ago this problem was stated for the first time, by Oort,[72] who used the law of conservation of momentum for its solution. Let us denote by v_0 the initial velocity of the shell, by $v(t)$ the velocity at the instant t ($t = 0$ corresponds to the instant of explosion), R is the radius of the spherical shell, M its mass and ρ the density of the surrounding interstellar medium which is assumed to be homogeneous. The law of conservation of momentum reads:

$$(M + \tfrac{4}{3}\pi R^3 \rho)v = Mv_0 \qquad (8.1)$$

This holds good under the supposition that the expanding shell "sweeps out" all the substance in front of it. Moreover, the shell is assumed to be free from all forces.

Taking into account that $v = dR/dt$ and integrating Equation (8.1) we obtain

$$\tfrac{1}{3}\pi R^4 \rho + MR = Mv_0 t \qquad (8.2)$$

The motion of the shell is entirely determined by Equations (8.1) and (8.2). Let us consider the important special case of a strongly decelerated shell where $\frac{4}{3}\pi R^3 \rho \gg M$. In this case we shall obtain from Equations (8.1) and (8.2)

$$v = \frac{3Mv_0}{4\pi\rho R^3}; \qquad R = \left(\frac{3Mv_0}{\pi\rho}\right)^{\frac{1}{4}}; \qquad R = 4vt \qquad (8.3)$$

To illustrate the results we shall apply these formulas to the system of filamentary nebulae in Cygnus. In this case it follows from observations that $R = 20$ psc, $v = 115$ km/s. Substituting these values in Equation (8.3) yields immediately the age of the system: $t = 44{,}000$ years. On the other hand, if $v_0 = 7 \cdot 10^8$ cm/s (in analogy to other supernovae) and $\rho = 2 \cdot 10^{-24}$ g/cm³, the mass of the gas shell ejected in the explosion would be $\sim 10 M_\odot$, which is in close agreement with an independent estimate obtained from an analysis of radio-astronomical observations (see § 7).

Though they are so elementary, Equations (8.1), (8.2) and (8.3), give in a first approximation quite a good description of the mechanical interaction between the gas shell ejected in the explosion and the interstellar medium. But this description is incomplete. The phenomena which appear in such a case are in fact very complex. Apart from this, the already difficult problem is complicated further by the necessity of considering the inhomogeneities in the interstellar medium, and of taking into account the presence of magnetic fields and relativistic particles in it and in the moving shell.

First of all it must be pointed out that so far we have no generally accepted unique theory to explain all processes caused by the motion of the shell in interstellar matter. Nevertheless there are sufficiently well-developed solutions to partial aspects of this problem. In many cases these solutions are of special interest and help us to understand details of the phenomena associated with the consequences of supernova explosions.

One aspect of the general problem was already discussed in § 5 when interpreting the phenomena observed in the system of thin-fibred nebulae in Cygnus. S. B. Pikel'ner's theory was briefly described there, which considers these filamentary nebulae as the intersections of the fronts of shock waves propagated in an inhomogeneous interstellar medium. In the present section we shall treat the problem of the propagation in interstellar medium of the shock wave produced by the explosion of a supernova of type II.

Before we apply the theory of shock wave propagation in a homogeneous medium to the real problem of the motion of a supernova's shell in interstellar medium, let us consider the following fact. As already stressed at the beginning of the present section, the kinetic energy of the gases ejected during the explosion of a supernova of type II is exceedingly high. All observational data (cf. § 5) indicate that in such an explosion at least one solar mass is ejected; in individual cases, however, tens and even hundreds (supernovae of type III, see § 2) of solar masses are ejected at speeds of 5,000 to 10,000 km/s. In the case of Cassiopeia A where the outburst was of a relatively modest power, the mass of gas ejected was at least equal to one solar mass, moving at a velocity of 7,000 km/s. The minimum kinetic energy of the ejected shell must therefore be $\sim 5 \cdot 10^{50}$ erg. Far more powerful was the outburst of the supernova which resulted in the formation of the filamentary nebulae in Cygnus or in the case of the formation of the object in the Magellanic Clouds N 49 (see § 7). In these cases the mass of the shells ejected must have been of the order of $30 M_{\odot}$, and their kinetic energies are of the order of 10^{52} erg. In the case of supernovae of type III, about which we know very little as yet, the mass of the ejected shell seems to reach $100 M_{\odot}$ which, with an ejection velocity of $\sim 10,000$ km/s (cf. § 2), leads to energies of the order of 10^{53} to 10^{54} erg.

Using Equation (8.1), which is based on the law of momentum conservation, we may estimate the deceleration of such shells in interstellar medium. In the process of this deceleration the kinetic energy of the shell and of the gas "swept together" by it decreases continuously, compared to the initial kinetic energy of the shell. The basic question will now arise: into which form is this energy converted?

However, strangely enough, this important problem has not been discussed until recently.

A special case of the expansion of a strongly decelerated supernova shell was investigated by S. B. Pikel'ner (cf. § 5), dealing with the system of fine-fibred nebulae in Cygnus. In this case the energy of the random (thermal) motion in the shock wave front is entirely converted into radiation. In the case of relatively young, insufficiently-slowed-down shells, however, this idea does not apply. This may be demonstrated by means of the example of Cassiopeia A. We know that the rate of expansion of the front of filaments nearest to the observer amounts to $\sim 6,000$ km/s while the opposite, rear front of the shell expands at a rate of 7,400 km/s (see § 5). The observed effect of deceleration finds a natural explanation in the assumption that the unperturbed density of interstellar matter, in which the shell is moving, amounts to $\rho \sim 10^{-24}$ g/cm^3. From the nature of the shell's deceleration it follows that it must have lost already ~ 20 per cent of its initial kinetic energy. If we assume the shell mass $\sim 1 M_\odot$ (which in all probability is too low) we find that the energy lost by the shell is of the order of 10^{50} erg.

Let us assume that the effective time within which an observable deceleration occurred is ~ 100 years (~ 30 per cent of the age of the shell). The power then released during the deceleration of the shell amounts to $\sim 3 \cdot 10^{40}$ erg/s. If this power had appeared in the form of radiation, as in the case of the filamentary nebulae in Cygnus, the bolometric absolute magnitude of Cassiopeia A would have been equal to -13. If an essential part of this energy had been emitted in the visual and photographic ranges then, even with an absorption A of about eight magnitudes (see § 5), the stellar magnitude of this object would have been ~ 7.5. In fact, however, this nebula is fainter than magnitude 15. The assumption that Cassiopeia A emits $3 \cdot 10^{40}$ erg/s, set free in the deceleration, in the X-ray or any other spectral range, cannot be justified since with the modern methods of extra-atmospheric astronomy a flux of $\sim 10^{-5}$ erg/cm$^2 \cdot$s would certainly have been discovered, whatever the spectral range in which it is emitted. Thus we may draw the conclusion that the energy set free in the deceleration of Cassiopeia A by interstellar matter is not emitted as radiation.

This important conclusion may also be obtained from theoretical considerations. First of all, note that the kinetics of shock wave formation at velocities of $\sim 10^8$ to 10^9 cm/s differs from that where the velocities are $\sim 10^6$ to 10^7 cm/s. For example, at a velocity of $7 \cdot 10^8$ cm/s the energy of each proton reaches 250,000 eV. With such huge energies the processes of elastic scattering in "pair" collisions with atoms of the medium in which the wave is propagated become negligible compared to the "collective" interactions of assemblies of ionized particles. The effects occurring in this case are described by the modern theory of instability of plasma beams.[130] If we take the finite temperature of the particles in the beams into account, it follows from this theory that the instability (which causes the transition of ordered motion of the particles in the beam to disordered motion) sets in (when a magnetic field perpendicular to the relative velocity of the beams is present) at two velocity intervals. The first interval begins at a velocity which is equal to the thermal velocity of the ions, and the second interval, in which we are interested, includes velocities exceeding the thermal velocity of the electrons. In the absence of a magnetic field a sharp front cannot be formed. It should be noted, however, that for our problem it is immaterial whether a magnetic field is present or not.

We may convince ourselves that the compression of gas behind the shock wave front will be adiabatic, on condition that the wave velocity is high enough and the time of existence of the wave is finite. The criterion of adiabaticity consists in the requirement that the time of essential cooling of the gas because of radiation exceeds the time during which the wave front has travelled a considerable part of the radius of the spherical shock wave. When the ion temperatures are very high, $T_i \sim 10^9$ (which corresponds to disordered velocities of protons $\sim 5 \cdot 10^8$ cm/s) and the densities are $\sim 10^{-22}$ to 10^{-23} g/cm^3 (which corresponds to the density of a shock wave propagated in a cloud of interstellar gas), the cooling period is very long. The electrons behind the shock wave are in fact heated very rapidly, within a period of $\sim 2\pi(\omega_e \cdot \omega_i)^{-\frac{1}{2}}$ (where ω_e and ω_i are the plasma frequencies of electrons and ions, respectively), by virtue of "collective" interaction with ions (chiefly protons), reaching a temperature which corresponds to the mean square velocity, equal to the velocity of the shock wave; this temperature is $\sim 10^6$. "Collective" interactions between electrons and protons may take place only so long as the proton velocity exceeds the thermal velocities of the electrons. A further increase of the temperature of the electron gas cannot be achieved by "collective" interaction but by means of "pair" collisions with ions.†
In this case the relaxation time is determined by the expression (see, for example, [84])

$$\tau_{ei} \sim \frac{m_i}{m_e} \frac{l_{ee}}{v_e} \tag{8.4}$$

where m_i and m_e are the masses of proton and electron, v_e is the thermal electron velocity and l_{ee} is the effective free length of electrons in the plasma, determined by

$$l_{ee} \sim \frac{(kT_e)^2}{e^4 N_e \, 3\ln(3kT_e/4l^2 N_e^{\frac{1}{3}})} \tag{8.5}$$

for example, if $T_e \sim 10^8$ deg and $N_e \sim 10^2$ cm^{-3}, $\tau_{ei} \sim 10^{12}$ s, which is much longer than the lifetime of such a comparatively young object as Cassiopeia A. On the other hand, electrons at a temperature of $\sim 10^8$ deg will lose energy through X-ray bremsstrahlung in the range of ~ 1 A.

---

† One cannot exclude the possibility that collective interactions may raise the electron temperature up to a value comparable to the ion temperature. This problem requires additional investigation.

Owing to the high degree of ionization other elements (e.g., oxygen, nitrogen) will not contribute to the X-ray emission as their abundance is too low. The energy loss per second and per electron, due to X-ray emission with continuous spectrum, will be equal to

$$\frac{3}{2} k \frac{dT_e}{dt} = \frac{k^2 K T_e^{1/2} g\mathrm{II} n_p}{2x_H} = 1.4 \cdot 10^{-23} g\mathrm{II} \left(\frac{T_e}{10^8}\right)^{1/8} \text{ erg/s} \qquad (8.6)$$

where $K = 3.2 \cdot 10^{-6}$, x_H is the ionization potential of hydrogen, $g\mathrm{II}$ is Gaunt's factor, ~ 1. From Equation (8.6) it follows immediately that the "de-excitation time" of the electrons owing to X-ray bremsstrahlung losses at $T = 10^8$ and $n_p = 10^2$ cm^{-3} will amount to $\sim 10^{13}$ s. The relaxation time is comparable with the de-excitation time only if the temperature $T_e < 4 \cdot 10^8$. It must, however, be kept in mind that the time of adiabatic cooling of the proton gas in early stages of expansion will be essentially smaller than τ_{ei}.

Owing to this, there is almost no "thermal contact" between the electrons and ions behind the shock wave front, in the case of high velocities. The plasma behind the front will be highly non-isothermal.† The ions will lose their energy only in inelastic collisions with atoms of the interstellar matter which they pass through, and in "collective" interactions with protons, produced in the ionization of interstellar gas through collisions.

Hence it follows immediately that the high-temperature ion gas appearing behind the shock wave front will lose almost no energy to radiation within the period of an essential displacement of the wave front. This indicates that the condition of adiabaticity will be satisfied (perhaps with the exception of the last stages of shock wave propagation, see below).‡

This shows us that the phenomenon of a supernova outburst in interstellar matter must be treated as a powerful explosion in a gas with constant specific heat. The constancy of the specific heat results from the fact that the ionization energy is much smaller than the kinetic energy of the ionizing particles. The author of the present book was the first who, in 1962, treated the outburst of a supernova in this way.[132]

The problem of a strong explosion in a medium with constant specific heat is known to have a self-modelling solution which differs in the fact

---

† See, however, the footnote on p. 414.
‡ The condition of adiabaticity will even be fulfilled if $T_e \simeq T_i$ (see footnote on p. 414).

that the characteristics of motion after the explosion change similarly.[133] Can we apply the self-modelling solution to the problem of supernova explosions in interstellar matter and, if we can, what are the limitations?

The condition of applicability of the self-modelling solution is that the problem does not contain more than two parameters with independent dimensionality, not counting the time after the moment of explosion and the distance from the origin of the explosion. In the case of supernova explosions the explosion energy and the density of the interstellar medium may be chosen as these independent parameters. Furthermore, we have to exclude the initial stage of the outburst when the moving shell of the supernova has not yet been slowed down sufficiently and has "maintained its individual character," i.e., when it is still discernible from the interstellar medium surrounding it. That is precisely the way it is also in the case of a strong explosion in the earth's atmosphere. The initial stage of the explosion, which lasts 30 microseconds, cannot be described by the self-modelling solution. On the other hand, when the shock wave has been propagated over a very large distance from the exploded star or when the density of this medium is sufficiently high, its velocity may become quite insignificant. The conditions of adiabaticity and constancy of the specific heat will be violated. Most of the energy released in the deceleration will be emitted in the form of radiation. It is not impossible that in the cases of the filamentary nebulae in Cygnus and, particularly, of S 147, we may already observe this phase of evolution of the shock wave.

Thus we have the right to apply the self-modelling solution of the problem of a strong explosion in a medium with constant density to a very wide range of evolution of the remnants of supernovae. This range begins when the moving shell has "swept together" a mass of interstellar gas which is several times greater than its own mass. In this stage the shell initially ejected in the explosion will no longer play a noticeable part in the pattern of the motion. In the following its significance will virtually come to naught. The other limit of applicability of the self-modelling solution must be rather close to the practically complete cessation of movement. When we know the limitations, we may, in our opinion, also apply the conclusions of the theory to the shock wave front which precedes the non-decelerated shell of such a young object as Cassiopeia A. In each concrete case one must, however, take the specific features of the object into account (shell structure, possible inhomogeneities in the interstellar medium and the like). These non-decelerated shells are of particular interest for astrophysics. Apart from Cassiopeia A the Crab nebula also belongs to them. The deceleration of such shells can be described in a first approximation by Oort's elementary formula (8.1). In front of the slowed-down shell a shock wave will be propagated at a velocity of $v_0/3$ with respect to the shell, this wave playing the part of a "piston." The physical conditions behind the shock wave front (and in front of the shell) may be derived from the self-modelling solution which we shall consider in the following.

It is interesting to draw the parallels between the outburst of a supernova in interstellar medium and a powerful explosion in the earth's atmosphere. Both explosions are adiabatic but for quite different reasons. In the second case the adiabatic character is due to the very high opaqueness of the glowing gas behind the front of the shock wave. In the astronomical case, however, adiabaticity is the result of the extremely low density of the interstellar medium and the resulting very slow de-excitation of the strongly heated gas behind the front. The low density of the medium in which the explosion takes place is an important feature, distinguishing the astronomical problem from the atmospherical one. By virtue of the very high temperature behind the shock wave front the mean free path of the ions may be very long in the early stages of development of the explosion of the supernova. It is obvious that in this case the presence of magnetic fields guiding the motion of the charged particles is of essential significance. In later stages of the explosion the temperature behind the front drops considerably (see below) and the mean free path of the charged particles becomes much smaller than the characteristic dimensions of the shock wave (e.g., the radius of the front).

Let us now discuss the fundamental results of the theory applying to our problem, which has been developed in [133]. We assume the interstellar medium homogeneous, with a particle concentration n_1, mainly consisting of hydrogen atoms. The density of this medium will then be given by $\rho_1 = n_1 m_i$ where m_i is the mass of a proton. We shall consider the explosion of a supernova as a sudden release of thermal energy at a point, identical with the origin of our co-ordinate frame, occurring at the time $t = 0$. According to [133] we shall then have the relationships:

$$R_2 = \left(\frac{2.2E}{\rho_1}\right)^{\frac{1}{5}} t^{\frac{2}{5}} = 10^{15}\left(\frac{E}{E_0 n_1}\right)^{\frac{1}{5}} t^{\frac{2}{5}} \tag{8.7}$$

$$T_2 = \frac{3}{25k}\left(\frac{2.2E}{kn_1}\right) R^{-3} = 1.44 \cdot 10^{21}\left(\frac{E}{n_1 E_0}\right)^{\frac{2}{5}} t^{-6/5} \tag{8.8}$$

$$\rho_2 = 4\rho_1 \tag{8.9}$$

where R_2 is the radius of the front, T_2 the ion temperature behind the front, ρ_2 the density behind the front, E the energy of the explosion, $E_0 = 0.75 \cdot 10^{51}$ erg is the amount of energy released in the explosion and taken as a standard; its value is typical for the remnants of supernovae of the type II with a mass $\sim 1 M_\odot$. The specific heat ratio $c_p/c_v = \gamma$ is assumed equal to $\frac{5}{3}$ for the interstellar gas. The physical contents of these equations is evident. Equation (8.9) represents the well-known discontinuity of density behind the front of a strong shock wave. Equation

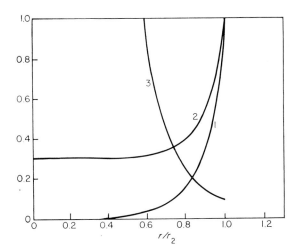

FIG. 54   Dependence of density, temperature and pressure on the distance to the explosion centre ($t = \text{const}$). Curve 1 shows the dependence of ρ/ρ_2, curve 2 that of P/P_2 and Curve 3 that of $0.1 T/T_2$. The subscript 2 refers to the conditions immediately behind the front.[134]

(8.8) indicates that the explosion energy (under adiabatic conditions) is converted into thermal energy of all the particles present within a sphere of radius R_2. Finally, Equation (8.7) describes the rate of expansion of the hot gas inside the sphere of radius R_2. The formulas (8.7) and (8.9) were verified experimentally in the nuclear explosions in the atmosphere.

In Figure 54 solutions to Equations (8.7) and (8.8) are represented in the form of graphs. Figure 55 shows the density, temperature and pressure at a definite instant of time as functions of the distance to the origin of the explosion. The time dependence of these parameters is shown in Figure 55 for a given mass element of the interstellar medium, after the shock wave front has passed through it.

From these graphs we may see in particular that behind the front the gas is concentrated within a relatively thin shell, measuring $\sim R_2/10$,

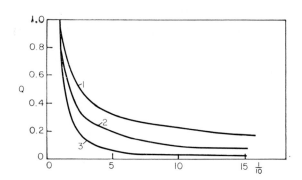

FIG. 55   Time dependence of density, temperature and pressure for a given mass element.   Curve 1 shows the time dependence of T/T_0, Curve 2 that of ρ/ρ_0 and Curve 3 that of P/P_0, where the subscript 0 corresponds to the moment when the mass element passes through the front.[134]

whereas the gas density in the central region is insignificant.   Differentiating Equation (8.7) with respect to time we obtain the velocity of the wave front:

$$v = \frac{dR_2}{dt} = \frac{2}{5}\left(\frac{E}{\rho}\right)^{1/5} t^{-3/5} \tag{8.10}$$

Equation (8.10) describes the deceleration of the shock wave.   From Equations (8.7) and (8.10) we may derive the following simple relation:

$$R_2 = \tfrac{5}{2}v(t)t \tag{8.11}$$

whereas from Oort's elementary formula (8.3) it follows for a strongly decelerated shell that $R_2 = 4v(t)\cdot t$.   The difference between Equations (8.11) and (8.3) may be explained by the fact that in Oort's simple theory which is based only on the law of conservation of momentum the adiabatic behaviour of the shock wave has not been taken into account, so that an incorrect result was obtained.

In this way the value obtained for the age of the decelerated remnants explosions was higher by a factor of 1.6 than that resulting from the simple considerations by Oort. For example, in the case of the filamentary nebulae in Cygnus, the observed values of $v = 115$ km/s and $R_2 = 20$ psc yield $t = 70,000$ years, whereas according to (8.2) $t = 44,000$ years.

Equations (8.10) and (8.11) give a sufficiently good description of an explosion in interstellar matter; that is, the outburst of a supernova.

A distinctive feature of the ideas developed above is the conclusion that the expanding old remnants of supernova explosions are relatively thin shells heated to very high temperatures which are determined by Equation (8.8). For example, in the case of the filamentary nebulae in Cygnus, $T \sim 2.5 \cdot 10^6$ deg, with $n_1 = 1$. The observed glow of the filaments must be interpreted as the result of the passage of a wave through relatively dense parts of the interstellar medium. This gives rise to a sharp increase in the number of collisions between electrons and atoms which, in its turn, results in a relatively rapid cooling of the gas behind the shock wave front (see § 5). But if the theory developed above is correct we must expect the presence of highly rarefied and very hot gas in the inner part of the system of fine-fibred nebulae (and likewise in other remnants of supernovae). We can easily convince ourselves that the optical effect of this gas is negligibly small. But in the far ultraviolet and in the X-ray range of the spectrum we may expect a measurable flux of radiation from such objects. Details of this problem will be discussed in the following.

The presence of a very hot rarefied gas in the region of supernova remnants may explain the ionization, heating and excitation in the filaments of such nebulae as Cassiopeia A and the Crab nebula.

Let us consider this problem by way of the example of Cassiopeia A. According to the ideas developed above, the comparatively dense, diffuse and stationary condensations of this nebula (see § 5) must be surrounded by a very hot rarefied plasma with $T_i \sim 10^9\,^\circ$K and $n_p \sim 0.1$ cm^{-3}. Note that the electron temperature of this rarefied hot medium must be much lower, namely $\sim 10^6$ to $10^7\,^\circ$K, since during the propagation of the wave equilibrium cannot be established between T_i and T_e.[†] The relatively high temperature of the dense condensations, which is responsible for the observed degree of ionization and the excitation of the atoms and ions, may be a consequence of simple heat conduction. Let us estimate roughly the effectiveness of this mechanism. If the mean

† See, however, the footnote on p. 414,

dimension of a condensation is equal to $3 \cdot 10^{17}$ cm, its effective surface will amount to $\sim 10^{35}$ cm^2. Since there are about two hundred such observable condensations, their total surface will be of the order of 10^{37} to 10^{38} cm^2.

The total flux of energy from the hot plasma in the condensations will be equal to $n_p v k T_i S \simeq 10^{38}$ to 10^{39} erg/s, where S is the effective surface of the condensations. If we assume that the total absorption of the light from Cassiopeia A amounts to eight magnitudes ($A_v = 8$) the luminosity of the condensations in the various lines will be of the order of 10^{38} erg/s.

Since most of the energy gained by a condensation in its bombardment by particles of the surrounding rarefied and hot plasma is consumed for heating and is then, in the stationary case, emitted as radiation, we see from the above estimate that this mechanism may support continuously the radiation of these condensations.

Let us now consider an effect which may be understood on the basis of the idea that the regions of the remnants of stellar explosions contain a very hot rarefied plasma. The fact that the relatively dense stationary condensations in Cassiopeia A are in equilibrium requires an explanation. We can imagine that, in the absence of external forces, such a condensation would inevitably be scattered as its own gravity is not able to compensate the gradient of gas pressure. Even the formation of stationary condensations requires the presence of external forces. It is quite natural to assume that the pressure of the hot plasma surrounding the condensations plays the part of the external forces. It is easy to see that at a temperature of $\sim 2.10^4$ deg of the stationary condensations and a particle density of $\sim 3 \cdot 10^3$ cm^{-3} (see § 5) the gas pressure of the condensations will be of the same order of magnitude as the gas pressure of the external hot and rarefied plasma. But it must be borne in mind that when these stationary condensations were formed through compression of inhomogeneities in the interstellar medium surrounding the exploding supernova, apart from the pressure of the hot gas a great part may be played by magnetic forces (see § 9).

With the help of Equations (8.7) and (7.10) we can derive a theoretical "luminosity function" of the radio sources which are remnants of supernovae of type II. Under "luminosity function" we understand the dependence of the number of radio sources in the galaxy on the power of their synchrotron radio emission per unit interval of frequency. For the sake of simple calculation we assume all sources similar, differing only in

their phases of expansion.   At a given frequency of outbursts of type II
supernovae the number dN of sources, whose radio-frequency emissivities
lie within the limits of L_ν and $L_\nu + dL_\nu$, will then be proportional to the
time interval dt within which the source dimensions increase from R to
$R + dR$, where R is the radius of the source at which the luminosity is
equal to L_ν.

According to Equation (8.7) we may write

$$t \propto R^{5/2}, \qquad dt \propto R^{3/2}\, dR \propto dN$$

Moreover, from Equation (7.10) it follows that

$$R \propto L_\nu^{-1/\beta}, \qquad dR \propto L_\nu^{-[(1/\beta)+1]}\, dL_\nu$$

and hence

$$dN(L_\nu) \propto L_\nu^{-(5+2\beta)/2\beta}\, dL_\nu \tag{8.12}$$

If we assume for example that $\beta = 3$, we have the following differential
distribution of the sources with respect to luminosity:

$$dN(L_\nu) \propto L_\nu^{-1.83}\, dL_\nu \tag{8.13}$$

The integral distribution reads

$$N(L_\nu > L_\nu^0) \propto (L_\nu^0)^{-0.83} \tag{8.14}$$

From Equation (8.14) it follows, for example, that the number
of sources whose power is at least two thousand times the power L_ν^0
must amount to about $\frac{1}{400}$ of the number of sources whose power
exceeds L_ν^0.   If L_ν corresponds to the power of the filamentary nebulae in
Cygnus, 2,000 L_ν corresponds to the power of Cassiopeia A.   From the
statistical analysis carried out in § 7 it follows that, in our galaxy, the
number of sources with a power equal to or higher than the power of
the filamentary nebulae in Cygnus must be of the order of several
hundreds, while Cassiopeia A is a unique object.   We can thus say that
Equation (8.12) describes satisfactorily the results of observations.

Future radio telescopes displaying essentially improved sensitivity
and directivity should enable us to study in detail the function $N(L_\nu)$
with the remnants of the type II supernovae in the Andromeda nebula
and the Magellanic Clouds.   Such an investigation would be of great value
for the research into the evolution of remnants of type II supernovae.

In 1964 Heiles criticized our paper on the interaction of supernova
outbursts with interstellar matter which has been discussed above.[134]

He drew attention to the importance of inelastic collisions between electrons and ions which are not protons. Such collisions may cause intense radiation in the X-ray range owing to which the problem on the propagation of a strong shock wave in interstellar matter may become non-adiabatic. In fact, however, we considered only the bremsstrahlung losses in a pure hydrogen plasma at high temperatures and showed that this cannot violate the adiabaticity. But let us discuss Heiles' arguments in greater detail.

First of all, in [134] the time was considered in which the condition of adiabaticity may be violated by bremsstrahlung alone (see above). A numerical integration of (8.6) over the volume yields an expression for the power emitted by the bremsstrahlung of an expanding shell

$$L_{ff} = 2.8 \cdot 10^{29} \left(\frac{E}{n_1 E_0}\right)^{4/5} t^{3/5} \quad \text{erg/s} \tag{8.15}$$

An integration with respect to time yields

$$\int_0^\tau L_{ff}\, dt = 1.75 \cdot 10^{29} \left(\frac{E}{n_1 E_0}\right)^{4/5} \tau^{8/5} \quad \text{erg} \tag{8.16}$$

If this expression is set equal to E we obtain the time after which the adiabatic theory will no longer be adequate for our problem:

$$\tau = 10^6 \left(\frac{E}{E_0}\right)^{1/8} n_1^{1/2} \quad \text{years} \tag{8.17}$$

This estimate depends a little on n_1 and very slightly on E_1. Millions of years after the explosion the radius of the wave front will be, according to (8.7), ~ 80 psc, much greater than all observed objects of this type. Hence we may draw the conclusion that the bremsstrahlung of a hot pure hydrogen plasma will not violate the condition of adiabaticity as this was already shown by us with the help of another method. The real inter-stellar plasma will also contain other elements, apart from hydrogen and helium, which occur in the form of insignificant impurities. When the plasma is very hot, these elements (in any case those with the greatest abundance) will be fully ionized. Their contribution to the bremsstrahlung of the plasma, which does not violate adiabaticity, will be small. As the wave front is propagated, however, the situation can change. First of all when the temperature behind the front drops to several 10^7 degrees (this is the case at about 5,000 years after the explosion, see Equation 8.8),

τ_{ei} will be smaller than the characteristic time of adiabatic expansion and the plasma becomes isothermal (i.e., $T_i = T_c$). Note, however, that owing to the beam instability the plasma may become isothermal much earlier. When the temperature behind the front becomes equal to $T \sim 5 \cdot 10^6$ deg, a great part of the nuclei of oxygen which, as to the abundance, comes next after hydrogen and helium, will get an electron by way of recombination. Owing to this the radiation intensity rises strongly because of an excitation of the O VIII resonance level by electron impact. This results in the emission of the line $\lambda\ 18.9$ (analogous to L_α) and other "hydrogen" lines. Let us consider this important problem in greater detail.

According to (8.8) a temperature of $T = 5 \cdot 10^6$ deg will be reached in $\sim 10^{12}$ s (or $\sim 3 \cdot 10^4$ years) after the outburst. The re-combination coefficient R_{87} for the O IX ion may be chosen as equal to $4 \cdot 10^{-13}$, [135] and the coefficient of ionization by electron impact

$$I_{78} \sim 8 \cdot 10^{-8} \frac{N_e}{T_e^{\frac{1}{2}}} \sim 3 \cdot 10^{-11} N_e$$

(if kT exceeds the ionization potential). The time ionization equilibrium takes to establish is equal to

$$\tau_u \sim \frac{1}{I_{78} + R_{87}} \sim 3 \cdot 10^{10}\text{s}$$

i.e., it is relatively short (compared to the time of expansion). The ionization equilibrium which is established in the plasma is therefore quite similar to that which exists in the solar corona. On the basis of the theory of this equilibrium (see [85]) we may write

$$\frac{O_7}{O_8} \equiv x_7 = \frac{R_{87}}{I_{78}}$$

where O_7 is the concentration of the O VIII ions and O_8 that of the O IX ions.

Since the O VIII ionization potential is equal to about 800 eV, the maximum concentration in this state of oxygen ionization will be reached at about the same temperature as in the active zones of the solar corona emitting the yellow Ca XV line (ionization potential 819 eV). In this case x_7 must be ~ 1. According to [85] the temperature at which calcium will occur mainly in the ionized state of Ca XV is equal to $5 \cdot 10^6$ deg.

Let us assume that O VIII too has its maximum at this temperature (in [134] this temperature was assumed equal to 10^7 °K). With $x_7 = 1$ it may be assumed that about one-third of all oxygen ions will be in the state of O VIII (an analogous situation is encountered in the case of the iron ions in the solar corona, see [85]).

The emissivity per unit volume of hot plasma in the O VIII resonance line may be given, according to [135], by

$$\varepsilon_{\text{O VIII}} = \frac{2.7 \cdot 10^{-15}}{T^{1/2}} N_e n_0 \frac{[\text{O VIII}]}{\Sigma[\text{O}_i]} \qquad (8.18)$$

where $n_0 \sim 5 \cdot 10^{-4}$ cm^{-3}, N_e is the oxygen concentration in all states of ionization,

$$\frac{[\text{O VIII}]}{\Sigma[\text{O}_i]}$$

is the fraction of O VIII ions.

Integrating (8.18) over the volume we shall have

$$\varepsilon_{\text{O VIII}} = 1.7 \cdot 10^{17} t^{9/5} \qquad (8.19)$$

where

$$\frac{n_0}{N_e} \frac{[\text{O VIII}]}{\Sigma[\text{O}_i]}$$

is assumed to be constant in the entire volume and equal to 0.1, $E = 2E_0$ and $n_1 = 1$. Integration with respect to time (under the same suppositions) and the assumption that the total radiative energy losses in the O VIII line are equal to the energy E yields a value of

$$\tau = 1.4 \cdot 10^{12} \text{ s} = 44{,}000 \text{ years} \qquad (8.20)$$

for the time after which adiabaticity is violated. The corresponding radius of the front will be equal to

$$R_2 = 26 \text{ psc}$$

Thus we see that when inelastic collisions between electrons and ions are taken into account the condition of adiabaticity is violated in the late stages of shock wave development. This particular fact attracted Heiles' attention. In which way will the shock wave then be propagated in the interstellar medium? The cooling rate of the gas behind the wave front will be higher; when the temperature has dropped to 3–$4 \cdot 10^6$ deg, the oxygen will be chiefly in the state of O VIII. The O VII ion has a resonance line at $\lambda = 21.6$ Å and another at $\lambda = 21.8$ Å. These lines (just as the O VIII line $\lambda = 18.969$ Å) were recently discovered in the solar X-ray spectrum.[136] At a temperature below $3\cdot10^6$ deg plasma emission will occur most likely in the O VII line. The lines of N VI and C V will be much less intense. When the temperature has dropped to $(1-2)\cdot10^6$ deg, i.e., when it has become similar to that of the solar corona, the intensity of the O VII emission lines will decrease considerably. At the same time the most abundant oxygen, nitrogen and carbon atoms are, as before, in the states O VII, N VI and C V and, like their lower states of ionization, they have very low potentials. The ionization potential of, e.g., O VII is equal to 739 eV and that of O VI is as low as 138 eV. The main radiative energy losses will now be connected with the excitation of various levels of the ions of iron, magnesium, neon, etc., and also with bremsstrahlung. With these temperatures behind the shock wave front we may use extensively the results of investigations of the emission of the solar corona at various waves.

The emission of some sufficiently rarefied plasma at constant temperature may be described by the expression

$$L = \left\{ \int N_e^2 \, dV \right\} \Psi(T) \tag{8.21}$$

where $\int N_e^2 \, dV$ is the "volume emissivity." The value of $\int N_e^2 \, dV$ for the solar corona can be obtained from radio-astronomical observations of the quiescent sun in the 10-cm band (see [137]). This value is $\sim 3\cdot10^{49}$ cm^{-3}. The flux of natural radiation from the corona at the boundary of the earth's atmosphere (mainly in the X-ray and soft ultraviolet ranges) amounts to ~ 1 erg/cm$^2\cdot$s.[85] Consequently the power of coronal emission per unit volume emissivity is of the order of 10^{-22}. On the other hand, if we assume that the radius of the shock wave front is $R_2 = 30$ psc and $n_1 = 1$ cm^{-3}, we find that the volume emissivity behind the front of a spherical shock wave is $\sim 5\cdot10^{60}$ cm^{-3}. If the plasma temperature behind the wave front is close to the temperature of the solar corona, the power emitted will be of the order of $5\cdot10^{38}$ erg/s, i.e., it is almost the same as in the O VIII line in earlier stages of cooling (see Eq. (8.16)). Since the thermal energy supply is essentially reduced, because of the emission in the O VII and O VIII lines, the cooling rate increases. At a temperature of $T_e \sim 10^5$ °K the He II emission line $\lambda = 304$ Å contributes very effectively to the cooling.

Thus, in the end, tens of thousands of years after the outburst of the type II supernova, the explosion energy (determined by the kinetic energy of the gas mass ejected) has been converted into energy radiation, mainly in the ultraviolet and the soft X-ray ranges of the spectrum. A certain part of the energy, however, will also be emitted in the visible range. Let us discuss this interesting problem in greater detail.

In the "coronal" stage of cooling, when the temperature behind the wave front has dropped to $\sim (1\text{--}2) \cdot 10^6\,°\text{K}$, we may expect that the well-known lines of the coronal spectrum are emitted; for example, Fe XIV, λ 5,303 and Fe X, λ 6,374 Å. The radiation flux on the earth amounts in each of these lines to about $5 \cdot 10^{-3}$ erg/cm$^2 \cdot$s, the power emitted from the volume inside the spherical front of the shock wave will therefore be equal to about $3 \cdot 10^{36}$ erg/s in each of these lines. The emission intensity is also easy to calculate; one obtains $\sim 5 \cdot 10^{-6}$ erg/cm$^2 \cdot$s or $\sim$ 30Rayleighs, which corresponds to the weak lines in the spectrum of the nocturnal sky.

Although our calculations are very rough and the theory is approximate, since it does not take into account the presence of magnetic fields and cosmic rays in the interstellar medium (see the following section), the conclusion that in certain cases coronal emission may be expected for the region behind the shock wave front deserves attention. It would be interesting to try to discover this weak emission for which special observations are necessary; suitable objects for such a careful investigation are the inner parts of the system of filamentary nebulae in Cygnus, IC 443 and S 147.

Let us return to the problem of the much more powerful ultraviolet and, in particular, the X-ray emission of the plasma behind the front of spherical shock waves, produced in the interstellar medium by the outbursts of type II supernovae. For this reason each stellar system in which such a supernova exploded must be a rather powerful source of hard photons. If, for example, we assume that in a given spiral galaxy one outburst occurs in a hundred years and that in each outburst an average mass of gas $\sim 1 M_\odot$ is ejected at a velocity of $\sim 7 \cdot 10^8$ cm/s, the mean power injected in this way into the intergalactic medium will be $\sim 10^{41}$ erg/s. According to the ideas discussed above this very power must be emitted in the form of hard photons. The energy will be mainly concentrated in the lines of O VIII (λ 18.97) and O VII (λ 20.60 and 21.80). Note that these X-rays will pass through the interstellar medium almost without being absorbed. The hydrogen atoms' absorption cross section for this radiation will in fact be 10^5 times smaller than for the limit of the series and amount to $\sim 7 \cdot 10^{-23}$ cm^2. Therefore, with $n_1 \approx 1$, the

optical thickness becomes similar to unity only after the radiation has
travelled a distance of $\sim 4{,}000$ psc in the medium.   It can be shown that
absorption in interstellar medium by other elements is also unessential.
The radiation will thus penetrate almost unimpeded into the intergalactic space.   Moreover, it can be assumed that radiation from super-

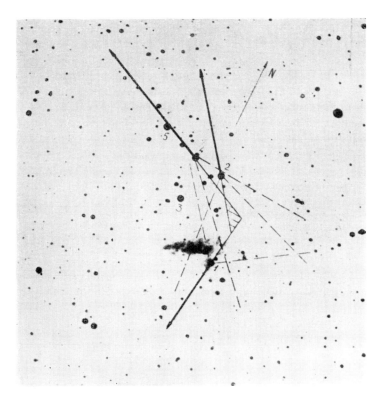

FIG. 56   Schematic representation of the proper motions of hot stars in the area
around NGC 6618.[141]

nova remnants at distances up to 4,000 psc may reach us.   The expected
flux of this radiation from Andromeda Nebula must amount to $3 \cdot 10^{-9}$
erg/cm$^2 \cdot$s or ~ 3 photons/cm$^2 \cdot$s.

Let us now consider an object at a distance of 3,000 psc.   According
to (8.16) its radiative power in the lines of O VIII and O VII will be

$\sim 3 \cdot 10^{38}$ erg/s and the flux at the boundary of the earth's atmosphere will be $\sim 3 \cdot 10^{-7}$ erg/s = 300 photons/cm$^2 \cdot$s. This is a very high value. But we obtain a still higher value of the flux if this source is identical with the inner zone of the filamentary nebulae in Cygnus. In this case the flux will be equal to $1.5 \cdot 10^4$ photons/cm$^2 \cdot$s. For comparison we may indicate that this value is only three times smaller than the flux of the solar line O VIII with a wavelength of 16 Å. The modern technique of rocket astronomy, based on the application of photon counters, enables us to reliably record fluxes of ~ 1 photon/cm$^2 \cdot$s from cosmic sources. The difficulty of this problem consists in the production of an inlet "window" which is sufficiently transparent in this spectral range. Such a window must be very thin, of a thickness ~ 1 μ. It may, however, be supposed that in principle this difficulty is not insuperable. The discovery of this radiation would be very important for all problems connected with the research into supernovae.

Younger objects with a plasma temperature $\sim 10^7$ °K must emit a sufficiently hard bremsstrahlung. The emission of a unit volume of hot plasma, per unit time and per unit interval of frequency, will be equal to[85]:

$$\varepsilon_\nu = 5.4 \cdot 10^{-39} \frac{e^{-h\nu/kT_e}}{T_e^{1/2}} N_e n_p gI \qquad (8.22)$$

where gI is Gaunt's factor.

A numerical integration over the shell of the spherical shock wave yields the spectral density of the power of a radiation whose photon energy is $h\nu > kT_e$:

$$L_\nu = 1.1 \cdot 10^{-2} \left(\frac{E}{E_0}\right)^{2/5} n_1^{8/5} t^{9/5} \text{ erg/s} \cdot \text{c/s} \qquad (8.23)$$

Let us consider the spectral range about $\lambda = 2.5$ Å the frequency interval $\Delta\nu = 5 \cdot 10^{17}$ c/s which in this range corresponds to $\Delta\lambda = 1$ Å. Let us further imagine a source, at a distance of 3,000 psc, its age being about 3,000 years (10^{11} s) and $E = E_0$. According to (8.8) we then have $T_e \sim 10^8$, $L_\nu \Delta\nu \sim 3.5 \cdot 10^{35}$ erg/s$\cdot$Å, and the flux at the boundary of the earth's atmosphere will be $\sim 3 \cdot 10^{-10}$ erg/cm$^2 \cdot$s per Ångström, which is an order of magnitude smaller than the X-ray flux from the Crab nebula, recently discovered in this spectral range (see Chapter III), and similar to the flux from the weakest galactic sources that may be discovered with modern methods.

We may expect that the number of remnants of supernovae of the type II in our galaxy, with an age between 10^{11} and $2 \cdot 10^{11}$ s, will amount to about thirty, so that the objects nearest to us must be at a distance of 2,000–3,000 psc. It is quite possible that in the near future, owing to the great progress of X-ray astronomy, the X-ray bremsstrahlung from remnants of type II supernovae will be discovered.

Summing up, we may say that the most important problem is the discovery of X-ray bremsstrahlung and X-ray spectral lines from the remnants of such supernovae. This opens a new era in research into these objects as it enables us to study the energy aspects of the phenomenon. Since the remnants of supernovae are sufficiently extended objects, one might succeed in obtaining their X-ray pictures which, of course, would be of extraordinary interest. We must, however, bear in mind that the theory developed above is of a highly approximate and preliminary nature, and results in the conclusion that hard photons must be emitted from the remnants of supernovae of the type II. As already stressed several times, this theory is very "one-sided" and ignores, in a first approximation, such important characteristics of the interstellar medium as the presence of magnetic fields and cosmic rays in it. Nevertheless we may have good reason to assume that the main conclusion of the theory, the presence of superhot rarefied plasma in the region of remnants of supernovae, is qualitatively correct.

The fine-fibred nebulae observed at several "old" remnants of type II supernovae arise, according to this theory, when the shock wave passes through relatively dense clouds of interstellar gas. In this case the plasma behind the front of the shock wave undergoes a relatively rapid cooling and the radiation is mainly concentrated in the visible range of the spectrum.

In regions, however, where the front passes through rarefied inter-stellar gas with $n_1 \sim 1$ and the medium is more or less homogeneous, the plasma behind the wave front is cooled down slowly. It may be expected that the physical conditions are described satisfactorily by the theory developed in this section.

As shown above, the "old" remnants of type II supernovae must have a temperature of $\sim (1-3) \cdot 10^6 \, ^\circ \mathrm{K}$ behind the front and the hard radiation is, as to its spectral composition, similar to the radiation from the solar corona. The latter is mainly concentrated in the range of 50–900 Å. It will therefore be absorbed by the interstellar gas and the interstellar gas will become ionized in this way. Since the power of the ionizing radiation is about the same as in the case of stars of the spectral class O, the radius of the Stremgren zone may reach 30 psc. The total contribution of old remnants to interstellar ionization is comparatively small since their number in the galaxy (which is of the order of several hundreds) amounts to only one-tenth of the number of hot stars of the spectral class O. Moreover, a great part of the remnants of supernovae of type II must be in associations where early-type stars are also concentrated. Their contribution to the ionization of the surrounding gas will therefore be small.

Owing to the enormous release of energy the outbursts of supernovae must exert a great disturbing influence on interstellar matter. First of all, in a region 50–70 psc in diameter, surrounding the exploding supernova, the physical conditions in the interstellar medium will differ essentially from the average for hundreds of thousands of years. Since outbursts of type II supernovae occur most frequently in associations, i.e., large complexes containing young massive stars surrounded by interstellar ionized gas, these complexes may be expected to display characteristic morphological features. Epik advocates the hypothesis that the well-known Barnard's loop, surrounding the Orion nebula and measuring ~130 psc in diameter, owes its existence to supernova outbursts.[62] According to Blaauw the age of Barnard's loop may amount to between two million and five million years.[62] We also know that several million years ago stars escaped from the Orion nebula, in all probability because of the "sling effect" (see § 4). Barnard's loop will hardly emit light as the result of radiative ionization due to hot stars. Between it and the early-type stars located in the Orion nebula lies a thick cloud of neutral hydrogen which may be observed at $\lambda = 21$ cm.[140] It is thus possible to observe traces of explosions of type II supernovae which took place several million years ago.

Gershberg showed that another well-known complex of diffuse nebulae, containing the most widely known nebula NGC 6618, also shows traces of relatively late outbursts of supernovae.[141] Just as in the case of Orion, three early-type stars fly away from NGC 6618 at high velocities. Figure 56 shows a schematic representation of the proper motion of the hot stars in this celestial area. The velocity vectors meet in the shaded triangular field. In this zone no bright nebulae can be observed, a fact which is attributed to the strong light absorption. The "kinematic age" of the runaway stars (see § 4) amounts to several thousands of years. The relationship linking the complexes NGC 6618 and Orion is also corroborated by the presence of a bright elliptic shell around the first nebula which is perfectly analogous to Barnard's loop.

Thus we see that the outbursts of supernovae may cause essential morphological changes in the diffuse nebulae; they may in particular give rise to the formation of peripheral structures around them. This fact has already been pointed out by G. A. Shayn and V. F. Gaze.[142]

§ 9 The influence of magnetic fields on the characteristics of remnants of type II supernovae

In the previous section the problem of the propagation of a shock wave in the interstellar medium has been treated as if this medium were free from magnetic fields and as if there were no relativistic particles moving in it. The energy density of the magnetic field and the cosmic rays (equal to their pressure) in the medium is relatively high. If $H \sim 5 \cdot 10^{-6}$ Oe, $W_m = H^2/8\pi \cdot 10^{-12}$ erg/cm^3, whereas the density of the thermal energy of the interstellar gas is $W_t \sim n_1 kT$ which, in zones containing ionized hydrogen, is of the same order of magnitude (with $n_1 \sim 1$ cm^{-3}), and in H I zones it is about 1 per cent of it.

What changes may be expected for the magnetic field in the interstellar medium when a shock wave passes through it? Since the magnetic lines of force "adhere" to the conducting interstellar gas the compression of this gas behind the shock wave front will inevitably entail a compression of the lines of force, i.e., the intensity of the interstellar magnetic field will rise. On the other hand, since the relativistic particles move along helical paths around the magnetic lines of force, this compression will involve an increase in concentration of the relativistic particles. If the magnetic field is sufficiently entangled the raised concentration of relativistic particles will be maintained for a longer time. Finally, the local intensification of the field will—by virtue of the conservation of the adiabatic invariant—entail an increase in energy of each relativistic particle which is proportional to $(H/H_0)^{1/2}$ and also an increase in H_I. The synchrotron radiation per unit volume depends strongly on H I and the concentration of relativistic particles which, under these conditions, will also depend on H. According to (6.13) $\varepsilon_v \propto (H/H_0)^{3.7}$ so that even a relatively slight increase in H involves a considerable increase in power of the synchrotron radiation. Under these conditions it cannot be regarded as impossible that a noticeable part of the synchrotron radiation from the

7+s.

remnant of a supernova may be attributed to the compression of interstellar matter by the shock wave and the intensification of the magnetic
field caused thereby.   It has so far been assumed that the relativistic
particles are generated in the explosion process or after it in the expanding
nebula itself, the magnetic field being connected with the shell ejected in
the explosion.   That this point of view is essentially correct has been
proved by observations of the secular diminution of the radio flux from
Cassiopeia A, which was predicted theoretically on the basis of the idea of
the "autonomous" origin of the relativistic particles and magnetic fields
during the outburst of the supernova (see § 7).   In the same section,
based on these conceptions, a distance system was obtained for the radio
sources connected with the remnants of supernovae.   The power of radio
emission, caused by the compression of interstellar matter, must increase
with time since the volume of the zone in which this medium is compressed
increases as the expansion continues.   Nevertheless, it may be expected
that in the late stages of expansion of the supernova remnants the compression of the interstellar magnetic field may be an important source of
the synchrotron radio-frequency radiation.

A theory of this effect was developed by van der Laan.[143]   He
reached the conclusion that the radio sources connected with the remnants
of supernovae may be subdivided into several types which form a certain
evolutionary sequence.

The first type is constituted by sources whose synchrotron radio
emission is caused by relativistic particles produced in the source itself
(when the supernova explodes or soon thereafter).   The evolution of
sources of this type is determined by their expansion and can be described
by the theory developed in detail in § 7.   The compression of interstellar
gas which is an inevitable consequence of the expansion of such sources,
results in an additional synchrotron radiation.   The power of the latter,
however, is small compared to the power of the synchrotron radio emission
of the "intrinsic" relativistic electrons.

In the expansion process the power of the synchrotron radio emission
of the "intrinsic" relativistic electrons decreases rapidly (cf. § 7) whereas
the power of the radio emission of the relativistic electrons "swept
together" increases slowly.   When they are comparable we are, according
to van der Laan's classification, concerned with sources of type II.   In
this case we may expect a relatively complex spatial structure of the
source: a central spheroidal body caused by the radiation of the "intrinsic"
relativistic electrons, surrounded by a shell in which emission is due to the

relativistic electrons "swept together." The characteristic features of
these two regions emitting radio-waves (as, for example, the magnetic field
strength and the spectral index) may be very different.

As the remnants of supernovae expand further, the radio emission
of the "intrinsic" relativistic electrons becomes negligibly weak as
compared to the radio emission from the interstellar relativistic electrons
"swept together." In this state the volume luminosity of the shell will
exceed that of the interstellar medium by about one order of magnitude
while the spectral index is the same as that of the medium.

Before we discuss the fundamental problem, which degree of the scheme
of the remnant radio source evolution sketched above corresponds to
reality, we consider this scheme from a mathematical point of view.
This consideration, first carried out in [143], is of particular interest as it
enables us to specify more precisely the theory of shock wave propagation
in interstellar matter discussed in the previous section, by estimating the
role played by the interstellar magnetic field and the relativistic particles.

The unidimensional problem considered in [143] was relatively simple
and evident. A consideration of the curvature of the shock wave front
does not involve any fundamental difficulties. The "non-collisional"
plasma (see § 8) containing a "frozen" magnetic field is compressed by a
"piston" (in our case a relatively dense ionized shell, ejected by the
explosion of a supernova) which moves at a constant velocity v_p in a
direction perpendicular to the homogeneous field of the interstellar
medium. Since the "piston" possesses a very high conductivity, the
magnetic lines of force of the interstellar medium cannot penetrate into it.
For this medium the usual equation of state

$$\frac{D}{Dt}(P\rho^{-\gamma}) = \text{const} \qquad (9.1)$$

falls into two equations since the magnetic field makes the medium
anisotropic. For the direction along the field Equation (9.1) is conserved.
For the direction perpendicular to H we have, according to [143]:

$$\frac{D}{Dt}\left(\frac{P_n}{\rho H}\right) = 0 \qquad (9.2)$$

where P_n is the gas pressure in the direction perpendicular to the magnetic
field and ρ is the density of the medium. Let us now consider a plane
layer of the medium, parallel to H, and derive the equation of motion for

it. Let us denote the initial position of the layer at $t = 0$ by x and its thickness by Δx. At $t > 0$ the co-ordinate and thickness of this layer may be given by y and Δy, with $y = y(t)$. Let us further denote by ρ_0, H_0 and p_0 the density, magnetic field and gas pressure, respectively, in the non-perturbed medium (see Fig. 57a). It will then follow from the law of conservation of mass that $\rho_0\, dx = \rho\, dy$. Since the magnetic field

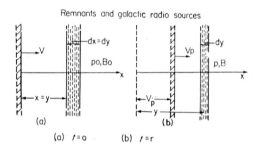

Remnants and galactic radio sources

(a) $t = 0$ (b) $t = \tau$

FIG. 57a   Diagram explaining the propagation of a shock wave in a medium with a magnetic field.[143]

"adheres" to the medium we shall also have the condition $H_0\, dx = H\, dy$. Consequently

$$\rho = \frac{\rho_0}{\partial y/\partial x}; \qquad H = \frac{H_0}{\partial y/\partial x}; \qquad \frac{H^2}{8\pi} = \frac{H_0^2/8\pi}{(\partial y/\partial x)^2} \tag{9.3}$$

where $H^2/8\pi$ is the magnetic pressure; from (9.1) and (9.3) it follows that

$$p = p_0\left(\frac{\rho}{\rho_0}\right)^2 = \frac{p_0}{(\partial y/\partial x)^2} \tag{9.4}$$

The total pressure $\Pi = p + (H^2/8\pi)$

$$\Pi = \frac{\Pi_0}{(\partial y/\partial x)^2} \tag{9.5}$$

The equation of motion of the layer will then read

$$\rho_0\, dx\, \frac{\partial^2 y}{\partial t^2} = -\frac{\partial \Pi}{\partial x}\, dx \tag{9.6}$$

Substituting (9.5) we obtain

$$\frac{\partial^2 y}{\partial t^2} = \left[\frac{V_0^2}{(\partial y/\partial x)^3}\right] \frac{\partial^2 y}{\partial x^2} \tag{9.7}$$

where

$$V_0^2 = \frac{(H_0^2/(4\pi) + 2p_0)}{\rho_0}$$

is the sum of the quanta of Alfvén and sonic waves. Our boundary condition may be written in the form

$$y(0, t) = V_n t \qquad (9.8)$$

it expresses that the gas layer comes immediately into contact with the piston and moves together with it. We also have the initial condition that the medium in front of the piston, at $t = 0$, is non-perturbed:

$$y(x, 0) = x \qquad (9.9)$$

Moreover, at a sufficiently great distance from the piston the medium will always be non-perturbed, i.e., for sufficiently large values of x and t we have

$$y(x, t) = x \qquad (9.10)$$

It may be expected on the grounds of dimension considerations that the equation of motion will have a solution of the form of $y/t = F(x/t)$. We therefore introduce the non-dimensional variables $\Psi = y/V_0 t$, $\xi = x/V_0 t$. In these new variables Equation (9.7) reads

$$\xi^2 \frac{d^2\Psi}{d\xi^2} \left(\frac{d\Psi}{d\xi}\right)^2 = \frac{d^2\Psi}{d\xi^2} \qquad (9.11)$$

To satisfy this equation we may either assume that $d^2\Psi/d\xi^2 = 0$ or $\xi^2 (d\Psi/d\xi)^3 = 1$. In the first case we shall have

$$y = k_1 x + k_2 V_0 t \qquad (9.12)$$

and in the second case

$$y = 3(V_0 t)^{2/3} x^{1/3} + k_3 V_0 t \qquad (9.13)$$

The solution (9.13) does not satisfy the condition (9.9) so that it must be discarded. Solution (9.12) will satisfy both the boundary condition and the initial condition if for the zone between the front of the wave and the piston $k_2 = V_{II}/V_0$ and behind the front $k_1 = 1$ and $k_2 = 0$ so that a possible solution has the form

$$y = \frac{x}{\eta} + V_{II} t \qquad (0 \leqslant x < R_s)$$

$$\qquad\qquad\qquad\qquad\qquad\qquad (9.14)$$

$$y = x \qquad\qquad (R_s < x)$$

where R_s determines the position of the front. The constant parameter $\eta = \rho/\rho_0$ determines the compression of the medium behind the front. With $x \to R_s$ we have

$$R_s = \frac{\eta V_{\text{II}} t}{\eta - 1} = V_s t \tag{9.15}$$

where $V_s = \eta V_{\text{II}}/(\eta - 1)$ is the velocity of the front relative to the non-perturbed medium.

In the transition from the zone $R_s - \varepsilon$ to the zone $R_s + \varepsilon$ the fundamental characteristics of the medium (temperature, density, pressure and magnetic field strength) display a discontinuity. It is thus in fact R_s which determines the position of the shock wave front.

The "densification parameter" η may be obtained from the conditions of momentum and energy conservation. These are the usual Rankin–Hugoniot conditions of classical gas dynamics which are generalized to the case of a medium in which a magnetic field is present. We must also take into consideration that relativistic particles exist in the medium. Taking the pressure of these particles into account changes the equation of motion (9.6) of the medium a little but leaves the solution (9.14) to this equation unchanged. The generalized Rankin–Hugoniot conditions read as follows:

$$\rho V = \rho_0 V_0 \qquad \text{(conservation of mass)} \tag{9.16}$$

$$\rho V^2 + \Pi = \rho_0 V_0^2 + \Pi_0 \qquad \text{(conservation of momentum)} \tag{9.17}$$

$$\rho V u^* + \Pi V + \tfrac{1}{2}\rho V^3 = \rho_0 V_0 u^* + \Pi_0 V_0 + \tfrac{1}{2}\rho_0 V_0^3$$
$$\text{(conservation of energy)} \tag{9.18}$$

where u^* is the intrinsic energy of the gas per unit mass. All the velocities are referred to the wave front. Let us denote by γ_g and γ_r the specific heat ratios of the "ordinary" and the relativistic gases. We shall then have

$$u^* = \frac{\left\{ \dfrac{P_g}{\gamma_g - 1} + \dfrac{P_r}{\gamma_r - 1} + P_m \right\}}{\rho} \tag{9.19}$$

where P_g is the pressure of the "ordinary" gas, P_r the pressure of the relativistic gas and $P_m = H^2/8\pi$ the magnetic pressure.

Since the mean free path of the particles of the "ordinary" gas is very short compared to the thickness d of the compressed zone between the wave front and the piston ($d \sim R_s - R_p$) the particle velocities will be chaotic even in the immediate proximity of the front. We therefore have $\gamma_g = \frac{5}{3}$. On the other hand, for the relativistic gas whose particles each have two degrees of freedom (because of their helical motion along the lines of force) $\gamma_r = \frac{3}{2}$. If the relativistic gas in the non-perturbed zone is isotropic and characterized by the energy density W_r, we have $P_{0r} = W_{0r}/3$. We also have

$$V_0 = V_s = \frac{\eta V_{\Pi}}{\eta - 1}, \quad V = V_s - V_{\Pi} = \frac{V_{\Pi}}{1 - \eta} \quad (9.20)$$

We will assume that the relativistic gas is compressed isothermally, i.e., $P_r = hP_{0r}$. In this case we obtain from (9.17) and (9.18) an expression for the pressure of the "ordinary" gas behind the front:

$$P_g = \rho V_{\Pi}^2\left(\frac{\eta}{\eta - 1}\right) - P_{0r}(\eta - 1) - P_{0m}(\eta^2 - 1) + P_{0g} \quad (9.21)$$

and

$$P_g = \frac{1}{5}\rho_0 V_{\Pi}^2 \frac{\eta(\eta + 1)}{\eta - 1} - \frac{4}{5}\eta(\eta - 1)P_{0m} + \eta P_{0g} \quad (9.22)$$

When we set (9.21) equal to (9.22) we obtain an algebraic equation of third order in h:

$$P_{0m}\eta^3 + (\rho_0 V_{\Pi}^2 + 5\Pi - 2P_{0m})\eta^2$$
$$- (4\rho_0 V_{\Pi}^2 - 10\Pi_0 - P_{0m})\eta + 5\Pi_0 = 0 \quad (9.23)$$

This equation has a single root which is of physical interest, $1 < \eta_1 < 4$. The value of η_1 may be found with the help of an arbitrary numerical method. In the case of an ordinary shock wave (without magnetic field and relativistic particles) $\rho = [(\gamma + 1)/(\gamma - 1)]\rho$; hence it follows that $\eta \sim 4$, a well-known result which we have applied already several times without proof. When the magnetic field and the relativistic particles are taken into account, a lower value is obtained for h.

We can draw a very important conclusion from Equation (9.18). Since $\eta \leqslant 4$, the gas pressure behind the front (and, consequently, also the temperature) is almost independent from both the magnetic field in the interstellar medium and the relativistic particles in it, provided the velocity of the shell ejected in the explosion of a supernova is sufficiently high. In fact we choose $H = 5 \cdot 10^{-6}$ Oe, $\eta = 4$ and $\rho_0 = 10^{-25}$ g/cm^3. In this case, even with $V = 100$ km/s (which corresponds to the velocity of an already strongly slowed down remnant of a type II supernova as, e.g., the system of filamentary nebulae in Cygnus) the first term of the right-hand side of (9.18) will be about six times greater than all other terms. This indicates that an estimate of the temperature behind the front made under the assumption that there is no magnetic field and no relativistic particles in the interstellar medium, is only about 15 per cent too high. With "younger" remnants of supernovae of type II the error due to the application of formulas of "non-magnetic" gas dynamics will be negligibly small. Only in very old objects whose fronts have radii $\geqslant 30$ psc the magnetic field of the interstellar medium and the relativistic particles contained in it exert a noticeable influence on the temperature behind the front. It is, however, incorrect to treat such objects as adiabatic problems (see § 8). Thus we see that the correction to the theory developed in the previous section for the magnetic field of the interstellar medium and the relativistic particles contained in it is quite insignificant. In particular, the fundamental conclusion of the theory remains true. It must also be taken into account that the relativistic particles may easily escape the compression zone, travelling along the lines of force. Therefore, if the magnetic field is not too complex in its structure, the magnetic pressure will be almost constant instead of being $\sim \rho^{3/2}$. In the region of remnants of supernovae of type II the very hot rarefied plasma, whose hard photon emission may be observed with the help of the methods of modern rocket astronomy, remains unchanged.

Let us now consider the conditions behind the front of the shock wave propagated in the magnetized interstellar medium. What will happen to a relativistic particle which passes through the wave front, coming from the non-perturbed region? Generally speaking, we must expect that the energy of each relativistic particle will be increased. This problem cannot be solved exactly since the structure of the front is unknown. It is, however, possible to estimate the lower limit of the energy increment if we take into consideration that the gas to which the lines of force "adhere" (along which the relativistic particles move in spirals) is compressed adiabatically. In this compression $du = -P\,dv$ where u and v are the specific energy and volume. In this case we shall obtain

$$P_r = (\gamma_r - 1)w_{\perp r} = \tfrac{1}{2}w_{\perp r} \qquad (9.24)$$

where $w_{\perp r}$ is the energy density of the relativistic gas connected with the motion of the particles in a plane perpendicular to H. The equation $du = -P\,dv$ may now be rewritten in the form

$$d\left(\frac{w_{\perp r}}{n}\right) = \frac{1}{2}\,w_{\perp r}\,d\left(\frac{1}{n}\right)$$

and an integration yields ($n \propto \eta$)

$$P_r = \eta^{3/2} P_{0r} \tag{9.25}$$

The meaning of this equation is evident: in the compression the concentration of the relativistic particles increases by the factor η while the energy of each individual particle—by virtue of the conservation of the adiabatic invariant—rises to the $\eta^{1/2}$-fold; this has already been mentioned at the beginning of this section.

In the previous section it was shown that at a certain (late) stage of expansion the adiabatic consideration becomes incorrect. It is then necessary to take into account the radiative cooling of the plasma behind the wave front. This radiative cooling behind the front may be taken into account in the following approximate way: Let us assume that the cooling is essential, which is the case with sufficiently "old" objects. Far away from the front (we move toward the "piston") the pressure of the "ordinary" gas drops and tends asymptotically to the "equilibrium" pressure which corresponds to the "standard" temperature of the H II zone of the interstellar medium which is of the order of $10^4\,^\circ$K. Immediately in front of the piston the medium, characterized by the "compression factor" $\bar{\eta}$, has the total pressure Π, which is the sum of the magnetic pressure

$$\bar{\eta}^2 \frac{H_0^2}{8\pi}$$

the pressure of the relativistic gas $\bar{\eta}^{3/2} P_{0r}$ and the pressure P_{0g} of the "ordinary" gas. The thickness of the medium characterized by these parameters will be equal to $\sim V_\Pi t / \bar{\eta} - 1$.

Immediately behind the front the characteristic parameters of the medium will be different. The density and pressure will be described by the formulas derived above, in which

$$V_0 = \frac{\bar{\eta} V_\Pi}{\bar{\eta} - 1}; \qquad V = \frac{\bar{\eta} V_\Pi}{\eta(\bar{\eta} - 1)} \tag{9.26}$$

where, as before, η denotes the compression behind the front. The quantity $\bar{\eta}$ is obtained from the condition of conservation of momentum in the transition from the non-perturbed zone to the "equilibrium" zone. For this purpose Equation (9.17) is used in which V_0 and V are

7*

determined by Equation (9.26) and η is replaced by $\bar{\eta}$, where $P_g = \bar{\eta} P_{0g}$. We thus obtain an algebraic equation in η:

$$P_{0m}\bar{\eta}^3 + P_{0r}\bar{\eta}^{5/2} + (P_{0g} - P_{0m})\bar{\eta}^2 - P_{0r}\bar{\eta}^{3/2}$$
$$- (\Pi_0 + P_{0g} + \rho_0 V_{\Pi}^2)\bar{\eta} + \Pi_0 = 0 \qquad (9.27)$$

which is solved numerically and possesses a single root in the expected interval of values $1 < \bar{\eta}^{1/2} < \infty$. Immediately behind the wave front the compression η is determined from Equations (9.17) and (9.18) and Equation (9.26) is used for V and V_1:

$$P_{0m}\eta^{5/2} - (P_{0r} - P_{0m})\eta^2 + (\rho_0 V_s^2 + 6P_{0r} + 5P_{0g} + C/P_{0m})\eta^{3/2}$$
$$+ (\rho_0 V_s^2 + 6P_{0r} + 5P_{0g} + 4P_{0m})\eta - 4\rho_0 V_s^2 \eta^{1/2} - 4\rho_0 V_s^2 = 0$$
$$(9.28)$$

where

$$V_s = V_{\Pi} \frac{\bar{\eta}}{\bar{\eta} - 1}$$

Let us now consider the problem in which way the synchrotron radiation of interstellar matter is changed by its compression due to the passage of a shock wave. In § 5 we derived a simplified expression for the increase in volume luminosity ε_v caused by a local increase in magnetic field strength. Following van der Laan we shall here derive a stricter solution to this problem. Let us assume that in the non-perturbed interstellar medium the relativistic particles display an isotropic distribution and a differential energy spectrum which can be described by the usual expression

$$N(E)\,dE = KE^{-\gamma}\,dE \qquad (9.29)$$

What changes does the energy spectrum undergo when the shock wave passes through the zone considered? Assume that a certain relativistic particle had the initial momentum P_0 and moved at an angle of θ_0 to the direction of the magnetic lines of force. Resolving the momentum into its two components parallel and perpendicular to the field, we obtain

$$P_0^2 = P_{0\parallel}^2 + P_{0\perp}^2 = P_0^2 \cos^2 \theta_0 + P_0^2 \sin^2 \theta_0 \qquad (9.30)$$

Let us assume that the momentum due to the motion in a plane perpendicular to the magnetic field increases by a factor of $x^{1/2}$ while the component $P_{0\parallel}$ remains unchanged. Then

$$P^2 = P_{\parallel}^2 + P_{\perp}^2 = P_{0\parallel}^2 + \chi P_{0\perp}^2 = P_0^2[1 + (\chi - 1)\sin^2 \theta_0]$$
$$(9.31)$$

Since

$$P^2_{0\parallel} = P^2_{\parallel}$$

then

$$\cos^2 \theta = \frac{\cos^2 \theta_0}{1 + (\chi - 1) \sin^2 \theta_0},$$

we obtain

$$tg\theta = \chi^{\frac{1}{2}} tg\theta_0$$

$$d\theta_0 = \frac{1 + (\chi - 1) \sin^2 \theta_0}{\chi^{\frac{1}{2}}} \cdot d\theta = \frac{\chi^{\frac{1}{2}}}{\chi - (\chi - 1) \sin^2 \theta} d\theta \quad (9.32)$$

Behind the wave front the motion of the relativistic particles becomes anisotropic. Their differential energy spectrum will now have the form

$$N(E, \theta)dE \, d\theta = K \frac{\sin \theta}{2} \left[\frac{\chi}{\chi - (\chi - 1) \sin^2 \theta} \right]^{(\gamma + 2)/2} \cdot \chi^{-1} E^{-\gamma} \, dE \, d\theta$$

$$(9.33)$$

Since the volume luminosity is given by

$$\varepsilon_v \propto K(H \sin \theta)^{\alpha + 1} V^{-\alpha} \quad (9.34)$$

(α is the spectral index), a substitution of (9.33) in (9.34) will yield

$$\varepsilon_v = \varepsilon_{0v} \left(\frac{K}{K_0} \right) \left(\frac{H}{H_0} \right)^{\alpha + 1} \chi^{(2\alpha + 1)/2} \int_0^{\pi/2} \frac{\sin^{\alpha + 1} \theta \sin \theta \, d\theta}{[\chi - (\chi - 1) \sin^2 \theta]^{\alpha + \frac{3}{2}}}$$

$$\times \int_0^{\pi/2} \sin^{\alpha + 1} \theta \sin \theta d\theta \quad (9.35)$$

where

$$\frac{K}{K_0} = \bar{\eta}; \qquad \frac{H}{H_0} = \eta; \qquad \chi = \bar{\eta}$$

The integral in the numerator of the right-hand side is obtained by a numerical method for different α and $\bar{\eta}$. The integral in the nominator is equal to

$$\frac{1}{2} \pi^{\frac{1}{2}} \Gamma \left(\frac{\alpha + 3}{2} \right) \bigg/ \Gamma \left(\frac{\alpha + 4}{2} \right)$$

If, for example,

$$\alpha = 0.5, \qquad \bar{\eta} = 2, \qquad \varepsilon_v \simeq 9\varepsilon_{0v}.$$

If the relativistic particles behind the front are effectively scattered from the inhomogeneities of the magnetic field whose dimensions are of

the order of the Larmor radius, their distribution becomes isotropic.†
In this case we shall have instead of Equations (9.33) and (9.35)

$$N(E)\, dE = K\left[\frac{1}{2} + \frac{1}{2}\frac{\chi}{(\chi - 1)^{\frac{1}{2}}} \sin^{-1}\left(\frac{\chi - 1}{\chi}\right)^{\frac{1}{2}}\right]^{\gamma - 1} E^{-\gamma}\, dE$$

and   (9.36)

$$\varepsilon_\nu = \varepsilon_{0\nu}\left(\frac{K}{K_0}\right)\left(\frac{H}{H_0}\right)^{\alpha + 1}\left[\frac{1}{2} + \frac{1}{2}\frac{\chi}{(\chi - 1)^{\frac{1}{2}}} \sin^{-1}\left(\frac{\chi - 1}{\chi}\right)^{\frac{1}{2}}\right]^{2\alpha}$$

(9.37)

It follows from Equation (9.37) that this "isotropization" of the relativistic particles behind the shock wave front diminishes the ratio $\varepsilon_\nu/\varepsilon_{0\nu}$ in the compression of the medium. This reduction is, however, insignificant (~ 25 per cent of the expected value of $\bar{h}$).

In order to compare the expected radio emission from the relativistic electrons "swept together" with the radio emission of "old" remnants of supernovae of the type II it is necessary to pass over from the uni-dimensional shock wave model considered above to the spherical-symmetrical problem. The inhomogeneity of the medium in which the spherical shock wave is propagated and also the anisotropic nature of the initial explosion leads inevitably to a disintegration of the shell into several pieces which then move independently. But each of these pieces of the shell will exercise the function of a "piston." It must still be kept in mind that the velocity of the "piston" in the medium, given by Equation (8.1), will decrease independently. Nevertheless the motion of each piece of the shell must be considered as the expansion of a spherical surface. Its surface will therefore grow proportionately to R^2. From the constancy of the magnetic flux it follows that the mean value of the magnetic field strength in such a piece will be

$$H(\varphi) = \left(\frac{R_s^2}{R^2 - R_\Pi^2}\right)H_0 \sin \varphi$$ (9.38)

where φ is the angle between the radius vector and the direction of the non-perturbed magnetic field. The volume of each piece will be equal to $V = C(R_s^3 - R_\Pi^3)$ where C depends on the angular co-ordinates. An application of the Rankin–Hugoniot conditions to these pieces in the "isothermal" case (when the cooling of the gas behind the front occurs

---

† This anisotropy produces a beam instability; in this process the relativistic particles
will be intensely scattered and thus their distribution becomes isotropic.

fast enough or when the pressure of magnetic field and relativistic particles in such a piece is much higher than the gas pressure) makes it possible to restrict oneself to the conditions of conservation of mass and momentum. It is obvious that the "isothermal" case applies to very "old" remnants of supernovae of the type II.

With $V_0 = V_s$ it follows from (9.16) and (9.17) that the mean gas density in the shell will be

$$\rho = \frac{\rho_0 R_s^3}{(R_s^3 - R_{II}^3)} \tag{9.39}$$

Eliminating V we have

$$\rho_0 V_s^2 + \Pi_0 = \rho_0 V_s^2 \left(\frac{R_s^3 - R_{II}^3}{R_s^3} \right) + \Pi \tag{9.40}$$

where the pressure outside the front

$$\Pi_0 = 2n_0 k T_0 + \frac{H_0^2}{8\pi} \sin^2 \varphi + P_{0r} \tag{9.41}$$

and the pressure inside the front

$$\Pi \simeq \left(\frac{R_s^2 \sin \varphi}{R_s^2 - R_{II}^2} \right)^2 \frac{H_0^2}{8\pi} + \left(\frac{R_s^3}{R_s^3 - R_{II}^3} \right) 2n_0 k T_0$$

$$+ \left(\frac{R_s^3}{R_s^3 - R^2} \right) \left(\frac{R_s^2}{R_s^2 - R_{II}^2} \right)^{\frac{1}{2}} P_{0r} \tag{9.42}$$

The first factor in the last term of the right-hand side of this equation corresponds to the intensification of the magnetic field caused by the increase in density in the shell. The relativistic gas is compressed in the ratio

$$\frac{R_s^2}{(R_s^2 - R_{II}^2)}$$

the second factor in the last term of the right-hand side is therefore corresponding to $\bar{\eta}^{\frac{1}{2}}$ in the case of the two-dimensional problem.

Let us now write Equation (9.40) in an explicit form:

$$\rho_0 V_s^2 \left(\frac{R_{II}}{R_s} \right)^3 - 2n_0 k T_0 \left(\frac{R_{II}^3}{R_s^3 - R_{II}^3} \right) + P_{0r}$$

$$\times \left[1 - \left(\frac{R_s^3}{R_s^3 - R_{II}^3} \right) \left(\frac{R_s^2}{R_s^2 - R_{II}^3} \right) \right] = \frac{H_0^2}{8\pi} (\sin^2 \varphi) \left[\left(\frac{R_s^2}{R_s^2 - R_{II}^2} \right)^2 - 1 \right] \tag{9.43}$$

This extensive expression is a generalization of Equation (9.27) to the spherical-symmetric problem. The expression for the volume luminosity ε_v of the synchrotron radiation of the relativistic electrons "swept together" will again be given by Equation (9.37) with the only exception that now

$$\frac{k}{k_0} = \left(\frac{R_s^3}{R_s^3 - R_{\Pi}^3}\right); \qquad \frac{H}{H_0} = \left(\frac{R_s^2}{R_s^2 - R_{\Pi}^2}\right) \sin \varphi; \qquad \chi = \left(\frac{R_s^2}{R_s^2 - R_{\Pi}^2}\right)$$

$$(9.44)$$

Before we turn to a comparison with observations we have to consider yet another problem, namely, whether the relativistic particles are retained by the compression of the shell. Generally speaking, it is quite possible that the relativistic particles leave the shell relatively quickly. The magnetic field in the shell is a part of the interstellar magnetic field. Moving along the lines of force, the particles should fly without hindrance from the compression zone where the field is relatively intense to a zone in which the field is relatively weak. The inverse motion of the relativistic particles is, however, limited by the adiabatic invariant. If the field behind the front has a very complex structure, the relativistic particles may be trapped in it for a longer period. Such a complex structure of the field may be brought about by a beam instability of the gas constituted by the relativistic particles. For this reason the motion of the relativistic particles is very soon made isotropic (after a period which is of the order of $\sim 1/(\omega_e \cdot \omega_i)^{1/2}$, see § 8) and, deforming the magnetic field, it gives rise to the appearance of a kind of "closed turbulent layer" or a "magnetic bottle." Such an effect, however, must occur in a much more distinct form in the case where the relativistic particles are generated during the explosion (instead of being a result of this "sweeping" by the shock wave). This "magnetic bottle effect" prevents the relativistic particles from freely leaving the zone of generation and flying out into interstellar space.

Let us now turn to the problem of the relativistic particles "swept together." The question is whether as a result of the effect of "sweeping together" of relativistic particles and field by the expanding shell of a type II supernova a synchrotron radio source may be formed which possesses an observable intensity. As already mentioned in the beginning of the present section, these objects may be found among the relatively "old" remnants of type II supernovae in which the power of the synchrotron radiation of the "intrinsic" relativistic electrons has already dropped considerably because of the expansion effect. As a suitable object of comparison between theory and observation van der Laan chose the thoroughly investigated system of filamentary nebulae in Cygnus. Equation (9.43) is applied to different parts of this system. The quantities R_p, R_s and V_s may be obtained immediately from observations. Consequently, Equation (9.43) becomes a relation linking the density of the interstellar gas with the magnetic field strength in the interstellar medium through which the corresponding part of the spherical shock wave is propagated. Equations (9.37) and (9.44) enable us to calculate the

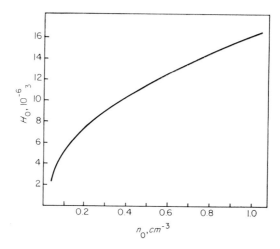

Fig. 57b   Relation of the strength of the magnetic field to the density of interstellar matter.

radio-emission flux from the relativistic electrons "swept together." According to Minkowski's observations, the parameters of one of the brightest parts of the system of filamentary nebulae in Cygnus, NGC 6960 (see Fig. 22), are the following: $R_p \approx 16$ psc, $R_s \approx 19$ psc and $V_s \approx 110$ km/s. From Figure 22 it follows that these nebulae are seen from the centre of expansion at an angle of about 70°. Figure 57b illustrates the relationship linking H_0 and n as obtained from Equation (9.43). On the arbitrary assumption that the extension of this part of the nebula in the direction of sight is half the extension in the direction of the image plane we may, as we know the distance of the nebulae (770 psc), estimate the volume of the region containing the relativistic particles "swept to-gether" and the field; we obtain a value of $V = 1.8 \cdot 10^{52} \, \text{cm}^3$. Moreover, from Equation (9.44) it follows that $k/k_0 = 2.5$; $H/H_0 = 3.4$; $\chi = 3.5$. With these values of k/k_0, H/H_0 and χ it follows from (9.37) that the volume luminosity is $\varepsilon_\nu \sim 30 \ \varepsilon_{0\nu}$. When we know the volume of the source, its distance and $\varepsilon_{0\nu}$ ($\varepsilon_{0\nu}$ may be determined from an analysis of the non-thermal radio-emission distribution of the galaxy) we may calculate the theoretical value expected for the radio flux from the electrons "swept together" in NGC 6960. It is equal to $F_\nu \simeq 16 \cdot 10^{-26}$ watt/m$^2 \cdot$c/s at a frequency of $\nu = 100$ Mc. In these estimations we assumed that $\sin \varphi \sim 1$. In other words, the direction of the non-perturbed interstellar magnetic field is almost parallel to the wave front observed as NGC 6960.

An analogous calculation was carried out in [143] for NGC 6992–5. The expected flux from the relativistic particles "swept together" was obtained as $F_\nu \simeq 10 \cdot 10^{-26}$ W/m$^2 \cdot$c/s at the same frequency. On the other hand, according to observations (see § 5) there are three radio sources in this region. The most powerful source "A" is situated in a zone of very weak optical emission. The radio flux from this source is $\sim 300 \cdot 10^{-26}$ W/m$^2 \cdot$c/s which is 70 to 90 per cent of the radio flux from the whole system of filamentary nebulae in Cygnus. It is known that the relativistic electrons which are responsible for the synchrotron radiation of this component are not "swept together" but are produced during or after the supernova explosion. The radio-emission component C (see § 5) is located around NGC 6992–5, noticeably shifted towards the centre of the system of the filamentary nebulae. This position of the source agrees with the idea that the synchrotron radio emission is generated in a broad zone behind the shock wave front characterizing the nebular system NGC 6992–5. The observed radio flux from component C, however, is with a value of $F_\nu = 50 \cdot 10^{-26}$ W/m$^2 \cdot$c/s at a frequency of 100 Mc, five times higher than the theoretical value. Attention should be drawn to the fact that the radio spectrum of component C is curved and thus quite different from the spectra of components A and B. As already stressed in § 5, this curvature of the spectrum cannot explain the presence of a thermal component in the radio-frequency radiation. According to [143] this spectrum might be an indirect argument in favour of the assumption that the radiation from component C is caused by relativistic electrons "swept together." There are indeed certain facts indicating that the spectrum of the synchrotron radio emission of the galactic disc is also curved in the range of low frequencies.[144]   If the compressed field behind the shock wave front is three to five times stronger than the non-perturbed field, the "bend" of the spectrum is shifted towards higher frequencies, since the energy spectrum of the relativistic particles either remains constant or changes little.   Nevertheless, the deviation of the calculated and the observed flux values by 500 per cent seem to us to be too high.

The component B is positioned near NGC 6960.   Its flux, however, is much higher than the flux from component C and exceeds the value calculated above by at least a factor of 5.   Moreover, this component displays a "direct" spectrum which is not in agreement with the hypothesis of relativistic particles "swept together."

Thus, even in such an "old" object as the filamentary nebulae in Cygnus, the contribution of the relativistic electrons "swept together" to the observed synchrotron radiation hardly exceeds a few per cent. One cannot exclude the possibility that observable radio sources which are "old" remnants of type II supernovae and display a noticeable effect of relativistic particles "swept together" do not exist.

It follows from observations that sources which can be identified with the remnants of type II supernovae have a clearly marked shell structure (see § 5).   This structure may be explained by the hypothesis that relativistic electrons and magnetic fields are "swept together."   As was shown, however, even with the "oldest" sources of this type the power of the synchrotron radio emission caused by the influence of a shock wave on interstellar relativistic electrons and magnetic fields is negligibly small compared to the power observed.   Moreover, even in the case of the youngest source of this type, Cassiopeia A, whose power of synchrotron radio emission is a thousand times higher than that of the "old" sources, the emitting zones display a shell structure.   The theory must explain this important peculiarity of the radio sources which are identified with the remnants of type II supernovae.   It was again van der Laan who, in paper [145], made the attempt to develop such a theory on the basis of his investigations which we discussed in detail.

In order to explain the shell structure of such radio sources we must have some, if very general, ideas on the origin of the magnetic fields existing there.   This important problem will be discussed in greater detail in § 19.   Van der Laan starts from the very general hypothesis that the magnetic field in the remnants of supernovae must be determined by the magnetic field of the exploding star and the "activity" of the remnant after the explosion. From this one may draw the conclusion that the various objects of this type which are in different stages of evolution may have essentially different magnetic fields of "intrinsic" origin. But if this is so, how does van der Laan explain the situation that in certain remnants of supernovae of type II the "proper" magnetic field becomes too weak to retain relativistic particles which are continuously injected from the inner zones? Some of these relativistic particles may be trapped by the magnetic shell of the interstellar medium which was "swept together" (see above), a shell in which the density of the relativistic particles will increase up to a certain limit which is determined by the equation of energy density of the relativistic particles and the magnetic field. It is a matter of fact that the initial energy density of the magnetic field in this shell exceeds the energy density of the relativistic particles of interstellar origin which are "swept together." Thus, for example, in the case of the filamentary nebulae in Cygnus, $H/H_0 = 3.4$ according to the above calculations and the magnetic energy density behind the shock wave front will be twelve times higher than that in the unperturbed interstellar medium. Moreover, $k/k_0 = 2.5$ and, consequently, the energy density of the relativistic particles behind the front will increase by the same factor. The magnetic shell "swept together" by the shock wave may therefore confine much more relativistic particles. If, however, the energy density of the relativistic particles becomes greater than the density of the magnetic energy, an instability will appear in the boundary of the shell and the "excessive" particles escape into the interstellar medium.

Let us denote by R the inner radius of the shell ejected in the explosion of the supernova, and by ΔR the thickness of the shell. Let us determine the relative thickness of the shell, $\Delta R/R = e(\Phi)$, where Φ is the angle between the radius vector drawn from the centre to a certain point of the shell and the direction of the interstellar magnetic field. Equation (9.43) describing the propagation of the shock wave will then read

$$\rho_0 V_{\text{II}}^2 \simeq \frac{4}{3} \left(\frac{1 + 5e}{4e^2} \right) \frac{H_0^2}{8\pi} \sin^2 \Phi \qquad (9.45)$$

where the factor $\frac{4}{3}$ has been introduced because of the supposition on the equality of magnetic energy and relativistic particle energy in the compressed shell, and the second component of the right-hand side of (9.43) is assumed to be small. We also have the condition of the equality of the energy densities of the relativistic particles and the magnetic field:

$$kK \int_{E_{\min}}^{E_{\max}} E^{-\gamma+1} \, dE \simeq \frac{H^2}{8\pi} \tag{9.46}$$

where k is the ratio of the energy densities of relativistic nuclei (mainly protons) and relativistic electrons in the compressed shell. In terms of the new variables Equation (9.38), which describe the constancy of magnetic flux, reads as follows:

$$H \simeq \frac{(1+e)^2}{e(2+e)} H_0 \sin \varphi \tag{9.47}$$

The shell volume may be given by the expression

$$V = 4\pi \int_0^{\pi/2} R \sin \varphi \cdot e(\varphi) R^2 \, d\varphi \simeq C_1 R^3 \tag{9.48}$$

where

$$C_1 = \frac{\pi^2 \bar{e}}{(1+5\bar{e})^{1/2}} + \frac{20\pi \bar{e}^2}{3(1+5\bar{e})}, \qquad \bar{e} = e\left(\frac{\pi}{2}\right)$$

The law of momentum conservation for the expanding shell assumes the form

$$P = M_0 V_{\Pi}(0) \simeq C_2 R^3 \rho_0 V(t) \tag{9.49}$$

where $C_2 = 4\pi/3 + C_1$.

If $e \leqslant \frac{1}{4}$ (a case which is of practical interest) then Equations (9.47) and (9.46) can be simplified:

$$H^2 = \left(\frac{1+4\bar{e}}{4\bar{e}^2}\right) H_0^2 \tag{9.50}$$

$$kKQ = \frac{H_0^2}{8\pi} \left(\frac{1+4\bar{e}}{4\bar{e}^2}\right) \tag{9.51}$$

where

$$Q = \frac{E_{\max}^{\tau-\gamma} - E_{\min}^{\tau-\gamma}}{2-\gamma} \qquad (\gamma \neq 2) \tag{9.52}$$

$$Q = \ln\left(\frac{E_{\max}}{E_{\min}}\right) \qquad (\gamma = 2) \tag{9.53}$$

If $\bar{e} < \frac{1}{4}$, Equation (9.45) can be rewritten in the form

$$V_{\text{II}}^2 \simeq \frac{(1 + 5\bar{e})}{6\bar{e}} V_0^2 \tag{9.54}$$

where

$$V_0^2 = \frac{H_0^2}{4\pi\rho_0}$$

Equations (9.49) to (9.54), together with the basic formula of the synchrotron theory (6.7) render it possible to write the following expression for the spectral density of the flux:

$$F_\nu = \frac{C_1\beta^2}{4} \left(\frac{2P\bar{e}}{C_2}\right) \left(\frac{1 + 4\bar{e}}{4\bar{e}^2}\right)^{(\alpha+3)/2} \frac{1.3 \cdot 10^{-22} u(\gamma)}{(1 + \bar{e})8\pi kQ}$$

$$\times \left(\frac{8.4 \cdot 10^{18}}{\nu}\right)^\alpha \frac{H_0^{2.66+\alpha}}{\{0.133 \cdot 10^{-24}(1 + 5e)n_0\}^{1/6}} \tag{9.55}$$

where β is the angular diameter of the shell. This extremely complex expression permits a calculation of the expected flux from radio sources from their observed characteristic parameters, under the assumption that van der Laan's hypothesis is true (according to it the magnetic field of the shell is the "compressed" field of the interstellar medium while the magnetic energy density in it is equal to the energy density of the relativistic particles). Van der Laan considers the inverse problem: assuming that this model is correct, he sets Equation (9.55) equal to the observed flux and calculates the characteristic parameters of several sources. He uses the sufficiently well-known objects 3C 392 and IC 443 as examples. He assumes $k = 60$, $P = 10^{43}$ g·cm/s and $n_0 = 1$ cm^{-3} for both sources and ~200 km/s and 120 km/s, respectively, for the expansion rates of the shells and arrives at the result that the agreement between calculated flux and observed flux is satisfactory if $\frac{1}{10} < \bar{e} < \frac{1}{6}$ (with IC 443) and $\bar{e} \sim \frac{1}{10}$ (with 3C 392). In the latter case e does not contradict the results of observations, whereas in the case of IC 443 the existence of such a shell is very problematic (see Fig. 48).

In connection with van der Laan's hypothesis, which explains the observed shell structure of the radio sources that have been identified with the remnants of type II supernovae, we may give some critical remarks. First of all the relation (9.43) and its modified form (9.45) apply to the isothermal case which is based on the assumption that because of the relatively intense radiation the gas behind the front cools down within a period that is much shorter than the age of the shell. But we showed in § 8 that to relatively young objects (to which IC 443 belongs and also the source 3C 392 which is known to be much younger) this is not true. These objects are characterized by the adiabatic propagation of a shock wave. In this case the density behind the front rises four-fold and so does H_0. Moreover, the width of the front will be very small. The inconsistency of van der Laan's theory with observations becomes particularly clear if we consider the example of Cassiopeia A. For it $\bar{e} \approx \frac{1}{4}$ (see § 6) (i.e., this shell is too thick) whereas $H > 2.5 \cdot 10^{-4}$ Oersted and $4H_0 \sim 5 \cdot 10^{-5}$ Oersted.

Finally, van der Laan's hypothesis is in obvious contradiction with the observed secular decrease in the radio flux from Cassiopeia A (see § 6). If the shell of Cassiopeia A actually had the nature suggested by van der Laan we could easily convince ourselves that the radio flux from it must increase with time, approximately following the law $F_\nu \propto t^3$, as behind the wave front H is always equal to $4H_0$ and the volume of the shell increases $\propto R^3$. Within the framework of van der Laan's scheme the magnetic energy density in the shell must always be equal to the energy density of the relativistic particles. The obvious disagreement of van der Laan's hypothesis with the observed characteristics of Cassiopeia A forces us to assume that it is not applicable to the other objects of this type either. This conclusion is in particular supported by another important fact, namely that all sources of synchrotron radio emission which have been identified with the remnants of supernovae of the type II constitute a uniform evolutional scheme. This would not be the case if, from a certain stage of expansion, the radio flux were increasing instead of decreasing. We thus see that the shell structure, or, more precisely, the "peripheral" structure of these sources, is a typical phenomenon. In our opinion this structure is formed for some reason or other by the "intrinsic" ("proper") magnetic field of the source and is independent (at least not directly dependent as was suggested by van der Laan) of the interstellar magnetic field "swept together" by the shock wave. The interaction between the "intrinsic" magnetic field which expands together with the shell and the interstellar medium may result in a compression of the latter. We think it very probable that the stationary condensations observed in Cassiopeia A have been formed in precisely this way.

CHAPTER III

The Crab nebula

§ 10   General information on the Crab nebula

In the previous chapter we discussed in detail the physical conditions in the remnants of type II supernovae. In the present chapter we shall consider the nature of the remnants of type I supernovae. It is obvious that in this case we are concerned only with galactic objects, since these remnants possess a comparatively short lifetime which is easily explained by the relatively small mass of the shell ejected. In our own stellar system we know at present three remnants of supernovae of type I: The Crab nebula (MI NGC 1952) and the two objects which have been identified with the remnants of the supernovae of 1572 and 1604. It must be mentioned that these three remnants differ essentially from one another, but we know that they cannot be viewed as different stages of evolution of objects similar in their nature. On the other hand, as was shown in the previous chapter, the remnants of supernovae of type II constitute a rather uniform group of objects whose various members are in different stages of evolution.

The Crab nebula is at present the object studied most carefully. This is due firstly to its relative proximity and secondly to a series of highly characteristic peculiarities (first of all, the powerful synchrotron radiation in a very wide frequency range, see § 12) which the remnants of the supernovae of 1572 and 1604 do not display. Since the statistical material available is very limited, we cannot say that the Crab nebula is a peculiar, non-typical representative of this group of objects. With the same right we might consider the remnants of Tycho's and Kepler's supernovae as peculiar objects. In the present chapter we shall discuss mainly the problems connected with the Crab nebula, where the question still remains open: Whether the results of an analysis of the physical conditions in the Crab nebula may be generalized to all remnants of type I supernovae.

206

During the last decades in the history of astrophysics the Crab nebula played a leading part.   It is no exaggeration to say that there is no other cosmic object which stimulated the development of the ideas and methods of modern astrophysics more than this astonishing nebula.   This statement applies to both theoretical and observational investigations. Remember that the Crab nebula was the first cosmic radio source to be identified with a galactic object (1949).   The Crab nebula was also the first identified X-ray source (disregarding the trivial case of the sun) (1963).   The radiation first discovered in the Crab nebula was an optical synchrotron emission, unprecedented in astrophysics (1953).   The strong polarization of this radiation, which had been predicted by theory, was fully verified by observations (1954).   The investigation of the optic synchrotron radiation of the peculiar metagalactic objects has today become almost the most fascinating and promising field of astrophysics (quasi-stellar sources, quasi-stellar galaxies, individual radio-galaxies). Before this discovery the only type of radiation known in astrophysics was the ordinary thermal radiation, and virtually all information on the universe had been obtained by analyzing this radiation.   The discovery of the non-thermal synchrotron radiation (and also the radiation generated by it which arises in the inverse Compton effect) extended considerably the field of effects accessible through investigations on the lines of observational astrophysics and revolutionized astronomy.   Finally, by way of the example of Crab nebula, the leading part played by the relativistic particles in the dynamics and evolution of cosmic objects was recognized for the first time.   At present it is well known that in galactic and metagalactic scales the cosmic particles play a part which is no less important than that of the classic components of matter, the stars, the interstellar and intergalactic gas and dust.   But we must not forget that the development of these basic ideas has been made possible mainly by the investigations of the Crab nebula.   We could give still other examples showing the exceptionally fruitful influence of the results of the research into the Crab nebula on the various fields of astronomy which are often not even connected with the problem of supernova outbursts.

The history of the identification of Crab nebula with the supernova of 1054 was already discussed in detail (cf. § 3).   Here we shall turn to a systematic consideration of the fundamental results of optical observations of this remarkable object.

The Crab nebula was discovered in 1731 by the English physicist and amateur astronomer John Bevis in his home observatory.   No details of this discovery have been handed down to us. It was independently discovered in 1758 by the so-called "comet hunter" Charles Messier.[145a] It was in this year that he devoted himself to a careful observation of Halley's comet, which reappeared in the sky after a 75-year absence, as predicted by theory. This astronomical event was at that time of paramount interest. Messier, during his observations, found a faint nebular object situated relatively close to the precalculated position of Halley's comet. This object was initially thought to be a comet; in

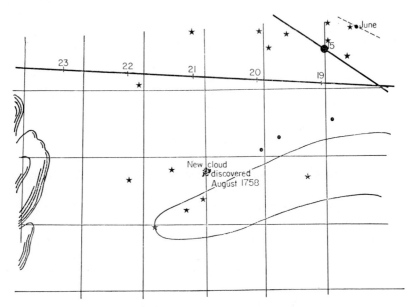

FIG. 58   Messier's map. [145a]

agreement with this the French astronomer wrote in his observation report: "...I found the comet of 1758, which ought to be between the horns of Taurus, on August 28th, below the southern horn, a small distance away from the star 'zeta' of this constellation. It appeared as a whitish elongated light spot, resembling a candle in its shape, and containing no stars."[145b]   Later on, in 1771, Messier published his first list of nebulae—misunderstood objects which caused some confusion in the observation of comets but which, in contrast to the latter, do not move relative to the stars.   Number one in this catalogue is the Crab nebula, with the following note added: "Observed by Doctor Bevis about 1731. Published in the English Astronomical Atlas." Messier seems to have heard of Bevis' discovery from Lalande who, during his visit to England in 1763, made the acquaintance of Bevis who showed him a copy of the stellar atlas *Uranographia Britannica*, composed by himself. This atlas contained not only the co-ordinates of a great number of stars determined by Bevis on the basis of his own observations but also sixteen nebular objects known at that time. The fate of this atlas is quite interesting. It was never printed as the owner of the printing house went bankrupt but, fortunately, he was able to give the galley proofs back to Bevis.... These copies were then partly used for the compilation of the rare English edition of the *Celestial Atlas* which was published in 1786. Copies of this atlas seem to have been possessed by Messier long before the *Atlas* itself was published.

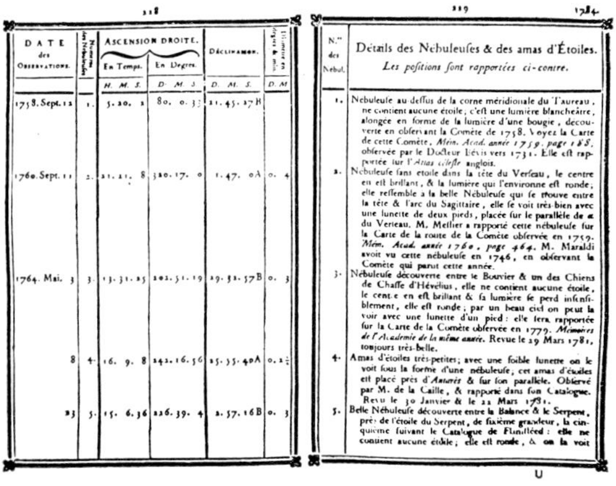

218

DATE des Observations.	Numéros des Nébuleuses	Ascension Droite. En Temps. H. M. S.	Ascension Droite. En Degrés. D. M. S.	Déclinaison. D. M. S.	Diamètre en degrés & min. D. M
1758. Sept. 12	1.	5. 20. 2	80. 0. 33	21. 45. 27 B	
1760. Sept. 11	2.	21. 21. 8	320. 17. 0	1. 47. 0 A	0. 4
1764. Mai. 3	3.	13. 31. 25	202. 51. 19	29. 32. 57 B	0. 3
8	4.	16. 9. 8	242. 16. 56	25. 55. 40 A	0. 2½
23	5.	15. 6. 36	226. 39. 4	2. 57. 16 B	0. 3

219 1784.

N.os des Nébul.	Détails des Nébuleuſes & des amas d'Étoiles. *Les poſitions ſont rapportées ci-contre.*
1.	Nébuleuſe au-deſſus de la corne méridionale du Taureau, ne contient aucune étoile; c'eſt une lumière blancheâtre, alongée en forme de la lumière d'une bougie, découverte en obſervant la Comète de 1758. Voyez la Carte de cette Comète, *Mém. Acad. année 1759, page 188*, obſervée par le Docteur Bévis vers 1731. Elle eſt rapportée ſur l'*Atlas céleſte* anglois.
2.	Nébuleuſe ſans étoile dans la tête du Verſeau, le centre en eſt brillant, & la lumière qui l'environne eſt ronde; elle reſſemble à la belle Nébuleuſe qui ſe trouve entre la tête & l'arc du Sagittaire, elle ſe voit très-bien avec une lunette de deux pieds, placée ſur le parallèle de α du Verſeau. M. Meſſier a rapporté cette nébuleuſe ſur la Carte de la route de la Comète obſervée en 1759. *Mém. Acad. année 1760, page 464*. M. Maraldi avoit vu cette nébuleuſe en 1746, en obſervant la Comète qui parut cette année.
3.	Nébuleuſe découverte entre le Bouvier & un des Chiens de Chaſſe d'Hévélius, elle ne contient aucune étoile, le centre en eſt brillant & ſa lumière ſe perd inſenſiblement, elle eſt ronde; par un beau ciel on peut la voir avec une lunette d'un pied: elle ſera rapportée ſur la Carte de la Comète obſervée en 1779. *Mémoires de l'Académie de la même année*. Revue le 29 Mars 1781, toujours très-belle.
4.	Amas d'étoiles très-petites; avec une foible lunette on le voit ſous la forme d'une nébuleuſe; cet amas d'étoiles eſt placé près d'*Antarès* & ſur ſon parallèle. Obſervé par M. de la Caille, & rapporté dans ſon Catalogue. Revu le 30 Janvier & le 22 Mars 1781.
5.	Belle Nébuleuſe découverte entre la Balance & le Serpent, près de l'étoile du Serpent, de ſixième grandeur, la cinquième ſuivant le Catalogue de Flamſtéed: elle ne contient aucune étoile; elle eſt ronde, & on la voit

U

FIG. 59 First page of Messier's *Catalogue of Nebulae*.[145b]

Figure 58 shows a part of Messier's map illustrating the trajectory of Halley's comet in 1758 (the straight line marked with the figures 19 to 23). Below the trajectory of the comet we find the newly discovered nebula. It is remarkable that Messier's drawing gives a relatively correct idea of the shape and structure of the Crab nebula. Figure 59 shows the first page of Charles Messier's famous *Catalogue of Nebulae* where the Crab nebula is listed as number one.

In the following century the Crab nebula was the object of many visual observations which, however, did not contribute essentially to the existing information. Several leading astronomers of that time, among them also Herschel[145c], assumed that this nebula might be resolved into stars. Lord Ross, an outstanding astronomer who made his observations in the first half of the nineteenth century with the largest of his instruments, drew attention to the filamentary structure of this nebula but, for some reason or other, he considered it an accumulation of stars at the limit of resolution into individual stars.[145d] Lassel did not share this opinion. He drew attention to the fact that the density of faint stars within the

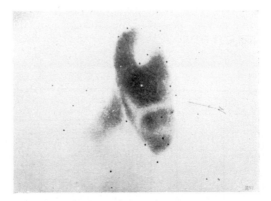

Fig. 60   Ross' drawing of Crab nebula.[145d]

bounds of the Crab nebula was virtually the same as in any other neighbouring part of the Milky Way.   In the middle of the nineteenth century the name "Crab nebula" was assigned to this object.   In 1844 Lord Ross published a drawing of the nebula in which it resembled a crab and in 1848 he called this nebula "The Crab."   This name has been generally used for more than a hundred years.   In Figure 60 we see a drawing of the Crab nebula made by Lord Ross.   It is interesting to compare this drawing with modern photographs (see, for example, Fig. 62).   It must be borne in mind that the drawings show the details of both very weak and very brilliant brightnesses.   Nevertheless the old drawings have much in common with the modern photographs.   In such a comparison it is useful to focus attention on the base stars which exist in this region. The most characteristic details of the nebula (for example, the "bay" in its eastern part) are seen equally well in both the drawing and the photograph.

The first photograph of the Crab nebula was obtained by Robertson in 1892 with the help of a 20-inch reflector. Later on this nebula was often photographed by various astronomers such as Keeler, Curtis and Ritchey, and these pictures proved very valuable for investigations of the nature of Crab nebula. As to its form it is a unique object. Figure 62 shows one of the best photographs that exist of the Crab nebula; it was obtained by Baade in the usual spectral range ($\lambda=3,600$–$5,000$ Å). The integral photographic magnitude of the whole nebula, obtained by Baade, is equal to 9.0.

FIG. 61   Photograph of the Crab nebula by Baade.[160]

The spectra of the Crab nebula were first obtained by Slipher in 1913 to 1915.[146]   It is interesting to read the description of the spectrum of this nebula given by this leading astrophysicist and observer: "The prominent nebular emission lines prove to be split into two components which forces us to assume the presence of a Stark effect caused by an electrical field." Today this interpretation may raise a smile but we must not forget that, when this was written, astrophysics was still in its infancy. Nevertheless, it was Slipher who discovered the important fact of the splitting of the emission lines in the Crab nebula's spectrum. In 1919 Sanford[147] obtained a spectrogram of this nebula with an exposure of 48 hours (!). (We must not forget that high-powered cameras were non-existent at that time.) According to Sanford the Crab nebula has a continuous spectrum with superimposed emission lines. He measured the wavelengths of several of these lines and six of them were correctly interpreted.

The first systematic spectral observations of the Crab nebula were carried out in the thirties by Mayall. These important observations will be discussed below.

In its general features the spectrum of the Crab nebula reminds us of that of the planetary nebulae. Its predominant lines are the nebular emission lines [O II], [O III], [N II], [S II], and the lines of the Balmer series of hydrogen. There exists, however, one important peculiarity which renders the spectrum of the Crab nebula essentially different from the spectra of planetary nebulae. This is the extraordinarily high intensity of the continuous component, a fact that was already pointed out by Hubble.[148] According to an estimate by Baade, the continuous spectrum amounts to at least 80 per cent of the total emission. Other authors give yet higher values. Barbier, for example, found that only a few per cent of the radiation from Crab nebula was concentrated in the emission lines.[149] The continuous spectrum of the planetary nebulae is, however, very weak. In any case more than 90 per cent of the radiation from the planetary nebulae is concentrated in the emission lines. As early as 15 years ago it was established that the continuous spectrum of the planetary nebulae is due to two-photon hydrogen emission,[150,151] and that the total intensity of this spectrum exceeds by only a little the intensity of the H_β line. Later on it could be shown that the continuous spectrum of the Crab nebula has a quite unusual origin and nothing in common with the continuous spectrum of the planetary nebulae (and all other previously known cosmic objects).

Particularly interesting results were obtained by Baade who, at the end of the thirties, began with a systematic photographic investigation of the Crab nebula, using various light filters made of glass with a broad pass band (from $\lambda = 400$–1,500 Å). The photographs obtained with filters for the range from $\lambda = 3,300$–6,500 Å did not show any unusual results. Though there were some slight differences in the details, these pictures resembled the ordinary photograph shown in Figure 61. The photograph, however, which was made with a filter transmissive for the $H\alpha$ line and the two [N II] lines "flanking" it (λ 6,548 and λ 6,584) showed various surprising details.   The application of a filter with a relatively narrow pass band (from λ=6,300–6,700 Å) resulted in a picture in which the "open-work" system of filaments could be discovered.   This photograph is shown in Figure 62.

Fɪɢ. 62   Photograph of the Crab nebula through a filter for λ = 6,300–6,700 Å.[160]

Using this photograph as a guide, Minkowski obtained a series of spectra of the Crab nebula in the range from λ=3,600–5,000 Å with various slit positions.   In these experiments it was discovered that when the slit traversed a "red" filament, the emission lines literally "flared up," while outside the fibres only the continuous spectrum is observed.

These observations show that the emission lines come from the system of fine filaments which surround from all sides like a shell in the centre of the nebula, whereas the continuous spectrum is emitted by the entire volume of the nebula.   The photometrical structure of the region that emits the continuous spectrum can be studied in the best way by means of a photograph obtained with a light filter in whose pass band there are no brighter lines.   The spectral range suitable for this purpose is the band from $\lambda = 7{,}200\text{--}8{,}400$ Å.   A photograph of the Crab nebula, exposed through such a light filter, is shown in Figure 63.   We see at once the striking difference in the photographs reproduced in Figures 62 and 63.   The region emitting the continuous spectrum and displaying a fairly rich photometrical structure was called an "amorphous mass," a

Fig. 63   Photograph of the Crab nebula through a filter for $\lambda = 7{,}200\text{--}8{,}400$ Å.[160]

designation which, in our opinion, is not very apt.   This region might only be considered "amorphous" in contrast to the "open-work" system of filaments which are the source of the emission lines.   Let us stress once again that the so-called "amorphous mass" possesses a rich and rather fine "striated" structure which is partly due to a projection effect as the structural elements emitting the continuous spectrum are distributed over the whole volume of the nebula.   The filaments emitting the line spectrum are, however, arranged in the periphery of the nebula, forming a thin shell so that the projection effect cannot influence them very much.

In this way Baade's observations showed that the Crab nebula behaves as if it consisted of two quite different parts: the "open-work" net of fine gaseous filaments arranged in the form of a shell at the periphery of the nebulae, and the so-called "amorphous mass" which occupies the whole volume of the nebula; its nature has been mysterious for a long time.

We see from Figure 63 that the system of filaments in the Crab nebula has a very regular elliptic contour; only the structural detail mentioned above, the so-called "gulf" in the south-eastern part of the nebula, disturbs a little the regularity of the elliptic form. From the outermost faint filaments Baade obtained the following values for the semi-axes of this ellipse: $a = 178''$, $b = 120''$, with an error of $\pm 5''$. The centre of the ellipse is positioned in the immediate proximity of the two faint stars of magnitude 15.9 which are located in the central part of the Crab nebula and possess a mutual distance of $4''.9$.

If the northernmost of these two little stars is chosen as the origin of a co-ordinate system, the centre of the ellipse will, according to Baade, possess the following co-ordinates: $\Delta\alpha = 4''.7$, $\Delta\delta = 0''.0$. For this determination Baade assumes a probable error of $\pm 3''$. If we transfer the origin of co-ordinates to the neighbouring southern star (for this we have good reasons, see §§ 12 and 13) the co-ordinates of the ellipse are the following: $\Delta\alpha = +6''.9$, $\Delta\delta = +4''.4$. The ratio of the semi-axes of the visible ellipse of Crab nebula is $b/a = 0.67$. If the spatial form of the Crab nebula is considered as an ellipsoid of revolution, the true ratio of the semi-axes of this ellipsoid must be smaller owing to the projection effect. In order to find the true ratio of the axes, Baade used spectrographic observations by Mayall who, taking his photographs with the slit oriented along the minor axis, obtained the characteristic slope of the emission line $\lambda\,3{,}727$.[152] The line emitted by the north-western part of the nebula displays a red-shift. This fact permits the conclusion that the principal plane of the ellipsoid of revolution makes an angle of $\sim 20\text{--}30°$ with the plane of the picture. The true value of b/a corrected for the projection effect must therefore be close to 0.60.

Though the "amorphous" mass does not display such a regular configuration as the filamentary system, it is much more elongated than the latter. Along the major axis of the nebula the traces of the amorphous mass may be pursued to the boundaries of the filamentary system, whereas in the perpendicular direction they fall a long way short of the periphery. In this connection we should like to mention the interesting

fact that the most intense filament lies for the most part in the direction
of the minor axis. We get the impression that the structural details of
the amorphous mass and the gaseous filaments "avert" one another.
This is particularly marked in the region of the "bay" in the south-
eastern part of the nebula which was mentioned before. The distinct

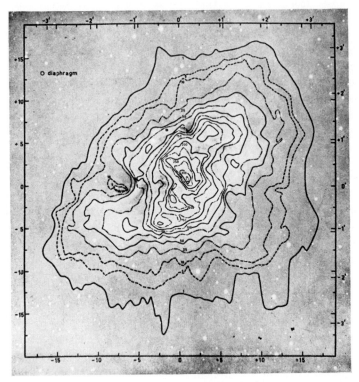

FIG. 64   Intensity distribution of the amorphous mass in the Crab nebula.[153]

outwardly curved arc found here is the outer boundary of the amorphous
mass, whereas in the perpendicular direction a very bright filament can be
observed. A rough estimate of the ratio of the semi-axes for the amorphous mass yields the value $b/a = 0.54$ and, if the projection effect is
taken into account, we obtain a value of $b/a \approx 0.50$, i.e., much less than
in the case of the filamentary system.

Woltier[153] used the calibrated photograph of the Crab nebula obtained by Baade with the help of a filter possessing a pass band in the
spectral range of λ 5,200–6,400 Å in which the emission lines of the
gaseous filaments are virtually absent, in order to obtain the intensity
distribution in the amorphous mass. Figure 64 shows the corresponding
isophotes; Woltier recalculated these isophotes in absolute units. In this
way he obtained the integral visual magnitude of the Crab nebula which
proved to be equal to 8.64 which is in agreement with other determinations. For example, according to [154], the photographic magnitude of the
Crab nebula is equal to 9.14 and the colour corresponds to a star of the
spectral class G 2. In this case the colour index must be equal to 0.64
and hence follows a visual magnitude of the Crab nebula of 8.50. It must
be stressed that the spectrum of the amorphous mass may only be represented as a Planck curve for a relatively narrow frequency range. In a
wide frequency range this spectrum is in principle different from the
Planck form, whatever the temperature (see § 1.2).

Comparing the photographs of the Crab nebula that were obtained
at a time interval of eight years, Lampland, in 1921, found that individual
details of this nebula had undergone a noticeable displacement.[46] In
addition to this, Lampland discovered surprising changes in the photometrical structure of the nebula which could not be attributed to the
simple motions of the individual filaments. This "metamorphosis" of
the photometrical structure of the nebula discovered by Lampland could
not be elucidated within the period of more than 30 years which have
elapsed since then. Only the explanation of the nature of the optical
radiation from the Crab nebula by the continuous spectrum led to a
comprehension of this strange effect; we shall discuss it in § 12.

The proper motions of the individual details of the Crab nebula were
already investigated in 1921 by Duncan,[47] who verified in an independent
way the fact of the expansion of the Crab nebula discovered by Lampland.
In 1939 Duncan could essentially improve the characteristic parameters of
expansion of this nebula, making use of the differences observed
after a period of 29 years.[158] A year later the results of a very
detailed investigation into this problem were published by the Pulkovo
astronomers A. N. Deych and V. V. Lavdovskiy.[159] According to these
measurements the mean proper motion obtained for a great number of
condensations of filaments amounts to 0".21 and is directed outwardly
along a radius drawn from the centre of the nebula. The vectors in
Figure 65 mark the proper motions of various filamentary condensations

8+s.

of the Crab nebula, investigated by Duncan.   This picture illustrates very
clearly the expansion of the filamentary system of the Crab nebula from a
single centre.

From the results of Duncan's measurements Baade selected those
which referred to condensations located near the endpoints of the major
axis of the Crab nebula.[160]   These measurements are obviously of great
interest.   After all corrections necessary he obtained a value of 0″.235
± 0″.008 per year for the proper motion of these condensations in the

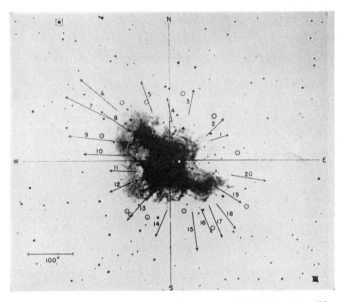

FIG. 65   Proper motion of the filaments in the Crab nebula.[158]

direction of the major axis of the nebula.   As Baade in his new paper
gives a value of $a = 178″ \pm 5″$ for the major semi-axis, the above value of
the proper motion in the direction of the major axis enables us to calculate
the age of the nebula (provided the expansion occurs at a constant rate).
A value of 758 years is obtained for this age.   On the other hand, assuming
a uniform expansion from the moment of the outburst in 1054 up to
Baade's observations in 1938, we obtain a value of 0″.201 ± 0″.006 per
year for the proper motion along the major axis, that is, 0″.034 ± 0″.010
per year less than that observed.   But, as there can be no doubt that this

nebula appeared in 1054, we are led to the conclusion that the filamentary system displays an accelerated motion. In a first approximation we may assume that this acceleration is constant. The time dependence of the radius of the nebula will then be given by $R = a_1 t + b_1 t^2$ where t is the time after the outburst of the supernova. Since, with $t = (1938 - 1054) = 884$ years, $R = 178'' \pm 5''$, $dR/dt = 0''.235 \pm 0''.008$ per year, $a_1 =$ and $0''.168 \pm 0''.015$ $b_1 = 0''.000038 \pm 000014$. In order to transform these angular units into linear ones, Baade uses the results of measurements of the radiation velocities in the Crab nebula carried out by Mayall (see below). In this way the expansion rate of the nebula is obtained as

$$V_R = 789 + 0.361t \text{ km/s}$$

and the acceleration amounts to

$$A = 0.0011 \text{ cm/s}^2$$

This very important result on the secular acceleration of the filamentary system in the Crab nebula cannot be explained on the basis of the usual notions of classical astrophysics. Baade himself made the very

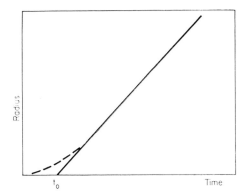

FIG. 66   Schematic representation of the time dependence of the Crab nebula's radius.[160]

naïve attempt to explain the acceleration of the Crab nebula he had obtained by the hypothesis of the light pressure, assuming one of these small stars found in the central part of the Crab nebula to be the source of radiation. This hypothesis, just like all the old hypotheses on the

nature of the Crab nebula, proved quite inapplicable.   Only the development of new ideas on the nature of the "continuous" optical emission
from this nebula enabled C. B. Pikel'ner, in 1955, to find a natural explanation of the secular acceleration of the Crab nebula and hence to derive an
independent estimate of its mass (see § 11).   Figure 66 gives a schematic
representation of the time dependence of the radius of the Crab nebula,
explaining Baade's results described above.

Let us now pass over to a more detailed discussion of the results of
spectroscopic investigations of the Crab nebula.

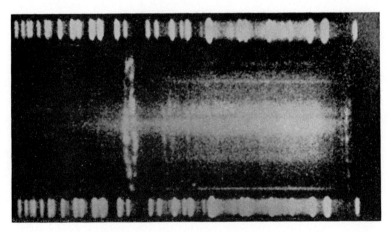

FIG. 67   Spectrum of the Crab nebula.[152]

First of all we shall focus our attention on the spectrum of its filamentary shell.   As already mentioned above, the effect of splitting of the
emission lines in the Crab nebula has already been discovered by Slipher
and Sanford.   An obvious explanation of this effect is afforded by the
expansion of the whole system of filaments with a sufficiently high
velocity.   Detailed investigations of the radiation velocities were carried
out by Mayall in 1936.[152]   The slit length of the spectrograph corresponded to 6'.2, which exceeds the major axis of the nebula.   Figure 67
shows the spectrum of the Crab nebula taken when the slit was oriented
along the major axis of the nebula.   It is clearly seen that the emission
lines in the centre of the nebula are split into two, whereas towards the
edges the components of each line approach one another which lends it

its peculiar shape. Moreover, the lines have a flocculate, "torn" shape which is explained by the fine-fibred structure of the emitting gas masses. The brightest line is the well-known nebular doublet [O II] λ 3,727. In the photographic part of the spectrum shown in Figure 67 this line is much more intense than all other emission lines. The very same situation is observed in the spectrum of the filamentary nebulae in the constellation Cygnus (see § 5). Besides the line λ 3,727, the lines [Ne III] λ 3,869 and λ 3,968, H_δ, H_δ [O III] λ 4,363, [He III] λ 4,686, $H\beta$, and the nebular

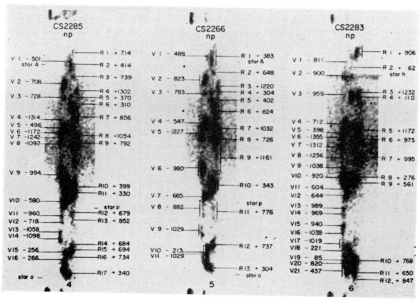

Fig. 68 Part of spectrum of the Crab nebula near the line λ=3,727 Å.[152]

lines [O III] λ 4,959 and λ 5,007 are also observed in the photographic part of the spectrum. Figure 68 shows a large-scale picture of the spectral range near λ 3,727 for the two orientations of the spectrograph slit mentioned above. Mayall also called attention to the fact that one cannot observe any systematic difference between the intensities of the "violet" and the "red" components of each line. This indicates that there cannot be any noticeable light absorption within the nebula. This, however, is a rather trivial statement since a noticeable light absorption could be observed only if the density of the cosmic dust were a hundred times higher than it is on the average in the interstellar medium.

Let us make the natural assumption that the maximum (in modulus) radial velocity measured in the central part of the nebula is equal to the linear velocity of expansion in a direction perpendicular to the direction

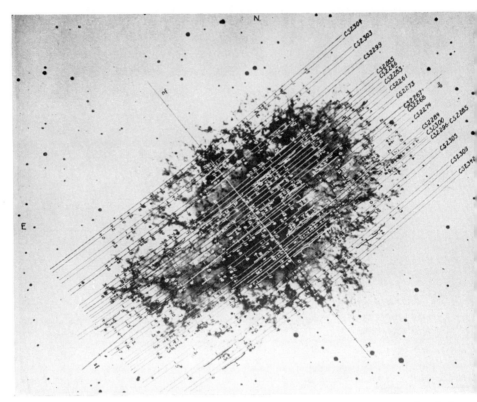

Fig. 69 Position of the spectrograph slit relative to the filaments in the Crab nebula.[53]

of observation. The latter is proportional to the velocity of expansion, in angular units, multiplied by the distance of the nebula. If we assume a value of $0''.201$ per year (see above) for the mean angular expansion rate and the modulus of the radial velocity $|V_R| = 1,116$ km/s, we obtain a value of 1,180 psc for the distance of the Crab nebula.[160] We must, however, take into consideration that this value has been obtained on several simplifying assumptions (for example, we ignored the ellipsoidal form of the filamentary shell). The true distance may be considerably larger, for example, 1,700 psc (see § 13).

Figure 69 shows the positions of the spectrograph slit for eighteen spectrograms obtained by Mayall.[53] In this figure the radial velocities are given in units of 100 km/s. In the photograph of the Crab nebula shown in Figure 70 the marks made along the various filaments indicate the directions and magnitudes of the radial velocities.[53] From this schematic representation we see that the system of filaments possesses

Fig. 70   Schematic representation of radial velocity distribution along the filaments in the Crab nebula.[53]

structural details of very large scale. Some of the strongest fibres may be pursued over very great distances. Such filaments, like huge "hoses," occupy the central part of the nebula.

On the basis of the measurements of radial velocities carried out by Mayall in the winter of 1954–55 at the same spectrograph as in 1936, Walraven constructed a rough model of the spatial structure of the filamentary system in the Crab nebula.

Figure 71 shows this coarse model of the spatial system of filaments.[53] The differences in the shading of the filaments indicates magnitude and direction of their radial velocities. It would be very important to

continue such interesting studies as they are a great help in elucidating
the physical processes accompanying the outbursts of supernovae.

Apart from the values of the radial velocities the spectrum of the
filaments of the Crab nebula (just as in the case of any other nebular
object) permits the investigation of the physical conditions of the gas in
the Crab nebula. In addition to the authors we referred to above, the
spectra of the filaments were also taken and studied by Minkowski.[162]

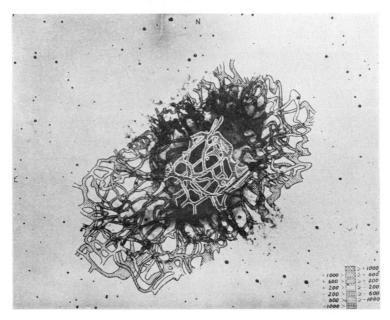

Fig. 71   Rough spatial model of the filamentary system in the Crab nebula.[53]

Besides the lines found by Mayall he discovered the relatively weak lines
of He I, λ 3,889 and λ 4,472, and a series of lines in the yellow and red
parts of the spectrum which had not as yet been investigated: He I
λ 5,875, [O I] λ 6,300, [N II] λ 6,548, Hα, [N II] λ 6,584 and the [S II]
doublet λ 6,711 to λ 6,728. Unfortunately Minkowski did not estimate
the relative intensities of the lines because of the disturbing effect of the
powerful continuous spectrum emitted by the nebula. The presence of
the relatively bright forbidden line [O I] (λ 6,300) in the spectrum of the

nebula attracts our attention.   The forbidden lines of ionized sulphur are
the most intense lines in the red part of the spectrum.   It must be noted
that in the spectra of the planetary nebulae these lines are always weaker
than the [N II] line.   This might indicate an anomalous chemical
composition of the filaments in Crab nebula.

The first attempt at a quantitative analysis of the spectra of filaments of the Crab nebula was made by Woltier.[163]   He based his studies
on the observational material obtained by Mayall in 1954–55 when investigating the spectrum of the Crab nebula.   These spectrograms were
calibrated and standardized.   The usual methods of photographical
photometry were used to study the spectra of about fifty condensations and nodes.   In Table 16 we compiled the line intensities of several
filaments.

In the first column of Table 16 the designations of the condensations
are listed (see Fig. 72).   The second and third columns give the rectangular
co-ordinates of each condensation, in minutes of arc.

The small south-western star in the central part of the nebula was
chosen as the origin of co-ordinates.   The fourth column contains the
radial velocities of the various condensations measured by Mayall, and
the fifth column the radii vectors of the condensations, in psc, drawn from
the centre of the nebula defined above.   The values of R were calculated
from the well-known values of V_R and the proper motions of the condensations.   In columns six to thirteen the absolute intensities of various
spectral lines are compiled.   These intensities were determined by way
of referring them to the intensity of the continuous spectrum of the Crab
nebula.   Absolute photoelectrical measurements of the latter were carried
out by Walraven[161] (see § 12).   The value of $1.20 \cdot 10^{-6}$ erg/cm$^2 \cdot$s was
chosen as the intensity unit in this system.

It must, however, be stressed that the intensities obtained by Woltier
are very unreliable.   The fact is that the spectrographs of the Crab nebula
were taken with a relatively wide slit ($\sim 10''$) while the filaments are very
thin.   The blurring due to the broad instrumental profile may therefore
be considerable.   It is obvious that this blur depends on the orientation
of the filament relative to the slit of the spectrograph.   This effect may in
particular alter the measured ratio between very bright and very weak
lines (owing to the non-linearity of the characteristic curve).   The
intensities given in Table 16 must therefore be corrected.   In individual
cases this correlation may be considerable.   According to Woltier the
intensities of the spectral lines given in Table 16 must be multiplied by a

8*

TABLE 16

No.	x	y	V_R	R	[O II] 3,727	[Ne III] 3,869	+ He I 3,889	[Ne III] 3,968	[S II] 4,075	+ Hδ 4,101	Hγ + [O III] 4,340	[O III] 4,363	He I 4,471	He II 4,686	Hβ 4,868	[O III] ~5,000
v6a	+0.65	−0.24	−870	0.73	4,200	776	437	343	118	195	260	68	237	738	645	High
v6b	+0.43	−0.40	−870	0.72	3,130	936		276	102		268			455	518	[8,900]
r11	+2.54	+1.14	+10	0.86	320	—						24				300
r3	−1.26	−1.55	+250	0.63	1,440	286	39	82	68		14	60			72	1,580
v2	−2.01	−0.79	−540	0.76	1,070	142				91					91	1,520
v9	+0.65	+1.67	+170	0.55	1,830	344	109	107	102	61	230	64	81	171	363	2,790
v10	+0.05	+1.23	−240	0.40	1,900	355		73	247		216	31			481	2,780
v5	−1.52	+0.14	−730	0.71	2,280	590		117	25	39	218		38	245	260	4,240
r11	+0.99	+0.56	+1,780	1.45	810	—										1,050
r5	+1.14	−0.35	+830	0.77	2,550	495	123	114	48	38	120		57	164	331	4,850
v4	+0.43	−1.40	−80	0.47	1,550	357		91	35	37	133	38	18	181	180	3,460
v6	−1.45	+0.61	−1,090	0.96	730	106	70				45				62	1,320
v4 + Z2	−2.33	+0.03	{+111 / −526}		820	100	18		27	7	78				70	960

factor of 5 for most of the filaments, though such a correction is, of course, quite uncertain.

Doubt might also be cast on the procedure for obtaining the relative intensities by referring them to the intensity of the continuous spectrum of the Crab nebula. This procedure requires the knowledge of the law of spectral distribution of the "continuous" emission from the amorphous mass, which was determined quite roughly in [163] (see § 12). Finally, one should also estimate the influence of interstellar absorption. The error due to ignoring light absorption in interstellar space is, however, small compared to other errors (first of all, the consideration of the width of slit of the spectrograph).

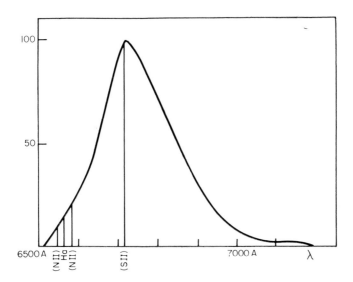

FIG. 72   Transmission curve of red filter.[163]

Nevertheless, Table 16 contains the only information on the intensities of the emission lines from the filaments of Crab nebula which are available for the present. The spectral range is in fact rather narrow. At $\lambda = 5,000$ Å the sensitivity of the plates used by Mayall decreases abruptly, so that important information about the line intensities in the infra-red range of the spectrum is absolutely lacking. This information was obtained by Woltier with the help of an indirect method, by analyzing

the photograph of the Crab nebula taken with a glass filter whose transmissivity was concentrated to the [S II] lines λ 6,711 to λ 6,728. This
photograph was obtained by Baade especially for this purpose. The
transmission curve of the filter is shown in Figure 72; the positions of the
fundamental emission lines of the Crab nebula in this part of the spectrum
are marked in this figure: [N II], Hα and [S II]. An estimate of the
absolute intensity of the [S II] lines was obtained by way of referring it to
the continuous spectrum for which a distribution law $I \propto \nu^{-1.15}$ is used
(the same law which was used in the determination of the absolute
intensities in the photographic part of the spectrum given in Table 16).
With the help of a rather complex and not quite reliable indirect method,
which we do not want to discuss here, Woltjer estimated the intensity
ratio of the lines Hα, [N II] and [S II] as 1:4:1 (averaged over six condensations). The absolute magnitude of the intensity of [S II], measured
in the same units as the lines listed in Table 16, is, averaged over six
condensations, equal to 1,185. It must be stressed that, in spite of the
great uncertainty of these estimates which are based mainly on purely
theoretical considerations, they contain sufficiently valuable information.

Regarding Table 16 one is immediately led to the conclusion that in
all condensations the lines [O II] λ 3,727 and [O III] λ 4,959 to λ 5,007 are
the most intense ones, the latter being the most intense lines in the
photographic part of the spectrum. Indirect data which we discussed
above enables us to draw the conclusion that the lines [N II] have an
approximately similar intensity to the lines [O III]. In a series of cases
the lines prove to be overlapping, which may also be seen from Table 16.

Although the spectra of the various condensations undoubtedly
display differences in the details, one can build up a kind of "synthetic"
average spectrum which is shown in Table 17.

This table contains the relative line intensities of the brightest filaments in the Crab nebula, referred to the intensity of the line λ 3,727,
taken as 100. Let us stress once more that this table does not show any

TABLE 17

	[O II]	[Ne III]	[S II]	He I	He II	O III	Hα	[N II]	[S II]
λ	3,727	3,869	$\begin{cases}4{,}068\\4{,}076\end{cases}$	4,471	4,861	$\begin{cases}4{,}959\\5{,}007\end{cases}$	6,563	$\begin{cases}6{,}548\\6{,}584\end{cases}$	$\begin{cases}6{,}711\\6{,}728\end{cases}$
I_λ	100	15.5	4.8	1.9	(7.5)	151	35	137	35

essential differences between the spectra of the individual filaments. That such differences must exist already follows from the simple fact that in the spectrum of the Crab nebula a sufficiently intense line of neutral oxygen (λ 6,300) is observed. It is very difficult to imagine that one and the same condensation should emit both the line [O III] and the line [O I]. We shall return to this problem in § 13 where we shall discuss the problem of the excitation mechanism in the filaments.

The line of ionized helium at λ 4,686, which is very important for the analysis of the physical conditions in the filaments, often comes out superimposed. The wavelength measurements of the "neighbouring" line (in such cases where the overlapping could be resolved) is about 4,660 A. It is very probably identical with the [Fe III] line λ 4,658. In the majority of condensations the intensity of the [Fe III] lines is several times smaller than that of the [He II] line. Owing to the rapid decrease in sensitivity of the plates towards the red side, the "nebulium" lines [O III] are not resolved into their components N_1 and N_2. Woltier was, in our opinion, excessively optimistic when assuming that the error in the determination of the intensities of not too weak lines listed in Table 16 was ~ 25 per cent. In all probability it is two to three times higher.

In Table 18 we find the measured mean values of Balmer's decrement determined for such condensations in which either the lines Hβ and Hγ or the lines Hγ and Hδ are observed simultaneously. The same table also contains several theoretical values of the decrement for the recombinative and the "collisional" mechanism of excitation under various

TABLE 18

		Hβ	Hγ	Hδ	B$_4$
Hβ $\geqslant$ 300		100	47.4	21.5	
300 > Hβ $\geqslant$ 125		100	49.5	13.8	
124 > Hβ		100	45.1	26.8	
Observational Mean		100	47.3	20.6	
$T_e = 1,0000°${B	250	100	51	31	0.17
	st	576	100	29.1	13.6	1.22
$T_e = 20,000°${B	259	100	50	30	0.40
	st	479	100	34.7	16.9	2.32

assumptions on the height of the electron temperature T_e. The first column of the upper part of the table gives the intensity values of Hβ for the filaments investigated, and the first column of the lower part the theoretical value of Balmer's decrement. The sixth column of the lower part of this table contains the values of the parameter and the deviations from Boltzmann distribution of the population of the fourth level of the hydrogen atom (on the basis of the emission of the Hβ line).

The symbol "B" in the first column of the lower part of the table indicates that the recombinative decrement was calculated on the assumption that the optical thickness in the lines of the Lyman series was very high (see [164]); the symbol "st" indicates the excitation mechanism of electron impact. The insufficient accuracy of the measurements of the relative Balmer line intensities does not, however, permit a final conclusion as to the excitation of hydrogen emission in the filaments of the Crab nebula. Nevertheless, the recombinative mechanism seems to be more likely, though electron impact may also play a certain part.

Another important problem is that of the electron temperature in the filaments. One may try to determine it with the help of a classical method often used in the physics of gas nebulae, i.e., from the intensity ratio of the [O III] lines. According to Seaton, in the case of not too high electron densities, this ratio is equal to [166]:

$$\frac{I_{\lambda\,4,959} + I_{\lambda\,5,007}}{I_{\lambda\,4,363}} \simeq 8.74 \cdot e^{3.30 \cdot (10,000/T_e)} \qquad (10.1)$$

For condensations in which $\lambda\,4,363$ is not superimposed by Hγ, the value of T_e determined in this way is close to $17,000°$. It must, however, be noted that the [O III] line $\lambda\,4,363$ may also be superimposed by the [Fe II] line $\lambda\,4,359$ so that the electron temperature in the filament may be lower. It would therefore be very desirable to obtain the spectrum of the filaments in the Crab nebula in a high resolution.

From the absolute intensities given in Table 16 we can determine the ion concentrations responsible for the emission of the corresponding lines, with the help of formulas well known from the physics of gas nebulae. For this purpose we must know the emission per unit volume of the filament investigated, in quanta of the corresponding line, and the electron concentration N_e. The first quantity may be obtained from the data of Table 16, under the natural assumption that the thickness of the filament in the direction of observation is equal to its diameter d. If the filaments are assumed to be of cylindrical shape with the radius $d/2$, the surface brightness I_λ will be linked with the sought volume luminosity by the relation:

$$\frac{\pi\, d^2 \varepsilon_\lambda}{4\pi\, d} = I_\lambda \qquad (10.2)$$

hence we obtain $\varepsilon_\lambda = 4I_\lambda/d$. The electron concentration may in principle be obtained from the intensity of the Hβ line. For this, however,

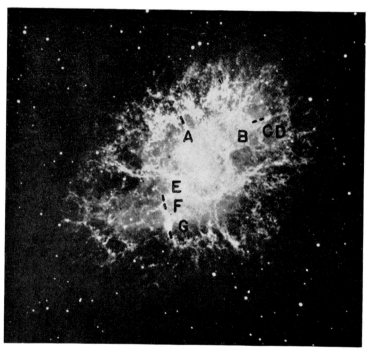

Fig. 73 Photograph of Crab nebula.   The dashes mark the condensations investigated by Osterbrock.[167]

we must know the excitation mechanism effective in the case of hydrogen, which as yet has not been fully elucidated.

The most reliable way of determining N_e is the use of a method developed by Seaton which is based on an analysis of the intensity ratio of the forbidden lines [O II] ($\lambda\,3{,}727$ and $\lambda\,3{,}729$).[166]   According to [166] the intensity ratio of the lines $\lambda\,3{,}727$ and $\lambda\,3{,}729$ depends on N_e in the following way:

$$r = \frac{I_{\lambda\,3{,}727}}{I_{\lambda\,3{,}729}} = 1.5\left[\frac{1 + 0.33\varepsilon + 2.30x(1 + 0.75\varepsilon + 0.14\varepsilon^2)}{1 + 0.40\varepsilon + 9.9x(1 + 0.84\varepsilon + 0.17\varepsilon^2)}\right]$$

(10.3)

where

$$\varepsilon = \exp\,(-1.96t), \qquad x = 10^{-4}N_e t^{-\frac{1}{2}}, \qquad t = 10^{-4}T_e$$

In 1957 Osterbrock obtained three spectrograms of filaments of the Crab nebula. These spectrograms were produced with the help of a high-power camera with a dispersion of 68 A/mm at $\lambda\,3{,}727$, at a 100-inch and a 200-inch telescope. Figure 73 shows a photograph of the Crab nebula, the lines marking the condensations which were investigated by Osterbrock. Table 19 contains the $\lambda\,3{,}727/\lambda\,3{,}729$ intensity ratios measured for various condensations and also the value of N_e obtained from Equation (10.3).

The measuring results refer to those parts of the bright condensations for which the dispersion of the intrinsic velocities is small so that both [O II] lines can be observed separately. These observations showed in particular that the line width in the filaments is considerable. For $\lambda\,3{,}727$ it amounts to ~ 1 A which corresponds to a velocity dispersion of about 100 km/s. The accuracy of the measured intensity ratios of $\lambda\,3{,}727$ and $\lambda\,3{,}729$ was estimated by Osterbrock as ± 6 per cent. The value of N_e can therefore be determined with an accuracy of ± 25 per cent which is quite good. The mean value of N_e for the bright condensations in the filaments is $N_e \sim 10^3$ cm^{-3}.

TABLE 19

	$\lambda\,3{,}727/\lambda\,3{,}729$	N_e cm^{-3}
A	0.96	820
B	0.58	3,700
C	0.97	790
D	1.03	630
E	0.67	2,400
F	1.07	550
G	0.95	850

The expression for the volume luminosity in the quanta of an arbitrary forbidden line whose basic configuration contains three energy levels is given by the formula

$$\varepsilon_{21} \frac{\dfrac{8.54 \cdot 10^{-4} \cdot \Omega_{(1 \cdot 2)}}{\omega_1} h\nu_{21} e^{-h\nu_{21}/kTe} N_e N_i}{1 + \dfrac{8.54 \cdot 10^{-4}\Omega_{12}}{\omega_2 A_{21}} N_e + \dfrac{8.54\Omega_{(23)}}{\omega_2} \dfrac{A_{31} \cdot e^{-h\nu_{32}/kTe} \cdot N_e}{A_{21} + (A_{32} + A_{31})}} \qquad (10.4)$$

An analogous expression also exists for the O II ion whose basic configuration contains two levels. In Equation (10.4) $\Omega(ik)$ is the collision parameter (see [164]), $\omega_i = 2J + 1$ is the statistical weight of the ith level characterized by the quantum number J, A_{ik} are Einstein's coefficients, N_1 is the concentration of the corresponding ions (or neutral atoms as in the case of O I) in the ground state.

On the basis of the "average" spectrum determined from observations (cf. Table 16) Woltier calculated the "average" chemical composition of the filaments with the help of Equation (10.4). The calculated relative concentrations of the various ions depend strongly on the electron temperature assumed and slightly on the electron concentration. The calculations were carried out for the following three values of T_e: 17,000°, 10,000° and 8,000°. In the case of helium the calculations were based on the assumption of a recombinative mechanism of emission, for which the corresponding formulas were used, which are well known from the physics of gaseous nebulae (see, for example, [164]). With the temperature of 17,000° both recombinative excitation and excitation by electron impact were taken into account in the calculation of the proton concentration. The results of the calculations are compiled in Table 20.

TABLE 20

Ion	Ho II	He I	He II	N II	O II	O III	Ne III	S II
$T_e = 17,000°$	10,000	4,820	1,370	0.77	0.71	1.36	0.52	0.19
$= 10,000°$	10,000	3,600	940	1.80	3.35	4.14	2.29	1.04
$= 8,000°$	10,000	3,400	770	2.40	9.10	8.90	6.80	2.90

In order to obtain the relative abundances of the various elements in all states of ionization it is necessary to make simplifying assumptions since by no means all states of ionization of an element emit lines in an observable

part of the spectrum. The supposition that virtually all hydrogen in the
filaments will be ionized seems natural. But we must not forget that the
[O I] line λ 6,300 is observed in the spectrum of the filaments. Since
the ionization potentials of hydrogen and oxygen are virtually the same,
regions containing luminescent neutral oxygen must also contain a great
number of hydrogen atoms. It is quite possible that in such condensations which contain luminescent neutral oxygen, the hydrogen is mainly
neutral. In this connection it would be extraordinarily important to
study the brightness distribution of neutral oxygen in the filaments of the
Crab nebula. The problem of the lines of neutral oxygen is in general
one of the most important questions in the investigation of the physical
conditions in the filaments of the Crab nebula.

Moreover, the following relationships are assumed for the concentra-
tion ratios: $N\,II/\sum N = S\,II/\sum S = O\,II/\sum O$ and $Ne\,III/\sum Ne = O\,III/\sum O$ (where, say, $\sum O$ denotes the concentration of the oxygen atoms
in all states of ionization). Finally, we assume that the concentration of
$O\,I + O\,IV$ is half the concentration of $O\,II + O\,III$. All these assumptions are more or less arbitrary. Only a detailed investigation of the
spectra of individual filaments with all their peculiarities permits a final
elucidation of the very important question as to the chemical composition
of the filaments in the Crab nebula. Until then, for want of something
better, we must be satisfied with Woltier's results. Practical astrophysical
investigations, however, have shown that parts of these rather rough estimates are correct and could be verified in later and more accurate measurements. Table 21 gives the relative abundances of various elements in the
filaments of the Crab nebula, taking all states of ionization into account.

TABLE 21

Element	H	He	N	O	Ne	S
$T_e = 17,000°$	320,000	20,000	109	100	39	27
$= 10,000°$	89,000	40,000	54	100	55	31
$= 8,000°$	37,000	15,000	26	100	76	32
Planetary Nebulae	170,000	32,000	40	100	15	9

In the last line of Table 21 the relative abundances of the most
frequent elements in planetary nebulae are given.[164] We see from Table
21 that the filaments in the Crab nebula do not display any particularly

anomalous chemical composition, unless too low a value has been chosen for T_e. In the case of $T_e = 8,000$ one might speak of a considerable hydrogen deficiency (compared with the planetary nebulae) and of a surplus of neon and sulphur. One gets, however, the impression that the abundance of helium is too high relative to that of hydrogen.

Thus we cannot say with absolute certainty that the chemical composition of the filaments in the Crab nebula is different from the chemical composition of the interstellar medium surrounding this nebula, though such a difference (mainly an anomalously high content of helium) seems rather likely. This problem is closely related to the problem of the origin of the filaments which may be expressed here in the form of a dilemma: do the filaments consist of interstellar gas, compressed by a shock wave, or do they form the shell ejected during the explosion which, therefore, will very likely display an anomalous chemical composition? This dilemma is still waiting for its solution with the help of methods of observational astrophysics.

At the end of the section we shall dwell on the question of the total mass of the gaseous filaments of Crab nebula. This problem was solved by Osterbrock[167] with the help of a "direct" method. From photographs showing the filamentary structure of the nebula, he estimated the total length of all bright filaments and obtained a value of 730″. After a correction for the projection effect (assuming a chaotic spatial orientation of the filaments) he obtained a value of 5.3 psc for the total length of the filaments. The mean visual thickness of the filaments is equal to 1″.4 which corresponds to a linear diameter of $2.5 \cdot 10^{16}$ cm. If the filaments are assumed to be cylindrical, one may find their total volume as equal to $7.8 \cdot 10^{51}$ cm³. With $\bar{N}_e = 10^3$ cm⁻³, on the supposition that in the filaments 1.5 free electrons fall on one heavy positive ion, the mean density is obtained as $\bar{\rho} = 5 \cdot 10^{-21}$ g/cm³ so that a value of $4 \cdot 10^{31}$ g or $0.02 M_\odot$ is obtained for the total mass of the bright filaments.

An estimate of the contribution of the faint filaments can be obtained in the following way: The total length of all faint filaments can be found from an analysis of the best photographs of the Crab nebula, obtained by Baade; the value obtained is equal to $4.2 \cdot 10^{4\prime}$ (± 50 per cent). Most of these faint filaments have an angular thickness $< 1″$, the true linear diameters are unknown. If the true angular thickness of the weak filaments is assumed as 0″.5 on the average, their total volume will be six times the volume of the bright filaments. It is plausible to assume that in all the faint condensations whose intensities are almost a hundred times lower than those of the bright ones, the value of N_e will be six times smaller than in the case of the latter, i.e., $N_e \sim 150 \text{ cm}^{-3}$. Hence follows for the total mass of the whole system of filaments a value which is within the limits of 0.05 and $0.1 M_\odot$. This estimate, which is based exclusively on the results of observations, is in close agreement with the theoretical estimate obtained from an analysis of the acceleration of the entire system of filaments (see § 12).

§ 11 The radio-frequency radiation from the Crab nebula and its interpretation

In 1948, when surveying the southern sky with the help of a "nautical" interferometer, Bolton discovered four new sources of radio emission.[168] One of these radio sources, the brightest in the constellation Taurus, was given the name Taurus A, following the nomenclature which was established at that time. In the next year, 1949, Bolton and Stanley, using the more modern interference technique, succeeded in an improvement of the co-ordinates of these sources, up to an accuracy of $\pm 30''$ in α and $\pm 7'$ in δ.[169] Within these limits of error the co-ordinates of Taurus agreed with those of the Crab nebula.[169] It is interesting to mention that in the same paper two other sources, namely Virgo A and Centaurus A, could be identified with the relatively nearby peculiar galaxies NGC 4486 and NGC 5128. In this way the very first identification of discrete cosmic radio sources with optical objects made it possible to recognize the two basic types of these objects: the radio galaxies and the remnants of supernovae.

The first observations at various frequencies of the metre band were made in 1950. Stanley and Slee could establish an essential difference between the radio spectrum of Taurus and the spectra of other radio sources known at that time.[170] Whereas in the case of the latter the spectral flux density decreases as the frequency increases according to the law $F_\nu \propto \nu^{-\alpha}$ where $\alpha \sim 1$, the spectrum of Taurus A proved to be plane,[170] within the limits of observational error. Later on, however, it could be established also that in the case of this radio source, the spectral flux density decreases with the frequency, but in this case much more slowly.

It is not necessary to discuss in detail all the measurements of the radio flux from the Crab nebula made at various frequencies between 1949 and the present. The most important results of the measurements of the flux from this radio source, in W/m²·c/s, carried out by various authors and at various frequencies, are compiled in Table 22.

Figure 74 shows log F_ν as a function of log ν, plotted after the data listed in Table 22. From this graph it follows that in the frequency range $2 \cdot 10^7 < \nu < 2 \cdot 10^{10}$ the spectral flux density can be represented quite well by the general expression $F \propto \nu^{-d}$ where the spectral index $d = 0.28 \pm 0.05$.

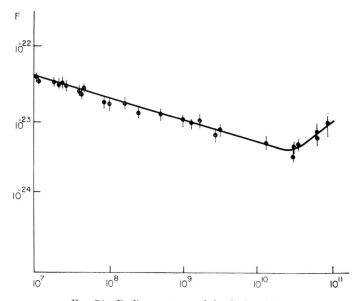

FIG. 74   Radio spectrum of the Crab nebula.

An essential peculiarity of the radio spectrum of the Crab nebula which was recognized only recently is the increase in spectral flux density accompanying an increase in frequency in the millimetre range. The cause of this interesting effect will be explained in the following and also in § 13.

Apart from the spectrum the most important parameter of any cosmic radio source is its angular dimensions. It must, however, be stressed that the latter are a very rough characteristic of the source which, together with the flux measured, gives us an idea of its mean brightness. The brightness, however, can in no way be assumed constant within the limits of the angular dimensions of the sources. The latter must display

TABLE 22

λ m	ν c/s	log F_ν	Reference
24.0	$1.25 \cdot 10^7$	−22.46	[171]
18.0	$1.67 \cdot 10^7$	−22.50	[171]
15.0	$2.0 \cdot 10^7$	−22.57	[171]
13.6	$2.2 \cdot 10^7$	−22.60	[172]
12.5	$2.4 \cdot 10^7$	−22.57	[171]
10.0	$3.0 \cdot 10^7$	−22.64	[171]
8.6	$3.5 \cdot 10^7$	−22.57	[171]
7.9	$3.8 \cdot 10^7$	−22.57	[173]
7.9	$3.8 \cdot 10^7$	−22.61	[174]
7.5	$4.0 \cdot 10^7$	−22.73	[170]

λ cm	ν c/s	log F_ν	Reference
21.0	$1.42 \cdot 10^9$	−23.05	[187]
10.2	$2.93 \cdot 10^9$	−23.17	[188]
9.6	$3.13 \cdot 10^9$	−23.18	[189]
9.6	$3.13 \cdot 10^9$	−23.08	[190]
9.4	$3.2 \cdot 10^9$	−23.06	[191]

λ m	ν c/s	log F_ν	Reference
5.0	$6.0 \cdot 10^7$	−22.73	[170]
3.78	$8.0 \cdot 10^7$	−22.75	[174]
3.50	$8.5 \cdot 10^7$	−22.64	[176]
3.50	$8.5 \cdot 10^7$	−22.73	[170]
3.0	$1.0 \cdot 10^8$	−22.73	[177]
3.0	$1.0 \cdot 10^8$	−22.73	[170]
1.88	$1.6 \cdot 10^8$	−22.73	[170]
1.43	$2.1 \cdot 10^8$	−22.86	[174]
1.20	$2.5 \cdot 10^8$	−22.90	[178]

λ cm	ν c/s	log F_ν	Reference
9.4	$3.2 \cdot 10^9$	−23.06	[192]
3.75	$8.0 \cdot 10^9$	−23.36	[180]
3.2	$9.4 \cdot 10^9$	−23.22	[193]
3.2	$9.4 \cdot 10^9$	−23.19	[190]
3.2	$9.4 \cdot 10^9$	−23.21	[194]
1.8	$1.67 \cdot 10^{10}$	−23.28	[196]
1.2	$2.52 \cdot 10^{10}$	−23.53	[195]

λ cm	ν c/s	log F_z	Reference
75	$4.0 \cdot 10^8$	−22.92	[179]
67	$4.4 \cdot 10^8$	−22.94	[180]
67	$4.4 \cdot 10^8$	−22.88	[181]
60	$5.0 \cdot 10^8$	−22.89	[174]
50	$6.0 \cdot 10^8$	−23.10	[182]
33.3	$9.0 \cdot 10^8$	−23.08	[183]
31	$9.6 \cdot 10^8$	−23.05	[184]
25	$1.2 \cdot 10^9$	−23.07	[180]
21.5	$1.39 \cdot 10^9$	−23.08	[180]
21.5	$1.39 \cdot 10^9$	−23.08	[185]
21	$1.42 \cdot 10^9$	−22.87	[186]

λ mm	ν c/s	log F_z	Reference
8.5	$3.5 \cdot 10^{10}$	−23.34	[197]
8.5	$3.5 \cdot 10^{10}$	−23.38	[198]
8.0	$3.75 \cdot 10^{10}$	−23.30	[199]
4.3	$7.0 \cdot 10^{10}$	−23.13	[200]
4.3	$7.0 \cdot 10^{10}$	−23.17	[198]
3.2	$9.4 \cdot 10^{10}$	−22.97	[198]

a rather complex brightness distribution and a rich "radio-photometrical structure" which is "blurred" owing to the insufficient resolving power of the radio-telescopes.

As already mentioned in § 5, in the ideal case it is the aim of radio-astronomy to obtain "radio-pictures" of the sources. Such an example is shown in Figure 37, the reproduction of a radio-picture of Cassiopeia A. Unfortunately, there does not as yet exist such a radio-picture of the source Taurus A, which has been identified with the Crab nebula; one may, however, expect that such a picture will soon be available. In the present situation we shall analyze all the observations from which we may derive some idea of the angular dimensions and the structure of the Crab nebula in the radio-frequency range. Though the resolving power of these observations was insufficiently high to obtain a radio-picture, they contain very valuable information.

Mills was the first who, in 1952, measured the angular dimensions of Taurus A with the help of a two-aerial interferometer with a variable base ranging from 0.29 to 10.01 km; the observations were made at a frequency of about 100 Mc.[203] With a base length of only 1 km the modulation depth of the interference pattern had already dropped to almost 50 per cent, and with a base length of 5.35 km there was no modulation at all. From these results one could conclude that the radio source's angular dimensions amounted to 4'. At that time these observations were very valuable as one could not *a priori* exclude the possibility that the radio source was not the nebula but a star—an ex-supernova. It was very essential that the angular dimensions of Taurus A proved to be similar to the angular dimensions of the Crab nebula.

Only one year later, in 1953, Mills made the first attempt to determine the rough structure of the brightest cosmic radio sources, among them also Taurus A. The observations were again made at the interferometer with variable base mentioned above; in this case the interferometer base had three different azimuths.[204] These observations showed that the brightness distribution does not display spherical symmetry. The source has a markedly elongated form, with a position angle of the major axis equal to 140°, which is close to the position angle of the major axis of the ellipse described by the filamentary system of Crab nebula (see § 10). Figure 75 shows the rough structure of the source as resulting from Mills' observations. The ellipse represents the isophote on which the brightness is half that in the centre. The axes of this ellipse measure 5'.5 × 3'.5. It is valuable to know that the brightness temperature in the centre of this ellipse amounts to about $4 \cdot 10^6 \,^\circ$K at $\lambda = 3$ m. Figure 75 shows us a photograph of the Crab nebula and, on the same scale and the same orientation, a rough representation of its radio picture, drawn according to Mills' observations.

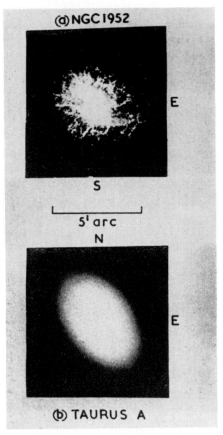

FIG. 75   Upper figure: Photograph of Crab nebula.   Lower figure: Rough radio picture of Taurus A.[204]

In 1954 Baldwin studied the angular dimensions of Taurus A on $\lambda = 1.4$ m; he worked with two interferometers with orthogonal bases of variable length.[205]   Unlike Mills he did not discover any deviation of the brightness distribution from the spherical symmetry.   It must be noted, however, that the accuracy of his observations was somewhat lower than that of Mills' studies. The base was considerably shorter ($\leqslant 300\ \lambda$) and, moreover, the observations were disturbed by a relatively close source which was identified with the nebula IC 443. The angular dimensions of the source (referred to the half-power points) were obtained as equal to $\sim 5'$.

A very effective method of measuring the angular dimensions of the Crab nebula and the brightness distribution in it consists in an observation of the variation of its flux when it is eclipsed by the moon. The Crab nebula is the brightest of the cosmic radio sources (disregarding the sun) which are eclipsed by the moon. The first observations during such an eclipse were made in 1956 by Soviet, English and French radio-astronomers; V. V. Vitkevich and V. A. Udal'tsov observed the eclipse on the 3.5-m wavelength.[206] According to these observations the angular dimensions of the source Taurus A are considerably larger than the angular dimensions of the Crab nebula. The source has the form of an ellipse with the axes $9'.5 \times 7'$ (for the half-power points) and the orientation of this ellipse coincides with the orientation of the nebula. The conclusion as to the large angular dimensions of the source Taurus A could not be verified by subsequent observations of other authors. It thus seems that an error had been made in the observations by the Soviet authors.

In the same year the radio-astronomers Costain and Elsmore (Cambridge) observed an eclipse with the help of interferometers on the wavelengths 3.7 m and 7.9 m.[207] These observations showed that whereas the angular dimensions of Taurus A observed on the shorter wavelength did not exceed the optical dimensions of the nebula, they were considerably larger if observed on $\lambda = 7.9$ m. Figure 76 shows the brightness distribution of the Crab nebula as observed on $\lambda = 3.6$ m (solid lines) and $\lambda = 7.9$ m (dashed lines, corresponding to the two possible interpretations of the results of observations). The upper part of the figure shows a sketch of the Crab nebula on the same scale. Another interesting result obtained from these observations is the absence of noticeable details in the intensity distribution on $\lambda = 3.7$ m. If there existed "patches" measuring $0'.5 \times 0'.5$ and being twice as bright as the central parts they should have been discovered. It must, however, be kept in mind that such observations are connected with great difficulties, particularly at greater wavelengths. The measurements on the 7.9-m wavelength therefore seem to be insufficiently accurate. In the following we shall discuss analogous observations made at the same frequency, which were carried out recently.

According to observations of an eclipse of the Crab nebula by the moon, carried out in the same year by Tuominen and Karras[208] on the 3.7-m wavelength, its angular dimensions are 3'.6 referred to the half-power points; the outermost limits of the radio-emitting region may be recorded up to 16'. The accuracy of these observations, particularly at the periphery of the nebula, was, however, low. Boischot and co-workers observed the

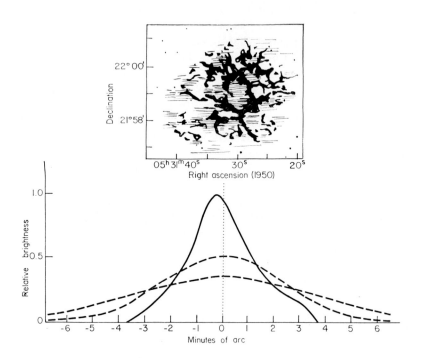

Fig. 76   Brightness distribution in the Crab nebula at λ 3.6 m and 7.9 m. Upper inset: Drawing of Crab nebula.

same eclipse at λ = 1.4 m with relatively high accuracy. According to these observations, 98 per cent of the flux comes from the region containing the optical nebula. The centre of gravity of the radio-emitting region is shifted by 25" from the geometrical centre of the Crab nebula, determined as the middle of the straight line connecting the two central stars. A somewhat larger displacement of the centre of gravity in the same direction was observed by Baldwin and also by Costain and co-workers (see Fig. 76).   The zone of the radio-emitting region which contains the centre of gravity also contains the brightest part of the amorphous mass of the Crab nebula (see Fig. 64).   French investigators were the first to find indications as to the presence of a large-scale structure of the Crab nebula in radio-waves.   Along the major axis of the nebula they discovered the presence of three relatively bright local formations.

Exceedingly interesting results were obtained from observations of several eclipses of the Crab nebula by the moon which occurred in 1964. In Cambridge, during the eclipse of April 16th of that year the radio-astronomers made their observations at the frequencies 408, 178, 81.5 and 26.5 Mc.[209]   Figure 77 shows us a schematic representation of the

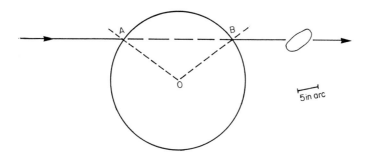

FIG. 77   Trajectory of moon relative to Crab nebula.[209]

moon's trajectory over the Crab nebula during this eclipse.   These observations were made with the help of interferometers of various types and sizes.   In Figure 78 we see the "curves of eclipse" as obtained at various frequencies by the radio-astronomers at Cambridge.   An analysis of these curves made it possible to obtain the one-dimensional brightness distribution projected onto the two directions OX and OY (see Fig. 79). Each point in this one-dimensional distribution is proportional to the radio flux from a slightly curved band, 11″ in width, intersecting the nebula in either the direction OX or the direction OY.   The one-dimensional distribution in the OX direction is obtained from an analysis of the "curve of eclipse" between the first and the second "immersion" contacts and in the OY direction from between the third and fourth contacts ("emmersion").

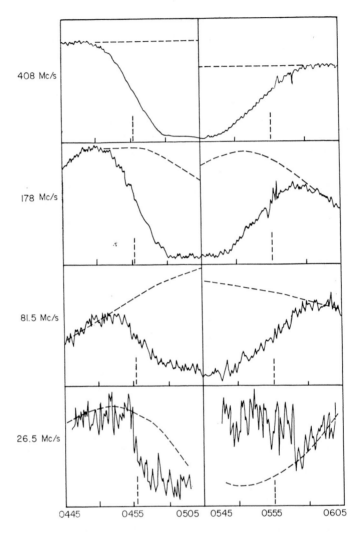

FIG. 78   Curve of eclipse of Crab nebula by the moon at various frequencies.[209]

Figure 80 again shows one-dimensional distributions along the above
directions obtained at various frequencies.   From these curves we may
see that in the OX direction ("immersion") the one-dimensional brightness distributions obtained at the frequencies 408 and 178 Mc are identical,

whereas at a frequency of 81.5 Mc this distribution displays a large concentration near the centre of the nebula.   The distribution at a frequency
of 26.5 Mc clearly indicates the presence of a source of relatively small
angular dimensions whose radio emission is superimposed on the radiation
from the more extended source.   This can be seen particularly well from
the one-dimensional distribution in the OY direction ("immersion").
Whereas the three higher frequencies show a noticeably "depressed"
distribution, the distribution obtained at the frequency 26.5 Mc possesses
a marked "peak" displaced to the south-east from the centre of the

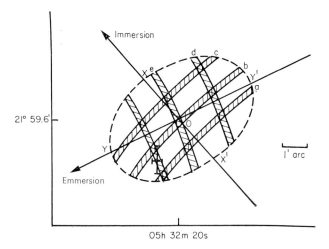

FIG. 79   Linear brightness distribution in Crab nebula.[209]

nebula and indicating the presence of a source of relatively small angular
dimensions at this place.   Combining the two one-dimensional distributions obtained in "immersion" and "emmersion" one may draw the
conclusion that this source is located at a distance of 1.2″ south-east of the
centre of the nebula.   In Figure 79 the position of the source is marked by
a cross near the intersection of the filaments *b* and *e*.   The presence of this
source may also be derived from the distributions obtained at higher
frequencies in "emmersion."   It is clearly seen that the centre of gravity
of the distribution is displaced eastwardly, the lower the frequency, the
bigger the displacement.   The displacement occurs in the direction of

The Crab nebula

the source of small angular dimensions, observed at a frequency of 26.5 Mc.

Possibly the most important result of the observations described above was that the Cambridge radio-astronomers discovered this relatively powerful radio source in Crab nebula, whose angular dimensions were smaller than 20″ or at least ten times smaller than the angular dimensions of Crab nebula itself. At a frequency of 26.5 Mc this small source yields 30–50 per cent of the total radio emission from the Crab nebula. Hence

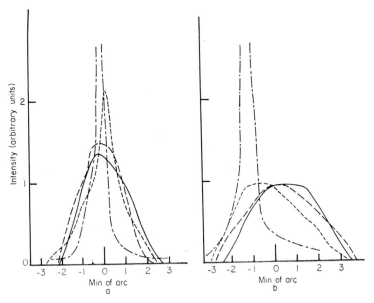

FIG. 80   Linear brightness distributions in the Crab nebula at various frequencies.[209]

it follows that its brightness temperature at this frequency is of the order of 10^9 °K, i.e., extraordinarily high.

The existence of a source of small angular dimensions in the Crab nebula was also indicated by independent interference observations by Hewish and Okoye, made at a frequency of 38 Mc.[210] Figure 81 shows the base-length dependence of the modulation depth observed. We see that with base lengths of from 1,000 λ to 1,500 λ the modulation of the signal does not disappear. This indicates the presence of a radio source in the Crab nebula whose angular dimensions are so small that they cannot be resolved by the interferometer. From these observations one may draw the conclusion that the source Taurus A consists of two components. The first component, which is relatively extended and has in its east–west direction the angular dimensions $3'.7 \pm 0'.5$, referred to the half-power points, the second component has the dimensions $\sim 30'' \pm 15''$. The ratio of the fluxes from the two sources is $4:1$. The dashed curve in Figure 81 shows on the same scale the results of interference observations

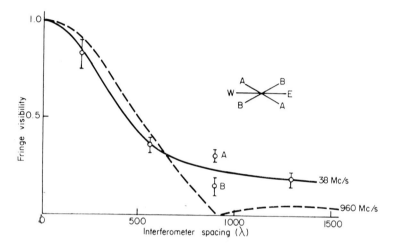

Fig. 81   Results of observation of the Crab nebula at a frequency of 38 Mc by means of an interferometer with variable spacing.[210]

by Maltby and Moffet which were carried out in California at the high frequency of 960 Mc.[184]   It follows from these observations that with an interferometer base equal to 900 λ the modulation depth decreased to zero.   Therefore, at this frequency, the Crab nebula does not contain any sources of small angular dimensions. The interferometrical observations made at Cambridge at a frequency of 408 Mc and with a base of up to 1,450 λ permit the conclusion that there must exist a source of very small angular dimensions in Crab nebula, which, at this frequency, yields about 2 per cent of the total flux.

Combining all the observations described above we may now build up the spectrum of the local source of small angular dimensions located in the Crab nebula (see Fig. 82). Up to a frequency of 408 Mc the spectrum of the small source drops steeply as the frequency increases. The spectral index in this range is $\alpha = 1.2$.

Figure 83 shows the spectra of the radio emission from the Crab nebula for six of its filaments (see Fig. 80), obtained in "immersion" and "emmersion." The dashed line in the upper part of the drawings represents the integral spectrum of the Crab nebula discussed above ($\alpha = 0.28$).

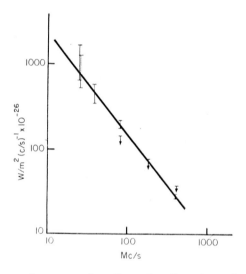

Fig. 82   Spectrum of a source of small angular dimensions, situated in the Crab nebula.[209]

The spectra of the filaments are relatively similar, with the exception of the filaments b and f at whose point of intersection the source of small angular dimensions is located, which possesses a spectrum that differs essentially from the integral spectrum. A really noteworthy peculiarity of these spectra is the "heap" of flux beginning at a frequency < 50 Mc.

New and important information on the nature of the source of small angular dimensions in the Crab nebula, possessing the steep spectrum, was obtained by systematic interference observations at a frequency of

38 Mc, carried out in 1963–64 at Cambridge.[211]   During these observations rapid oscillations of the flux could be discovered: "scintillations" of the radio flux from the Crab nebula.   Since the base of the interferometer was 10 km, only sources of sufficiently small angular dimensions could be recorded.   In order to exclude a possible influence of factors due to the

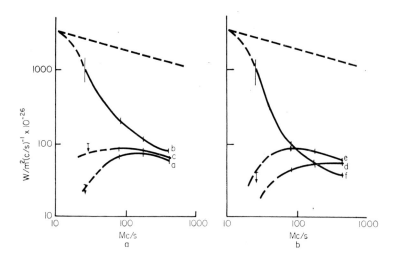

Fig. 83   Spectrum of various parts of the Crab nebula.[209]

apparatus, parallel observations were made of a relatively nearby source of likewise small angular dimensions, 3C 123, for the purpose of comparison.   In Figure 84 the radio-flux records from the Crab nebula are compared with those from 3C 123.   These records show that, unlike the Crab nebula, the source 3C 123 does not display an observable scintillation of the flux.

The fluctuations of the radio flux possess a characteristic period of about two seconds.   Their amplitude has an annual periodicity (see Fig. 85).   This figure shows the intensity variations of the fluctuations for various months, each point being the result of an averaging over a week. The strongest fluctuations of the flux can be observed in April and August. They vanish completely between the end of May and the beginning of July.   It is well known that on June 15th the solar corona projects itself

9+s.

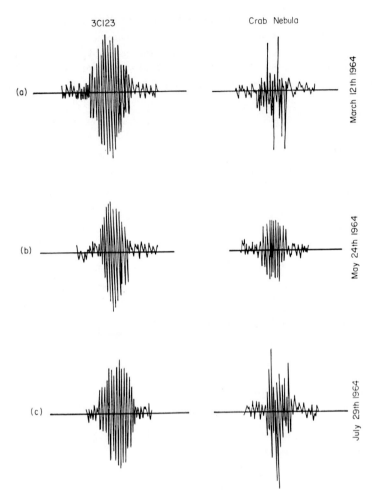

FIG. 84   Scintillations of the radio-frequency radiation flux from the Crab nebula and from 3C 123 at a frequency of 38 Mc.[211]

on the Crab nebula. It is therefore quite evident that the absence of flux fluctuations in this period must be connected with the covering of the Crab nebula by the solar corona.

It is also well known that these fluctuations are caused by a scattering of the radio emission from travelling inhomogeneities of electron concentration in the direction of propagation of this radiation. It can be shown that these inhomogeneities are not of ionospheric origin. The scintillations are caused by non-uniformities of the interplanetary plasma. Scintillations will be observed if the angular dimensions of the radio source are smaller than $v\tau/r$ where $v = 3 \cdot 10^6$ cm/s is the velocity at which the inhomogeneities in electron concentration move, $\tau \sim 2$ s is the characteristic time of scintillation and $r \sim 10^{13}$ cm is the effective distance of the inhomogeneities in an interplanetary medium. Hence follows a quite astonishing result: the angular dimensions of a source of low-frequency

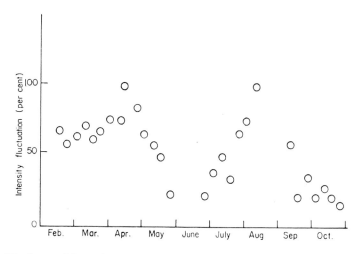

Fig. 85   Seasonal dependence of the radio flux scintillation amplitude at a frequency of 38 Mc, for the Crab nebula.[210a]

radio-waves, located in the Crab nebula, can in any case not exceed 0″.1! Consequently its linear dimensions will not be larger than 10^{-3} psc. Since, according to [210], the flux at a frequency of 38 Mc from a small source amounts to about 20 per cent from the total flux (see above), the brightness temperature of such a source will be higher than 10^{14} °K, i.e., extraordinarily high. In what follows we shall discuss the nature of this remarkable detail of the Crab nebula, which, at present, is still far from elucidated.

Now we shall consider the fundamental results of investigations of the intensity distribution of radio emission from the Crab nebula at higher frequencies.   At 8 mm the first brightness distribution studies were carried out by A. D. Kuz'min and A. Ye. Solomonovich with the 22-m precision reflector of the Physical Institute of the Academy of Sciences.[199]   The radiation pattern of the aerial was 2′ which permitted a rough estimate of the angular dimensions of the nebula.   On the condition that the brightness distribution is Gaussian, the Soviet researchers obtained a value of $4'.5 \pm 1'$ for the angular dimensions of Taurus A (referred to the half-power points) at this frequency; the centre of gravity of the source was found to be displaced by almost one minute of arc relative to the optical centre, in a westerly direction.

Barrett, who made his observations at $\lambda = 1.8$ cm with a radio-telescope whose radiation pattern was 3′, obtained a value of $4'.1 \times 3'.4$ with an error of $0'.5$ for the two co-ordinates α and δ of the angular dimensions of the Crab nebula, under the same suppositions as the authors of the papers described above.

Important investigations of the brightness distributions were also made at the wavelengths 3.2, 6.5, 8.7 and 9.4 cm, by radio-astronomers at Pulkovo who, for these studies, used their well-known aerial with the "knife" radiation pattern.[212,213,214]   The width of this diagram in right ascension was equal to 1′, 2′ and 2′.9 at the wavelengths 3.2, 6.5 and 8.5 cm, respectively; i.e., it was small enough.   The most important result of these observations is the conclusion that the boundaries of the radio source do not exceed the limits of the optical nebula and are relatively sharp.   Referred to the intensity level of ~ 5 per cent of the central part, the angular dimensions of Taurus A are equal to $5'.5$, the source being inside the system of filaments.   The brightness distributions on the wavelengths 3.2 cm and 8.7 cm are almost Gaussian; to the east, however, the intensity decreases more rapidly with distance to the centre of the nebula.   The angular dimensions of the source (relative to the half-power points) at $\lambda = 3.2$, 6.5 and 8.7 cm, amount to about $3'.5$ with a probable error of $0'.2$.   Just as the other observers, the radio-astronomers of Pulkovo could ascertain a westward shift of the centre of gravity of the radio-emitting zone of about 30″.

Observations on the 9.1-cm wavelength were made by Californian radio-astronomers with the help of radio-telescopes with knife-shaped radiation patterns, $2'.3$ in width.[215]   From these observations it could be concluded that at this frequency the Crab nebula has the form of an ellipse with axes of $4'.3 \times 2'.7$, with an angle of position of the major axis of about 150°, which is rather close to the direction previously observed by Mills for the metre band. In α and δ the angular dimensions are 3'.25 and 3'.9, respectively. Repeated measurements with a narrower radiation pattern (1' in width) made it possible to obtain the brightness distribution of the source with respect to the right ascension. A striking feature of this distribution is its asymmetry. The angular dimensions of the source referred to in the half-power points are close to 3'.2.

The brightness distribution was investigated quite often in the 21-cm band. So, for example, Lequeux studied the brightness distribution in the Crab nebula with the help of an interferometer with variable base and azimuth.[94] It could be verified that at this frequency too the nebula

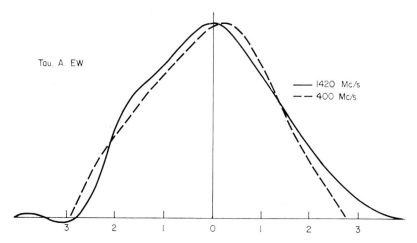

FIG. 86   Brightness distribution in the Crab nebula at a wavelength of 21 cm and 75 cm.[194]

shows the form of an ellipse with axes of 3'.9 × 2'.7 (referred to in the half-power points) and the angle of position is almost the same as with the optical system of filaments. The radio emission is localized in a zone with the angular dimensions 6' ± 0'.5, i.e., it coincides with the zone of optical emission. The intensity distribution of radio emission from the Crab nebula in the 21-cm band obtained in the observations described above is shown in Figure 86. We see from this figure that the brightness distribution of the Crab nebula at this wavelength is steeper than in the optical range. It may also be concluded from Figure 86 that in the radio picture of the nebula its western part is the brighter one.

Analogous investigations were carried out at the same frequency by Labrum and co-workers[216] who also worked with an interferometer (width of "knife" pattern 1'.5). Labrum's results are represented in Figure 87 together with the brightness distribution in the optical range. One sees clearly the displacement of the centre of gravity of the radio-emitting region to the west by about 50", relative to the optical centre. The angular dimensions of the source, referred to half the central brightness, are 3'.6 ± 0'.05; the eastern boundary of the source possesses sharper contours.

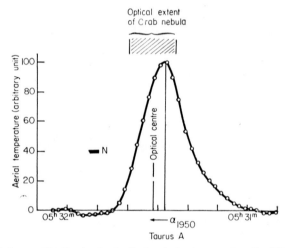

FIG. 87   Brightness distribution in the Crab nebula at a wavelength of 21 cm obtained by a radio-telescope with "knife" radiation pattern.[216]

The intensity distribution in the Crab nebula was also investigated at the California Institute of Technology, by means of an interferometer of variable base, operating at $\lambda = 31.3$ cm.[184]   The brightness distribution in an east–west direction was almost Gaussian and the source has the angular dimensions 3'.7 ± 0'.4 (for the half-power points).

At almost the same wavelength (33 cm) Boischot studied the brightness distribution of the Crab nebula during its eclipse by the moon in 1956.[183]   He also discovered a displacement of the centre of gravity of the radio-emitting region, relative to the optical centre, by 50" ± 15" in a north-westerly direction.

In the same year Seeger and Westerhout observed the eclipse of the Crab nebula by the moon, at a wavelength of 75 cm.[179]   In these observations it could be established that the boundaries of the radio source are almost coincident with the boundaries of the optical nebula and lie within the dashed contour in Figure 86.   At the same time the brightness distribution in radio-frequency radiation is "more planar" than in optical radiation.   Consequently, the intensity ratio between radio-frequency and optical radiations increases towards the periphery of the nebula.

Let us sum up the main results of the radio-astronomical observations:

1. The region in which the radio-frequency radiation is located is almost coincident with the optical boundaries of the nebula and lies within the shell formed by the system of gaseous filaments.

2. The angular dimensions of the nebula in the map plane may be represented in the form of an ellipse with the axes $3'.5 \times 2'.5$ (referred to in the half-power points); the angle of position of the major axis is similar to the angle of position of the major axis of the optical ellipse formed by the system of isophotes (see § 1).

3. The radio-brightness distribution is "more planar" than the optical brightness.

4. The centre of gravity of the radio-emitting zone in the centimetre and decimetre bands is displaced relative to the geometrical centre of the nebula (i.e., the point in the middle of the straight line connecting the two central stars) by about $50''$.   In this area we also find the brightest part of the amorphous mass of the nebula (see Fig. 64).

5. A source of very small angular dimensions (maybe $< 0''.1$) with a very steep spectrum has been discovered in the metre band.   Owing to the presence of this source the centre of gravity of the nebula in the metre band is shifted systematically in a south-easterly direction.

6. We are not justified in assuming that the angular dimensions of the Crab nebula in the metre band are notably different from the angular dimensions in the decimetre and centimetre bands.

Let us consider now the problem of the nature of the radio-frequency radiation from the Crab nebula.   In 1953 the author of the present book suggested a well-founded theory of the synchrotron nature of the radio emission of this nebula which was soon generally accepted.[217]   We shall repeat here the corresponding calculations on the basis of the most recent data of observation.   We shall use the fundamental formula (6.7).   Since the spectral index of the radio emission from the Crab nebula is close to

0.3, the exponent in the differential energy spectrum of relativistic electrons is $\gamma \approx 1.6$. Consequently, the non-dimensional parameter $U(\gamma) = 0.16$. The effective angular dimensions of the radio source in the Crab nebula are given by $\varphi = 3'.5$. We see from Figure 74 that the spectral flux density at the frequency $\nu = 10^9$ c/s is $F_\nu = 10^{-23}$ W/m²·c/s = 10^{-20} erg/cm²·s·c/s. For the distance to the nebula we assume a value of $r = 1{,}130$ psc. The extension of the nebula in the direction of observation will then be equal to about 1 psc or $3 \cdot 10^{18}$ cm. The solid angle at which the Crab nebula is seen is given by $\Omega = 6 \cdot 10^{-7}$ steradian; hence follows a value of $\bar{I}_\nu = F_\nu / \Omega = 1.5 \cdot 10^{-14}$ erg/cm²·s·steradian for the visual mean intensity. Let us further assume that $H_\perp = 7.5 \cdot 10^{-4}$ Oe; the choice of this value for the magnetic field is not unfounded as we shall see in the following section. Substituting all these values in Equation (6.7), the following is obtained for the parameter of the energy spectrum of the relativistic electrons which are responsible for the radio emission of the nebula:

$$K = 9.6 \cdot 10^{-9} \qquad (11.1)$$

The energy density of these relativistic electrons is determined by the expression

$$W_{\text{rel.el.}} = \int_{E_1}^{E_2} KE^{-(\gamma-1)}dE = 2.5K\{E_2^{0.4} - E_1^{0.4}\} \qquad (11.2)$$

where E_2 and E_1 are the maximum and minimum values of the energies of the relativistic electrons possessing a spectrum with $\gamma = 1.6$. It follows from Figure 74 that the spectrum of the form $F_\nu \propto \nu^{-0.3}$ ranges up to $\nu \sim 3 \cdot 10^{10}$ c/s. With $H_\perp = 7 \cdot 10^{-4}$ Oe, a value of E_2 determined by the relation

$$\nu_2 \sim \frac{eH_\perp}{2\pi mc}\left(\frac{E_2}{mc^2}\right)^2 \qquad (11.3)$$

corresponds to this value of ν; numerically we obtain $E_2 = 1.5 \cdot 10^9$ eV = $2.4 \cdot 10^{-3}$ erg, $E_2^{0.4} \sim 0.1$. For our calculations this value is not important.

In this way we find that $W_{\text{rel.el.}} \simeq 2.4 \cdot 10^{-9}$ erg/cm³. Note that the mean magnetic energy density W_m, with $H_\perp \sim 7.5 \cdot 10^{-4}$ Oe, will be equal to about $3.3 \cdot 10^{-8}$ erg/cm³; i.e., it is almost fourteen times higher than $W_{\text{rel.el.}}$. This important problem will be discussed in § 13, after the discussion of the synchrotron emission from the Crab nebula in the entire frequency range.

As the radio-frequency radiation from the Crab nebula is of synchrotron nature it may be expected that it is linearly polarized. First attempts made to discover the polarization of this source in the decimetre band did not yield positive results.[218] Westerhout, who tried to detect the linear polarization on a wavelength of 22 cm, did not obtain a measurable effect.

We must, however, bear in mind that mechanisms may be effective in the source which depolarize the radio emission. In the first place such a mechanism will consist of a Faraday rotation of the plane of polarization (see § 6, Equation (6.14)). Since this effect has its greatest influence at relatively low frequencies, it may explain the negative results of the first attempts, described above, which were made to discover the polarization of the radio-frequency radiation from Crab nebula. At that time (in 1956) one had already discovered the polarization of the integral optical radiation from the Crab nebula which, as will be shown in the following section, is of synchrotron nature. For the optical radiation the frequencies are high enough so that depolarization due to Faraday rotation is inessential. We may hope that at higher radio frequencies the depolarizing mechanisms will not be effective any longer, so that the degree of polarization of the radio flux from the Crab nebula will be almost the same as that measured in the optical frequency range.[103]

And, in fact, even the first polarization observations at relatively high frequencies led to the discovery of a linear polarization of the radio flux from this source, so that the synchrotron nature of this radiation was verified. In 1957 Mayer, McCullough and Sloanaker discovered the linear polarization of the radio-frequency radiation from the Crab nebula on the 3.15-cm wavelength, with the help of the 16-m. precision radio-telescope of the Marine Laboratory in Washington.[219] The degree of polarization was found to be relatively high, about 7 per cent. The angle of position of the electrical vector was 149°, which was 11° different from the analogous angle of position for the optical polarization (see the following section).

Soon after the observations described above, in 1959, A. D. Kuz'min and V. A. Udal'tsov discovered a linear polarization of the radio-frequency radiation from the Crab nebula on the 10-cm wave, with the help of the stationary 30-m reflector of the Lebedev Institute of Physics in the Crimea. The degree of polarization of this radiation was obtained as 3.5 per cent and the angle of position of the electrical vector was found to be 142° ± 9°.[220]

9*

In the subsequent years a great many observations were made of the radio-frequency radiation from the Crab nebula. In this connection we should like to mention the observations by Hollinger, Mayer and Mennella (Marine Laboratory, Washington), who, in 1963, studied the linear

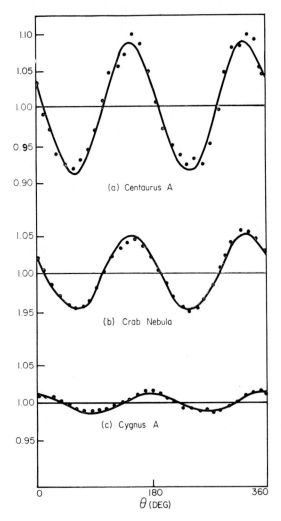

Fig. 88 Dependence of radio flux from the Crab nebula on the angle of position of the electrical vector of the aerial.[221]

polarization of the radio-waves from the Crab nebula on wavelengths of
5.31 and 5.56 cm.[221]   For these wavelengths the degrees of polarization
and the angles of position are equal to 5.4 per cent $\pm$ 0.3, 140° $\pm$ 2° and
5.1 per cent $\pm$ 0.3, 141° $\pm$ 2°, respectively.   The graph of Figure 88
demonstrates the presence of a linear polarization of the radio-frequency
radiation from Crab nebula on the 5.56-cm wavelength.   The ordinate
gives the radio flux measured in arbitrary units, the abscissa the angle
of position of the electric vector of the aerial used in these observations.
The dots correspond to the results of observations averaged over thirty-
three full rotations of the aerial.

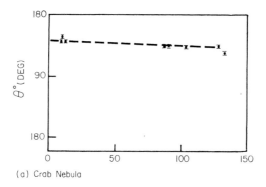

(a) Crab Nebula

Fɪɢ. 89   Angle of position of the electrical vector as a function of the wavelength squared.[222]

Observations of the polarization of radio-frequency radiation from
Crab nebula made by Morris and Radhakrishnan,[222] in 1963, on the
relatively long wavelength of 21 cm, are very valuable for the problem
considered.   As indicated above, the first observations by Westerhout did
not yield any positive results for this frequency range, so that one may
conclude that the degree of polarization must be insignificant.   More
accurate observations made in 1963 permitted the establishment of a
degree of polarization of 1.5 $\pm$ 0.2 per cent and a position angle of the
electrical vector of 92° $\pm$ 4° for the radio emission from Crab nebula at a
frequency of 1,390 Mc.
    The great differences of the angles of position of the electrical vector
at various frequencies are explained by the Faraday rotation in the
interstellar medium through which the radio-waves are propagated.   This

is illustrated by the graph of Figure 89 which shows this angle of position as a function of the wavelength squared, plotted according to the published observations at various frequencies. We see from this drawing that the points which correspond to the various observations lie in a straight line. The slope of this straight line enables us to determine the "measure of rotation" of the interstellar medium between the Crab nebula and the sun, extrapolated to very high frequencies (where the Faraday rotation is inessential). The value of the angle of position was found to be equal to 148° ± 1°. It should be mentioned that, unlike the "differential" Faraday rotation described above and caused by the magnetized plasma present inside the radio source, the Faraday rotation in the interstellar medium does not cause depolarization.†

It must be expected that the degree of polarization of the radio-frequency radiation emitted from the various zones of the Crab nebula is different. The Pulkovo radio-astronomers N. S. Soboleva, V. A. Prozorov and Yu. N. Pariyski,[223] were the first to investigate the distribution of the polarized radio-frequency radiation over the source. The observations were made in Pulkovo using an aerial with a "knife" radiation pattern of $1' \times 6'.5$ and $2'.9 \times 18'$ at the wavelengths 3.2 cm and 8.7 cm, respectively. These observations showed that the zone with a considerable linear polarization is much smaller than the source. The angular dimensions of the source of polarized radiation (referred to in the half-power points) are 2.2 ± 0.2. The highest degree of polarization on the 3.2-cm wavelength proved to be 11.5 per cent. Since the surrounding areas of the nebula emit virtually no polarized radiation and the observations were made in the "knife" pattern, the degree of polarization in the central zone, which is $2'.2$ in diameter, must be 1.5 times higher and reach 17 per cent. If the resolving power of the radio-telescope had been higher, the individual details in the central part would have shown a higher degree of polarization, just as is observed in the optical frequency range (see the following section). According to the observations in Pulkovo the centre of gravity of the polarized radio-frequency radiation is shifted eastwards by $30''$ relative to the centre of gravity of the non-polarized radio-frequency radiation. The integral degree of polarization at $\lambda = 3.20$ cm is equal to 7.6 per cent; this value is similar to the result of American observations made at a wavelength of 3.15 cm (see above).

---

† This is valid if the width of the receiver pass band is not very large. Otherwise the differential rotation up to the various frequencies at the pass band limits may cause depolarization.

The results described above of investigations by the radio-astronomers in Pulkovo were fully verified by the paper of Morris and co-workers,[224] who studied the intensity distribution of the polarized radiation at $\lambda = 10.6$ cm from the Crab nebula. The angular dimensions of the zone emitting polarized radiation of this wavelength was $1'.9$ (for the half-power points); this is only half as large as the zone emitting non-polarized radiation.

When we turn to the theoretical interpretation of the results of polarization observations of the Crab nebula, we have to pay attention to the serious difficulties arising in this case. Although the fact of a linear polarization of the radio-frequency radiation is an obvious proof of its synchrotron nature it is so far impossible to explain the wavelength dependence of the degree of polarization observed.

It follows from the observations that the depolarization of the radio-frequency radiation with increasing wavelengths does not occur during their propagation in the interstellar medium but in the source itself. The natural assumption that depolarization is caused by a differential Faraday rotation in the nebula meets with great difficulties. Since the degree of polarization of the radio flux at a wavelength of ~ 5 cm is known to be lower than at a wavelength of 3.2 cm (see above), we must, in order to explain the depolarization by a Faraday rotation, assume that the angle of this rotation is $\Psi \sim 1$ for $\lambda \sim 5$ cm. This requires a value of $N_e \sim 1$–2 cm^{-3} which does not contradict the observations. It is, however, difficult then to explain why the degree of polarization drops relatively slowly with the wavelength. With $\lambda = 21$ cm, $\Psi \propto \lambda^2$ must be ~ 20 and the degree of polarization to be expected must be considerably lower than the 1.5 per cent observed. But the most serious objections against an explanation of the observed depolarization by differential Faraday rotation is that the angle Φ of position of the electrical vector is not wavelength dependent. The observed dependence of Φ on λ can be explained completely by the rotation of the plane of polarization of the radio-frequency radiation from Crab nebula in the magneto-active interstellar medium (see Fig. 89). The angle of position of the electric vector of the radio emission from Crab nebula in the case of zero interstellar Faraday rotation, Φ_0, proves to be equal to $148° \pm 2°$ for all wavelengths from 3 to 21 cm, which differs by only $\sim 10°$ from the angle of position of this vector in the optical polarized synchrotron radiation (see the following section). It can be shown that if the differential Faraday rotation in the nebula were stronger, one could not observe a regular dependence of Φ on λ as the angle Φ would then be a rapidly oscillating function of λ.

Recently V. I. Slysh developed a very radical hypothesis on a new explanation of the observed decrease in the degree of polarization of the radio-frequency radiation from the Crab nebula which accompanies the increase in wavelength. This hypothesis will be discussed at the end of § 13 after a general discussion of the synchrotron radiation of the Crab nebula.

We shall now pass over to a consideration of the very complex and at present not yet solved problem of interpreting the source of low-frequency radio emission of very small angular dimensions whose existence follows from observations during an eclipse of the Crab nebula by the moon, and from the flux scintillations observed at a frequency of 38 Mc (see above). First of all it is difficult to understand why this source, whose linear dimensions are so small ($< 10^{15}$ cm), is not located in the centre of the nebula where one might expect a singularity, connected with the peculiar object that exists there, the ex-supernova. The observed position of the small source in the region of the very bright filament of the Crab nebula is not understood either.

For example, we cannot assume that the low-frequency radio source is located inside the filament where $N_e \sim 10^3$ cm^{-3} and $T_e \sim 17{,}000\,^{\circ}$K (see § 10), since this filament will display an optical thickness equal to ~ 10 for a frequency of 26 Mc.

Since the brightness temperature at the frequency 38 Mc is $T_b > 10^{14}\,^{\circ}$K, this radiation cannot be considered as produced in a synchrotron mechanism. In fact, it follows from thermodynamic considerations that the brightness temperature cannot exceed the "temperature" of the gas consisting of the emitting relativistic electrons. Hence we see that if this radiation were of synchrotron origin, the mean energy of the relativistic electrons would be $> 10^{10}$ eV. Relativistic electrons of such a high energy, however, would need a field of $H_{\perp} \sim 10^{-8}$ Oe to be able to emit in the band of ~ 10 m; this value of the field strength is 10,000 times lower than in the nebula, which can hardly be admitted. It should be mentioned that analogous difficulties arose recently in radio-astronomy when investigating the quasi-stellar sources, in connection with the variability of their radio fluxes.

In § 14 we shall return to a discussion of the nature of this small low-frequency radio source in the Crab nebula.

The problem of a possible secular decrease in radio flux from the

Crab nebula is also of great interest. We know that an analogous effect was predicted theoretically for Cassiopeia A (see § 7) and this effect could be observed later on. In 1962 Mayer and other radio-astronomers repeated their measurements of the radio fluxes from several bright sources, among them also Taurus A, which had been made for the first time in 1953 with the 16-m precision radio-telescope of the Marine Laboratory in Washington.[119] The observation wavelength was 9.4 cm. They verified the secular decrease of the flux from Cassiopeia A which has been discussed already in § 6. The source M 17, the Orion nebula, Centaurus A and Virgo A do not display any variations of flux within the limits of error of observation. Taurus A (the Crab nebula), however, has obviously reduced its flux within nine years. If we denote by F_1 the flux value measured in 1953 and by F_2 that measured in 1962, we have, according to the American measurements, $2(F_1 - F_2)/(F_1 + F_2) = 0.047 \pm 0.038$, which corresponds to a mean annual reduction of flux of ~ 0.5 per cent. On the basis of the simple theory developed in § 6 the annual flux decrement to be expected is given by $\Delta F/F = 2(2\alpha + 1)/T$, where $\alpha \sim 0.3$ is the spectral index of the expanding source and $T \sim 900$ years is its age. It follows from this formula that for the Crab nebula the mean flux decrement must amount to ~ 0.3 per cent per year. This holds true on the supposition that this change in flux is caused solely by the adiabatic expansion in a constant magnetic flux and without any continuous injection of new relativistic particles. The last two conditions are, however, not satisfied in the case of the Crab nebula (see § 13).

If we assume that injection occurs at a constant rate throughout the time of existence of the nebula it is easy to show that the theoretical change in radio flux (on the assumption that the magnetic field decreases as R^{-2}, see § 6) will be half as high. In the case of the Crab nebula we will thus obtain a value of 0.15 per cent per year, and this is too small to be measured at present. There is yet another fact which complicates our theory, namely the possibility of a considerable deviation of the law governing the time dependence of H from $H \sim t^{-2}$. This law is based on the assumption of a constant magnetic flux. So far, however, the problem of the origin of the magnetic field in the Crab nebula has not found its final solution. We may assume with good reason that a field which, in some way, is permanently "generated" by a possible ex-supernova, may have maintained its activity up to now (see § 19). If this is the case the magnetic field will lose its intensity, as the nebula expands, much more slowly than according to the t^{-2} law. Under certain conditions the simultaneous effects of injection of relativistic particles and a "generation" of the magnetic field might result in a secular increase in power of the radio emission from Crab nebula, at least at some stage of its evolution. In any case the theoretically expected secular decrease in radio flux from the Crab nebula must be at least half as high as in the simple case of an adiabatic expansion considered in § 6.   The results of the American researchers discussed above, however, seem to indicate a secular decrease in flux which is three times higher than the highest possible value resulting from the theory.   Nevertheless, it must be borne in mind that such subtle observations are connected with great difficulties.   Since the inevitable errors of these observations are very high, the problem of the secular variation of the radio flux from the Crab nebula must still be regarded as unsolved.

§ 12   The optical emission from the Crab nebula possessing a continuous spectrum

On the basis of an analysis of photographs of the Crab nebula which were taken through different light filters, Baade divided the Crab nebula into two parts: the system of thin filaments arranged in the form of a shell surrounding the central part of the nebula, and the so-called "amorphous mass" distributed over its entire volume.   Whereas the emission of the gaseous filaments is concentrated in individual forbidden and allowed lines and, as to its spectral composition, does not differ from the emission of other nebulae that were produced as a result of supernova explosions (e.g., the filamentary nebulae in Cygnus), the emission of the "amorphous mass," whose power is thirty times higher than the emissivity of the filaments, has a purely continuous spectrum.   An analysis of the emission of this amorphous mass will, as we shall show in this section, finally give rise to a radical change of all our ideas on the nature of the Crab nebula and confront modern astrophysics with completely new and, moreover, important phenomena.

The first serious investigation of the continuous spectrum from Crab nebula was carried out in 1941 by Minkowski.[162]   A relatively rough photometrical comparison of the continuous spectrum from Crab nebula with the spectra of stars of various classes enabled him to obtain the spectral intensity distribution for this amorphous mass.   According to [162], the energy distribution between λ 4,000 and λ 5,000 resembles that of the spectral class F7, whereas the energy distribution between λ 5,500 and $\lambda\,6,500$ corresponds to $\alpha < 0$.   Assuming a value of 0.15 for the photo-electric coefficient of interstellar reddening of light, Minkowski obtained a colour of the amorphous mass, corrected for interstellar absorption, which corresponded to the spectral class F0.   On the assumption that interstellar absorption varies according to the law $1/\lambda$, and that the intensity distribution of the stellar reference spectra corresponds to that of an absolutely black body, it was found in [162] that, corrected for interstellar absorption, the colour between $\lambda\,5,500$ and $\lambda\,6,500$ corresponds to the spectral class G0.   The following absolute spectro-photometrical gradients in the Greenwich system were obtained for the continuous spectrum of the Crab nebula: $\Phi = 1.75$ for $\lambda = 0.45$ μ and $\Phi = 2.2$ for $\lambda = 0.60$ μ.   The corresponding colour temperatures will be 8,400 and 6,700 °K.   It must be stressed that this determination of the colour temperatures is very incorrect and rough.   We shall now describe the results of far more accurate observations of the intensity distribution in the continuous spectrum of the Crab nebula.

Minkowski based his considerations on the naïve assumption that the decrease in colour temperature with increasing wavelength was a direct observable proof that the continuous spectrum was produced in a sufficiently hot plasma in free–free and free–bound transitions.   At that time, however, other mechanisms of emission of a continuous spectrum by a gas were unknown and it was never questioned whether or not it was the gas that emitted it.   With this interpretation of the continuous spectrum it must be very valuable to observe the discontinuity of intensity at the boundary of the Balmer series.   Minkowski tried to observe such a discontinuity.   But the conditions of observations in the ultraviolet range near $\lambda = 3,600$ Å were very unfavourable because of the interfering effect of the emission of the nocturnal sky and the light from the town.   It seemed that a very small intensity discontinuity was discovered: Minkowski estimated it as 1.15.   In 1945, however, high-quality spectro-photometrical observations made by Barbier in the range $\lambda = 3,300$–$4,700$ Å showed that within the limits of error of observation (which amounts to several per cent) there is no Balmer discontinuity.[149]   Figure 90 shows the frequency dependence of the continuous spectrum of the Crab nebula obtained by Barbier.   According to [149] the colour temperature of the Crab nebula is equal to $5,600 \pm 1,000$ °K for the range $\lambda = 4,700$–$3,300$ Å, a result which differs essentially from that obtained by Minkowski.

Some information on the intensity distribution of the emission of the amorphous mass in the Crab nebula with respect to the spectrum may also be obtained from the colour index. Unfortunately, reliable data were not available at that time. Thus, for example, according to Hubble the photographic magnitude of the nebula is 11.2,[148] Lundmark gives a value of 9.4,[49] while Baade found 9.0 (see § 10). For the visual magnitude Holetschek gives a value of 8.5,[226] Würtz found 8.1[227] and Lundmark 8.5.[49] Though these data are insufficiently reliable, the colour index of the nebula is in all probability positive which speaks in favour of its relatively low spectro-photometrical temperature.

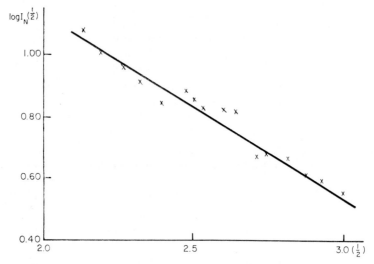

Fig. 90   Dependence of the continuous optical spectrum of the Crab nebula on the frequency.[149]

Applying the theory of the free–free and free–bound transitions to the continuous spectrum of the Crab nebula described above, Minkowski developed several models of the amorphous mass of this nebula. The method of calculation was the same as in the classical problem of the luminescence of planetary nebulae which are ionized by the ultra-violet radiation from the star that forms the nucleus of the nebula. The results of these calculations, whose details we shall not discuss here, are compiled in Table 23; D denotes the Balmer discontinuity, X the hydrogen content (in per cent of mass), L and L' are the upper and lower limits of the bolometric luminosity of the Crab nebula (the upper limit is obtained under

TABLE 23

D	X	T_e	$N_iN_eV \cdot 10^{-60}$	N_e (cm^{-3})	N_i (cm^{-3})	$M/M_\odot$	$L/L_\odot$	T	$R/R_\odot$	$L'/L_\odot$	T'	$R/R_\odot$
1.2	1.0	250,000°	24	1,600	1,600	13	12,000	410,000°	0.021	6,800	340,000°	0.024
	0.6	135,000°	13	1,300	1,100	14	29,000	560,000°	0.018	7,600	350,000°	0.023
	0.14	55,000°	4.0	800	500	15	52,000	670,000°	0.017	9,900	380,000°	0.023
	0.0	25,000°	1.6	600	300	13	56,000	690,000°	0.016	9,900	380,000°	0.022
1.1	1.0	420,000°	33	1,900	1,900	15	17,000	460,000°	0.020	10,200	390,000°	0.022
	0.6	280,000°	19	1,500	1,300	16	33,000	580,000°	0.018	11,700	410,000°	0.021
	0.14	100,000°	5.0	900	600	17	52,000	680,000°	0.017	11,700	410,000°	0.021
	0.0	45,000°	1.9	700	300	14	58,000	700,000°	0.016	10,200	390,000°	0.022

the supposition that the nebula is at all frequencies transparent for the natural radiation, the lower limit is obtained by excluding the recombination on the ground level of the hydrogen atom), T and T' are the temperatures of the central star obtained when L and L', respectively, are used, R and R' are the upper and lower limits of the central star's radius, determined analogously. The calculations were made under the supposition that the star radiates like an absolutely black body.

In 1953 Greenstein and Minkowski revised this paper.[228] They drew attention to the extreme unreliability of the spectro-photometrical gradients used in [162] and to the strong dependence of the calculated T_e-value on them. Thus, for example, in [162] a value of $\Phi = 1.75$ was used for $\lambda = 0.45$ μ. If Φ were in fact equal to 1.35, that is, by only 0.45 smaller than the value assumed, the calculation would yield infinity for T_e. An error of the gradient of 0.40, however, corresponds to an error of the colour index of only 0.09 which is quite possible in photographic spectro-photometry. Moreover, doubt is cast on the Balmer discontinuity obtained by Minkowski, which, after Barbier's investigations, is quite natural. In the new calculations carried out in [228] the assumed chemical composition of the hot plasma which must constitute the amorphous mass had been changed a little. Altogether three models were considered: the pure-hydrogen model (a_1), the pure-helium model (a_2) and a "standard" model consisting of 15 per cent hydrogen, 80 per cent helium and 5 per cent other elements (per cent in numbers of atoms). The results of the calculations by Greenstein and Minkowski are compiled in Table 24.

TABLE 24

| | "Standard" Mixture | | | | a_1 | a_2 | |
$10^{-4}\,T_e$	D	N_i	N_e	$M/M_\odot$	D	D	Φ
10	1.20	450	880	17.3	1.43	1.10	1.48
20	1.10	530	1,030	20.4	1.20	1.05	1.41
40	1.05	620	1,200	24.1	1.09	1.02	1.37
100	1.02	770	1,500	30.0	1.04	1.01	1.35
200	1.01	1,810	1,810	36.1	1.02	1.01	1.35

If, for example, one had discovered a Balmer discontinuity of $D = 1.04$ in the continuous spectrum of the Crab nebula, this would have indicated that $T_e \sim 600{,}000$ °K, if the chemical composition of the plasma corresponds to the "standard mixture," and $T_e = 10^6$ °K in the case of a pure hydrogen plasma and $T_e = 250,000\,°\mathrm{K}$ in the case of a pure helium plasma.

We shall now describe by way of a brief summary the ideas on the nature of the Crab nebula which, in 1953, were the result of analyses of its continuous spectrum and its line spectrum, obtained by the usual methods of theoretical astrophysics. In its periphery the nebula possesses a network of gaseous filaments arranged as a shell and expanding at a speed of $\sim 10^3$ km/s. The particle concentration in these gaseous filaments is $\sim 10^3$ cm^{-3} and the kinetic temperature $\sim 10^4\,°\mathrm{K}$. The entire volume of the nebula is filled by a very hot and rather dense plasma which emits only a continuous spectrum. This is the "amorphous mass." Its mechanism of emission is the free–free and free–bound transitions in the strongly ionized gas. From the fact that this component of the Crab nebula does not emit a line spectrum and that there is no noticeable discontinuity at the boundary of the Balmer series it may be concluded that the temperature of this plasma is not lower than 100,000 °K. The intensity observed of the radiation with the continuous spectrum which is emitted from a region of given volume requires a relatively high electron concentration of $N_e \sim 10^3$ cm^{-3} so that a value of ~ 20–$50 M_\odot$ is obtained for the total mass. In analogy with the planetary nebulae, the researchers dealing with this problem assumed this plasma to be ionized and its radiation therefore to be maintained by some "central star," the hypothetical remnant of the supernova. This was assumed to be identical with the south-western star of magnitude 16 positioned in the central part of the nebula. Under these suppositions it was necessary to assume its radius $< 0.02 R_\odot$ and its surface temperature $> 500,000\,°\mathrm{K}$. In fact, attempts were also made to explain the high temperature and density of the amorphous mass without the help of a very hot stellar nucleus possessing such unusual characteristics. Oort, for example, in 1951, suggested that the nebula may have conserved the high temperature which corresponds to the temperature of the interior of the exploding star. He assumed that the process of cooling of such a very hot mass of gas should take a very long time. But he ignored the fact that only the effect of adiabatic cooling of a rapidly expanding gas will result in a very low temperature if no additional heat sources are present. If, for example, the initial temperature in the core of the exploding star was as high as $\sim 10^9\,°\mathrm{K}$, with a radius of $\sim 10^{11}$ cm, it is a consequence of the adiabatic equation $pv^\gamma = \text{constant}$ that, with a radius $R \sim 10^{18}$ cm (the present dimension of the Crab nebula), $T \sim 10^2$.

According to Ramsay the high temperature of the amorphous mass may be maintained by the radioactive decay of certain unstable isotopes which might have formed during the explosion of the supernova.[229] This hypothesis, however, is today of merely historical interest. But the idea that radioactive processes may be important in explosions of type I supernovae was further developed later on (see §§ 18 and 19).

The interpretation of the spectra of the Crab nebula described above meets with a series of insuperable difficulties which we shall discuss in the following:

1. The mass of the very hot plasma which is responsible for the emission of the Crab nebula with the continuous spectrum is much too great (20–$50 M_\odot$). The Crab nebula is in fact the remnant of a supernova of type I. These supernovae belong to population II as they, in particular, explode in elliptical galaxies. All stars of population II are relatively old objects. Therefore, according to the modern theory of stellar evolution which is well supported by observations, their mass cannot exceed 1.5–$2 M_\odot$. It is quite obvious that the mass of the gaseous remnants of stellar explosions cannot exceed the mass of the original star by a factor of 10 or more.

2. It is difficult to understand the absence of any emission lines in the spectrum of the amorphous mass. If, for example, this mass consists mainly of hydrogen, one must expect very intense emission lines of the Balmer series of recombinative origin. In fact, the emission per unit volume in the Hβ line will at $T = 10^4 \,^\circ\mathrm{K}$ amount to $\sim 1.2 \cdot 10^{-25} \, N_e N_i$ erg/cm$^3 \cdot$s which, in the case of a sufficiently high value of T_e, depends on T_e according to the law $\varepsilon_{H\beta} \propto T_e^{-3/2}$. The emission due to free–free transitions in a fixed spectral range (e.g., the visible) is $\varepsilon_{ff} \propto T_e^{1/2}$. With $T_e = 10^4 \,^\circ\mathrm{K}$ the power of this radiation in the visible range of the spectrum is of the same order of magnitude as the power of emission in the Hβ line. For this line not to appear on the background of the continuum caused by free–free transitions, the plasma temperature must amount to at least several tens of millions of degrees. But if we assume such an extremely high T_e value, new difficulties arise. For example, since $\varepsilon_{ff} \propto T_e^{-1/2}$ (in a limited spectral range) the total mass of the gas must be enlarged three- to fourfold, but even without this it would be much too high. Of course, one cannot exclude the possibility that the relative abundance of hydrogen in the hot plasma is low. In this case, however, an analogous problem arises when we have to explain the absence of helium

emission lines. If the temperature lies within the limits of $3 \cdot 10^5$ to $3 \cdot 10^7 \,°K$ one must expect to find forbidden emission lines of highly ionized iron, calcium, nickel and the like which are observed in the spectrum of the solar corona. Their absence requires a temperature exceeding $10^7 \,°K$ and yet greater masses.

3. It is very difficult to understand in which way the relatively cold gas filaments ($T_e \sim 10^4 \,°K$) can "survive" as they are surrounded by the hot plasma which is assumed to constitute the amorphous mass. A "co-existence" of hot and cold plasmas is well known to be observed in the solar atmosphere. The relatively cold protuberances, whose temperature is about the same as that of the filaments in the Crab nebula, are very often surrounded on all sides by the hot ($T_e \sim 10^6 \,°K$) coronal plasma. But in this case the density of the "cold" plasma of the protuberances is about two orders of magnitude higher than that of the "hot" plasma of the corona so that the gas pressures are equal and the protuberances may exist in a state of mechanical equilibrium. The presence of magnetic fields prevents them from being heated by a mechanism based on heat conduction.[85] The situation encountered in the Crab nebula is quite different. The gas densities in the filaments and in the model of the amorphous mass are there almost equal. It must also be taken into consideration that at present the filaments are arranged in the periphery of the nebula as if they are enclosing the amorphous mass from all sides. Consequently, there must have been a time when they, while expanding, had been in "the very midst" of the amorphous mass. Why were they not destroyed by the pressure of the amorphous mass, why did they not mix up with it? Their total mass is almost a thousand times smaller than the mass of the hot plasma which, according to the Minkowski–Greenstein theory, is responsible for the continuous-spectrum radiation from the Crab nebula.

4. The Crab nebula is a powerful radio source. This radio emission can in no way be regarded as the thermal emission of a hot plasma which is assumed to constitute the amorphous mass. Calculations show that in this case the flux of the radio-frequency radiation from the Crab nebula must amount to about one-thousandth of the flux observed. This proves that the radio emission from the Crab nebula cannot be explained by a hypothetical hot plasma forming an amorphous mass. What is more, the polarization observations on the 20-cm wavelength (which, in fact, were made after 1953, see § 11) fully exclude the possibility of the existence of any kind of plasma with a free electron concentration $N_e > 1 \; cm^{-3}$

(see § 11).   The radio-astronomical observations are thus not in agreement
with Minkowski's hypothesis.

5. The existence of noticeable changes in the photometrical structure
of the Crab nebula discovered by Lampland[46] several decades ago (see
below) can in no way be explained on the basis of the classical ideas on the
emission mechanism of gas nebulae.

In 1953, the numerous difficulties listed above led the author of the
present book to the conclusion that the interpretation of the radiation
of the amorphous mass suggested by Minkowski, which is based on the
classical concepts of the physics of gas nebulae, is incorrect.   Instead of
the classical ideas a completely new theory was suggested, radical in
nature, which gave the entire research into the problem of the Crab nebula
a wholly new direction.[230]   The initial considerations were the following:
when it is impossible to consider the observed radio emission from the
Crab nebula as a continuation of the optical emission of its amorphous
mass, why should it not be possible to consider its optical emission as a
continuation of the deliberately non-thermal radio emission to ranges of
higher frequency?   We had just suggested and established the hypothesis
of the synchrotron nature of the radio emission from the Crab nebula
and other remnants of supernovae.[217]   We therefore tried to explain the
optical emission of the amorphous mass by a synchrotron mechanism.
It has been shown above that the spectral flux density in the continuous
optical spectrum of the Crab nebula is lower by a factor of about 400
than the flux density in the metre band.   On the other hand, the spectral
density of the radio emission decreases as the frequency increases.   If between $\nu = 100$ Mc and $\nu = 10{,}000$ Mc, which corresponds to 7 octaves,
the spectral flux density decreases to almost $\frac{1}{4}$, why does it not drop to
$\frac{1}{100}$ within the following 15 octaves separating this part of the spectrum
from the optical range ($\nu \sim 7 \cdot 10^{14}$ c/s)?   According to the data available
at that time (see, for example, Fig. 90) in the optical range the spectral flux
density decreases as the frequency increases, following a power law of
the form $F_\nu \propto \nu^{-\alpha}$, where $\alpha \sim 1$.   This is much steeper than in the
radio-frequency range ($\alpha \sim 0.3$, cf. § 11).

Radio-frequency radiation is produced when relativistic electrons
with an energy of 10^8 to 10^9 eV move in a magnetic field of $H \sim 10^{-3}$
to 10^{-4} Oe.   It is natural to assume that the relativistic electrons in
the Crab nebula possess a sufficiently wide energy spectrum ranging up to
10^{11} to 10^{12} eV and even farther.   Since the frequency at which the

synchrotron emission of a relativistic electron is strongest is proportional to the square of its energy E (with $H_\perp$ = constant), at the same magnetic field strength in the Crab nebula electrons with an energy of $\sim 3 \cdot 10^{11}$ eV will already emit in the optical frequency range by means of the synchrotron mechanism. Let us now estimate the concentration of ultra-relativistic electrons which are held to be the source of the optical emission of the amorphous mass; this emission is suggested to be produced by a synchrotron mechanism.

Let us draw attention to the fact that about 40 per cent of the radiation flux from the Crab nebula (mainly from its amorphous mass) comes from a central zone with the angular dimensions of 2'. On the supposition that $m_{ph} = 9.0$ and $F_\nu \propto \nu^{-1}$, the spectral flux density near $\lambda = 4,250$ A ($\nu = 7 \cdot 10^{14}$) is equal to $2.25 \cdot 10^{-23}$ erg/cm$^2 \cdot$s. Since the spectral index of the optical synchrotron radiation is equal to about unity, the exponent γ in the energy spectrum of the relativistic electrons in the energy range of 10^{11} to 10^{12} eV must be close to 3. Now we possess all data necessary to calculate the quantity K from the fundamental formula (6.7) of the synchrotron theory and with it to determine the concentration of relativistic electrons. We have $U(\gamma) = 0.087$. The corresponding calculations yield $K = 2.6 \cdot 10^{-9}$; for $H_\perp$ we assumed a value of $7.5 \cdot 10^{-4}$ Oe (see § 11) and $\gamma = 2.6$. We also have

$$N(E > E_1) = K \int_{E_1}^{\infty} E^{-2.6}\, dE = 5 \cdot 10^{-9} \text{ cm}^{-3}$$

where $E_1 = 3 \cdot 10^{11}$ eV. The energy density of the relativistic electrons with $E > E_1$ will be equal to

$$w_{\text{rel.el.}} = K \int_{E_1}^{\infty} \frac{dE}{E^{\gamma-1}} = 1.66 K E_1^{-0.6} = 2.6 \cdot 10^{-9} \text{ erg/cm}^3$$

The energy density of the "softer" relativistic electrons, responsible for the radio-frequency emission, was of the same order of magnitude.

Though these calculations are only preliminary estimations, they show us that, obviously, no hot and dense plasma is needed to explain the optical emission of the amorphous mass in the Crab nebula. A small number of relativistic electrons of sufficiently high energy are able to produce optical radiation of such an intensity as is observed. If we assume that on each relativistic electron contained in the amorphous mass falls one proton, the mass of the substance (in the form of relativistic particles) necessary to produce the observed luminescence of the Crab nebula amounts to only $\sim 10^{23}$ g; this is $\frac{1}{10,000}$ of the mass of the terrestrial globe and 10^{-9} of the gas mass of the filaments in the Crab nebula. Of course, besides the relativistic particles there must also be ordinary gas in the "amorphous mass" which does not manifest itself by optical emission. The "mass" of this gas, however, will be small. We may therefore draw the conclusion that the "real" Crab nebula (i.e., the remnant of the super-nova of 1054, namely the gaseous shell ejected in this process plus the interstellar medium "swept together") is identical with the system of filaments. The so-called "amorphous" mass is almost imponderable. It is a source of unusual non-equilibrium radiation which falls partly into the optical frequency range. It owes its nature first of all to the exceptional state of the interior of the Crab nebula and to the presence of relativistic electrons of super-high energies and a relatively strong magnetic field.

All the numerous difficulties mentioned above to do with interpreting the continuous optical radiation from Crab nebula were connected with the assumption that it was emitted by a relatively dense and very hot plasma by way of a thermal mechanism. These difficulties fall away automatically as the new interpretation of the Crab nebula's optical radiation with the continuous spectrum does not require the assumption of the existence of such a plasma. In this connection we should like to mention yet another difficulty which we did not discuss above. It seems incomprehensible why there should be nebular patches of quite insignificant brightness (cf. § 15) only where supernovae exploded in 1572 and 1604. As these supernovae are also of the type I, we may ask why they differ in such a radical manner from the supernova of 1054. The answer to this question in the framework of the new theory is the following: the energy spectrum of the relativistic particles in the Crab nebula is comparatively flat (the spectral index of the Crab nebula in the radio-frequency range is very small, $\alpha \sim 0.28$, whereas the radio sources attributed to the outbursts of Kepler's and Tycho's supernovae possess a much higher spectral index, cf. § 15), the energy spectrum of the relativistic electrons will therefore be much steeper. The Crab nebula must therefore contain much more relativistic electrons of sufficiently high energies ($E > 10^{12}$ eV) than the remnants of the supernovae of 1572 and 1604. It is another question how we can explain the difference in the energy spectra of the relativistic particles in the various remnants of supernovae. The answer to this question is connected with the explanation of the acceleration mechanism of the charged particles of sub-relativistic energies in the remnants of supernovae.   It is, however, quite natural that the conditions of acceleration will differ in different objects.

The fact that the difficulties of the old theory do not arise with the new one (though this is of course important) does not mean that the new theory is the only one among all possible theories that is correct.   For this it would be necessary, on the basis of the new concepts, to predict effects which have so far been either fully unknown or absolutely incomprehensible.   Such a prediction was actually made.[232]   If the Crab nebula's optical emission with the continuous spectrum is of synchrotron origin, it must be polarized.   This polarization may be observed unless the magnetic field displays an extremely complex fine-cellular structure.   As the magnetic field structure in the Crab nebula had not been known beforehand, this problem could only be solved by particularly directional observations.   For example, the theory could not predict the value of the average degree of polarization (which, for example, might be investigated by a photoelectrical method, using a diaphragm whose size is equal to the angular dimensions of the nebula).   At that time the polarizations in the centimetre radio-frequency band of the Crab nebula's radiation had not yet been measured.   We must not forget that polarization measurements in the radio-frequency range were carried out after analogous optical measurements and were stimulated by the new theory (see § 11).   Note that if the results of polarization measurements of the optical radiation from the Crab nebula had been negative, this would not have disproved the new theory.   Such results might have been interpreted by the extremely complex and chaotic structure of the magnetic field in the Crab nebula.   The fact is that, as regards the centimetre band, no-one has yet discovered any linear polarization in the radiation of such a bright source as Cassiopeia A, though today it is beyond any doubt that its radio-frequency radiation is of synchrotron origin.

This was the situation when the Soviet astrophysicists and observers, V. A. Dombrovski and M. A. Vashakidze, independently and by means of different methods, began to measure the possible polarization of the optical radiation from the Crab nebula.   V. A. Dombrovski made his observations at the end of 1953 at the Byurokan Observatory.   He used a photoelectrical method, working with a very large diaphragm of 3′.   About 50 per cent of the radiation from all the nebulae passed through this diaphragm.   A considerably high degree of polarization, about 13 per cent, was discovered immediately.   The electric vector was found to make an angle of about 20° with the galactic equator.   The polarization remains unchanged when the diaphragm is displaced a little within the limits of the representation of the Crab nebula.[231]   Analogous results were obtained by M. A. Vashakidze at the Abastuman Observatory; he applied a photographic method.[233]   Vashakidze was the first to stress that the degree of polarization of the individual parts of the Crab nebula is so high that its representations differ with different orientations of the polaroids.

At that time also other polarization observations of the Crab nebula were made by Soviet astronomers.   G. A. Shayn, S. B. Pikel'ner and R. N. Ikhsanov studied the polarization of this object by means of a photographical method, with the 40-cm astrograph of the Crimean Astrophysical Observatory.[232]   A polaroid was arranged in front of the plate and photographs were taken with three different orientations of it.   The diaphragm of the microphotometer measured 0.1 mm which, with a focal length of 140 cm, corresponded to 13″.   In this way the distribution of the degree of polarization over the nebula was investigated for the first time.   It was found that within the nebular area the polarization displays strong changes in magnitude and direction.   This excludes the possibility of explaining the polarization by oriented dust particles in the interstellar space, by which, as is well known, the polarization of stellar radiation is explained.   The polarization of the Crab nebula's radiation, however, is too strong to be explained by interstellar effects.   According to [232] the mean degree of polarization of the optical radiation from the Crab nebula amounts to 8 per cent, which is similar to the radio-flux polarization in the centimetre band discovered later on.   Unfortunately, for instrumental reasons, it was not possible to carry out quantitative measurements of the polarization at the various points of the nebula.   Only at four points, where the polarization proved to be particularly high, was its degree measured.   The arrows in Figure 91, which at present is only of historical interest, indicate the directions of the electrical vectors relative to the brightest gaseous filaments.

It must be stressed once again that it is impossible to explain the discovered polarization of the Crab nebula by an influence of the dust component of the interstellar medium.   In this celestial region the interstellar absorption (and thus also the interstellar polarization connected with it) is quite insignificant.   It is likewise impossible that any considerable amount of dust is present in the nebula itself.   This follows from the (on the average) equal brightnesses of the two components of the lines λ 3,727 emitted by the "front" and "rear" halves of the expanding nebula (see Fig. 68).   The relatively high polarization observed of the radiation from the Crab nebula must therefore be caused by the specific mechanism of emission alone, which is also responsible for the continuous spectrum.

It was also in 1955 that E. Ye. Khachikyan studied the polarization of the Crab nebula at the Byurokan Observatory, with the help of a graphical method; for this purpose he used a small Schmidt camera, 20 cm in diameter.[234]   The diaphragm of the microphotometer applied corresponded to an area of 20″ on the negative.   He also found that the degree of polarization varied considerably within the boundaries of the

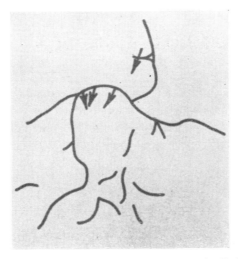

FIG. 91   Schematic representation of polarization in the Crab nebula.[232]

nebula, in individual zones reaching values of 50–60 per cent, which is a record value in astrophysics.   Such a high degree of polarization is observed in the zones of highest brightness of the amorphous mass.   In addition to this, Khachikyan discovered that for large parts of the nebula the directions of the electrical vector were similar, which indicates an essential uniformity of the magnetic field in the Crab nebula, a result which is rather unexpected.   The mean degree of polarization of the whole nebula as obtained by Khachikyan was about 20 per cent; this result is obviously too high, as was shown later on in more careful investigations.

In this way the Soviet observers could soon verify the noticeable effect of a polarization of the continuous-spectrum radiation from Crab nebula, an effect that had been predicted by the new theory. This success was not so much due to the perfection of the methods they applied or to the large dimensions of the telescopes used (quite the contrary!) but to the high degree of polarization on the light emitted by this nebula. It is beyond any doubt that the level of astronomical technique at the end of the nineteenth and the very beginning of the twentieth centuries should have been high enough to discover the polarization of the optical radiation from the Crab nebula if anybody had realized that this radiation must be polarized. Maybe it was better that this polarization was not discovered by chance at that time. Such an untimely discovery might have confused all contemporary astronomical conceptions, which might have impeded the the progress of astronomical investigations. We must also remember that special theory of relativity did not exist at that time and the synchrotron mechanism of radiation is one of the consequences resulting from it.

In 1954, during the festivities on the occasion of the restoration of the Pulkovo Observatory which had been completely destroyed in the war, the author of the present book discussed the new theory of the optical emission of the Crab nebula and the verification of this theory by polarization observations with Professor Oort who attended the festivities. Immediately after his return to Holland, Professor Oort, who had previously been occupied with the problem of the Crab nebula and was extremely interested in the new theory, organized a programme of observations of this nebula at the Leyden Observatory. Just about that time a photoelectrical device had been prepared designed for a systematic observation of the interesting brightness variations discovered (but never published) by Baade in 1938 and long before that by Lampland, in 1921 (see below). This programme was replaced by the programme of polarization investigations with the aim of verifying and improving the results of the Soviet astronomers. The results of these studies were published by Oort together with Walraven in a voluminous article.[235] In the photoelectrical polarization observations carried out by the Dutch researchers, relatively large diaphragms of various sizes were used. On the basis of careful measurements with diaphragms, 1' and 0'.5 in diameter, a mean degree of polarization equal to 9.3 $\pm$ 0.3 per cent was found, a result close to that obtained by Shayn, Pikel'ner and Ikhsanov.[232] The degree of polarization P varied in the individual zones from a few per cent to 34 per cent (P averaged over the 0'.5 diaphragm).

It is very likely that with a smaller diaphragm one would have found still higher degrees of polarization of individual parts of the nebula. Although different orientations of the electrical vector could be observed, there is undoubtedly some tendency of the vectors to be parallel in large areas of the central region.   Inside a zone with a radius of 1″ in the centre

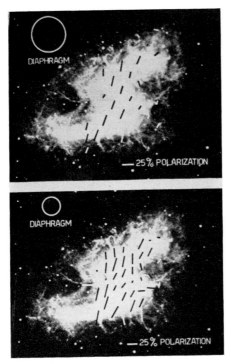

Fɪɢ. 92   Photoelectrical observations of polarization in the Crab nebula with 1 and ½ diaphragms.

of the nebula the degree of polarization was found to be independent of the distance from the centre.   In this zone the degree of polarization is also independent of the surface brightness.   In the outer regions of the nebula the degree of polarization averaged over the size of the diaphragm decreases rapidly.

The results of the photoelectrical observations by Oort and Walraven are shown in photographs of the Crab nebula obtained by Baade (see

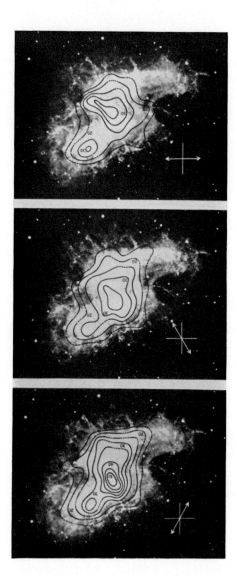

Fig. 93 Isophotes of the Crab nebula in polarized light for various orientations of
the polaroid.[235]

Fig. 92).   The circles denote the sizes of the diaphragms used.   In these photographs the lengths of the lines are proportional to the degree of polarization observed and their directions coincide with the directions of the electrical vectors.   Figure 93 shows the isophotes of the Crab nebula in polarized light.   The isophotes of the nebula obtained without polaroids are shown in Figure 65.   The strongest polarization is observed near the centre of the Crab nebula.   Figure 94 shows the intensity distribution of the polarized radiation along a certain direction for two orthogonal orientations of the polaroids.   The sharp peak of the solid curve indicates

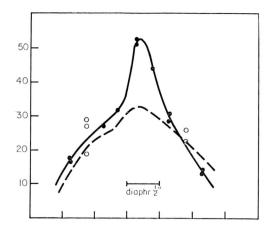

FIG. 94   Intensity distribution of polarized radiation from the Crab nebula for two directions.

a very high degree of polarization.   Oort's and Walraven's investigations are of great importance for the introduction of new ideas on the nature of the Crab nebula to foreign astronomers.   These investigations were carried out with great care and the authority of Oort as a leading European astronomer "opened all doors" for the new theory.

At last, in September 1955, polarization observations of the Crab nebula were also carried out with the world's largest telescope, the 200-inch reflector on Mount Palomar.   Baade obtained a series of excellent photographs taken at various orientations of the polaroids.[235a]   He used a filter transmissive in the range $\lambda = 5,400$–$6,400$ Å where the contribution of the emission lines from the gaseous filaments is insignificant.   Figure 95

10 + s.

shows us four of these photographs obtained with different orientations of the polaroids indicated by the arrows. These photographs are bound to astonish us. On one or two photographs individual bright details have completely vanished whereas on the others they are seen very clearly. Certain regions of the Crab nebula are transformed beyond recognition

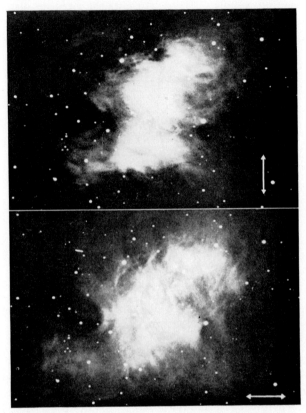

Fɪɢ. 95 Photographs of the amorphous mass in the Crab nebula obtained with various orientations of the polaroids.[235a] (See also opposite page.)

when the polaroid is rotated. For example, the great bright detail in the north-western part of the nebula, on which three stars are projected, vanishes completely when the polaroid is rotated through 90°. Extremely large changes are also caused by such a rotation in the south-eastern part of the nebula.   The changes are so extreme that one has the impression of viewing the photographs of different objects.   These considerable changes in the intensity distributions demonstrate quite clearly that the radiation from individual parts displays an almost complete linear polarization.

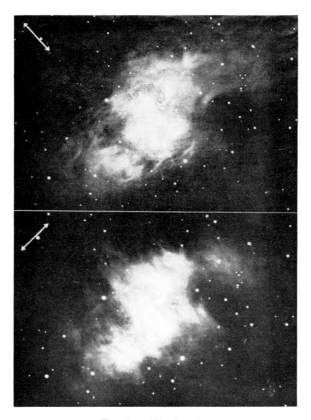

FIG. 95   *(Continued.)*

The plates on which these photographs were taken were calibrated so that Woltier (to whom Baade gave the original negatives) could carry out the photometrical processing of these observations.   The results are shown in Figure 96.   The lines represent the degrees of polarization and the directions of the electrical vector.   The circle in the upper left part

represents the size of the diaphragm of the photometer with respect to
which the measuring results have been averaged. The rms error of the
measurements of the degree of polarization in the brightest central part
of the nebula are estimated as 2.8 per cent, and the mean error of the
determination of the angle of position as 4° (for an area with a degree of
polarization of 20 per cent).

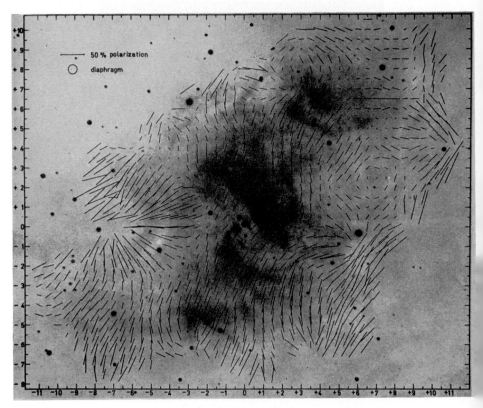

FIG. 96   Polarization of the Crab nebula obtained from photographic
observations.[153]

Careful electro-photometrical observations of the polarization of the
Crab nebula's optical radiation were made in 1957 by Walraven[236a] and,
independently, by Hiltner.[237a] Without entering into details, we shall
report Hiltner's results which seem to be more reliable (see Fig. 97).

According to the theory of synchrotron radiation, the direction of the electrical vector is perpendicular to the direction of the magnetic field in the emission zone.   The relatively regular character of the polarization in the Crab nebula permits the construction of a system of lines which are orthogonal to the polarization vectors observed, which gives us an idea of the magnetic field structure.   Such a "magnetic map" of the Crab nebula was composed for the first time by Oort and Walraven (see Fig. 98).

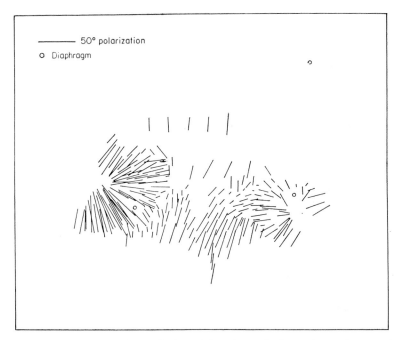

FIG. 97   Polarization of the Crab nebula obtained from electrophotometrical observations.[237a]

It must, however, be borne in mind that, because of the projection effect, it is very difficult to compose such a map.   Nevertheless, there are some very interesting peculiarities of the magnetic field structure which attract our attention.   First of all, the directions of the magnetic fields coincide with the directions of the individual parts of the amorphous mass. This is particularly marked in, e.g., the zone of the "bay" in the southeastern part of the nebula.   Hence we may immediately draw the conclusion that the individual "clusters" of relativistic electrons move along the magnetic lines of force; these act as kind of "guide lines" for this motion, preventing the relativistic particles from diffusing in a perpendicular direction.   This picture may only be observed when the energy density of the magnetic field exceeds the energy density of the relativistic particles.   Otherwise the pressure of the latter would "scatter" the lines of force and after some years the relativistic gas would leave the region of

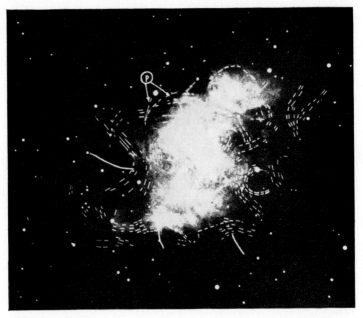

FIG. 98   Schematic representation of the magnetic fields in the Crab nebula.[235]

the nebula.   The position of the lines of force relative to the gaseous filaments in the Crab nebula is very interesting.   A schematic representation of the positions of the brightest filaments and the magnetic lines of force is given in Figure 98.   It is obvious that the magnetic lines of force are curved outwardly in the form of giant arcs, in the space between the filaments.   This configuration of the filaments and the lines of force is of course not random.

In fact it is as if the filaments were sustaining an expansion of the field; the lines of force bend themselves around the filaments and "swell" in the space between them. The whole picture resembles the inter-relations between quiet protuberances and magnetic fields in the solar atmosphere. It is well known that the quiet protuberances are found in regions where the field is horizontal, which is explained by stability considerations. S. B. Pikel'ner showed that this field pattern in the Crab nebula is determined by the relationship between the forces of pressure of the relativistic particles and the "counteraction" of the gaseous shell.[352] The field looks as if it were "bulged" by the cosmic rays at its "weak" spots. The gas slides down along the lines of force into the "valley" thus forming the filaments. In the zones of low gas density this density decreases still further, the lines of force bulge forward and the filaments are compressed.

In the end a state is established where the lines of force seem to be "fixed" in the filaments, forming arcs in the space between them; their tension is, even without the help of the gas, compensated by the pressure of the relativistic particles.

Knowing the thickness of the gaseous shell containing the filaments, and also the mean distance between the filaments, it is possible to estimate the ratio between the energies of the field and of the relativistic particles. The estimates obtained in [352] permit the conclusion that in the Crab nebula the energy of the field is comparable to the energy of the relativistic particles. If, for example, the energy of the latter were considerably higher than the field energy, the arcs would stretch themselves at greater distances and could not in general be in a steady state. In the opposite case, if the field energy were higher, the curvature of the arcs would be less strong.

In the paper by Oort and Walraven mentioned above, attention was drawn for the first time to the quite peculiar group of effects concerning the emission of the Crab nebula. These apparently misunderstood phenomena, which were discovered as early as 1921 by Lampland, did not attract the researchers' attention for a long time. Lampland was the first to pay attention to the surprising metamorphosis in the brightness distribution of the Crab nebula.[46] Comparing his photographs of the Crab nebula obtained in 1913 and 1921, he discovered great changes in the brightness of individual parts of it. It must be stressed in this connection that the question is not about the regular expansion of the filaments (see § 11) but the changes in brightness and configuration of whole regions of the nebula. For example, 10″ in a north-western direction from the central star he discovered a detail which in the course of eight years raised its brightness considerably and became much narrower. "This small condensation," writes Lampland, "developed out of a small diffuse mass which can be seen on the photographs of 1913. The change in structure of this detail gives us the impression that its inner boundary moved away from the central star and the detail itself seems to be compressed to a brighter, smaller mass with sharper contours." Lampland also discovered changes on a larger scale. For example, a large detail of the dimensions 48″ × 15″ positioned 45″ north-west of the central star seemed to display considerably sharper contours than in the earlier negatives.

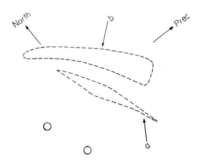

FIG. 99   Schematic representation of the photometrical structure of the central part of the Crab nebula.[235a]

Only 20 years later Baade began to study the variations of the brightness distribution in the Crab nebula. In the winter of 1942–43 he discovered and investigated the interesting changes occurring in the central part of the nebula. From time to time small and bright condensations arise in this zone, which are usually of elongated form and travel very fast through the Crab nebula (we must, of course, take its distance into consideration). Figure 99 shows a schematic representation of the rough photometrical structure of the central part of the nebula. The two small circles indicate the central stars; Baade and Minkowski suggest that the little south-western star ought to be the ex-supernova. The angular distance between the two little stars (which, in all probability, are optical binaries) is equal to 4″.9. Baade's observations showed that the structural detail of the nebula which, in Figure 99, is denoted by "*b*," is a more or less stationary formation.   Its centre is located at a distance of about 10″ from the south-western star.   The other detail, denoted as "*a*," behaves quite differently.   It changes its position, contours and brightness. Baade describes the changes of this detail in the following words:

"It appears as a bright elongated spot (sometimes, however, it is round) which is always in the space between the central star and the detail '*b*.' So, often as I observed it, I never found it to be closer than 7″ from the straight line connecting the two little stars.   In the following the detail '*a*' moves westwardly in a direction almost perpendicular to the straight line mentioned above.   During this motion its brightness decreases continuously.   Usually the detail '*a*' fades away as it approaches and almost reaches the 'permanent' detail '*b*.'   Only in a single case did I observe the detail '*a*' joining detail '*b*.'   At the end of 1944 I made the attempt to describe the development of detail '*a*'."

The further report reads as follows:

"…1944, October 11th.   The elongated 'plait' [of almost the same form as shown in Figure 99] is at a distance of $\alpha = 7''.17$ from the straight line connecting the two little stars.

"1944, November.   Observations disturbed by bad weather.

"1944, December 18th.   The detail '*a*' maintained its initial form but its brightness decreased considerably.   It moved westwardly and is now positioned at a distance $d = 8''.18$ from the straight line mentioned above.   According to the survey at a blink comparator the motion of the detail between October and December was considerable.

"1945, January 15th.   Detail '*a*' is still distinguishable but it has become so faint that it can no longer be measured by the microphotometer. Comparisons at the blink comparator, however, show that it continues its westward motion.   This January photograph shows a bright new detail '*a*' which is at a distance $d = 7''.06$ from the base line."

According to a rough estimate by Baade, the integral stellar magnitude of the detail "*a*" right after its appearance was, by 1, lower than the central star which corresponds to about $\frac{1}{1,500}$ of the optical radiation flux from the whole Crab nebula.

From the fact that within 68 days the detail was displaced by 1″.01, taking into account that the distance to the Crab nebula is $\sim 1,000$ psc, it follows that the velocity component perpendicular to the direction of observation of the "plait's" motion was equal to 26,000 km/s or

~ 0.1 c! Remember that the velocity of expansion of the system of gaseous filaments in the Crab nebula is $\sim 1,000$ km/s. From this we see that we are concerned here with some quite new phenomenon which has nothing to do with the expansion of the nebula's filaments.

From the above description it follows also that this phenomenon is of periodic or quasi-periodic character, recurring within a period of about three months. It seems that Lampland was the first to observe the variations in the zone of detail "b" (see above).

It is interesting that Baade, who observed these peculiar phenomena in the central part of the Crab nebula for many years, never reported on them in a publication. Obviously they must have seemed to him to be somehow transcendental, not in agreement with the ideas one had at that time on the nature of this nebula, in the formation of which they play such a great role.

At the end of 1962 we had the opportunity to see reproductions of several negatives of the Crab nebula obtained in polarized light by Munch with a-200 inch reflector. Munch had systematically photographed the nebula since 1959 with the aim of determining the phenomena in its central part discovered by Baade. Though the orientations of the polaroid had not been chosen in the best way, it is beyond any doubt that detail "a" is strongly polarized. It is remarkable that the direction of its motion is perpendicular to the direction of the magnetic field. These photographs essentially complete Baade's observations. First of all, it follows from the survey that formations analogous to the moving "plait 'a'," but less intense, are also observed south-east of the central star. One gets the impression of the latter being the centre of a spherical wave in the surrounding space, which is propagated at a velocity of ~ 0.1 c. It is extraordinarily interesting that in individual cases one can observe something like an "outburst" of synchrotron radiation from the central star. It is almost certain that this outburst is a real phenomenon, it can also be seen on another photograph that was obtained with the polaroid turned through $90°$. It is very improbable that this "outburst" has only been projected onto the star by chance. These photographs show clearly that active processes of high power take place in the central part of the Crab nebula, the ex-supernova being the centre of this activity. In § 14 we shall return to this problem which is extremely important for all the questions connected with the outburst of supernovae.

As already indicated above, the relatively fast changes of the photometrical structure of the Crab nebula are not limited to its central part.

Oort and Walraven compared the photographs of this nebula obtained in 1899 and reproduced in the publications of the Lick Observatory[236b] with Baade's photographs obtained in 1942 with the 100-inch telescope. They discovered a striking change in details of the amorphous mass in various parts of the nebula. These changes were so obvious that they could not be explained by any possible photographic effects. The contours and intensities of individual details had varied while the general structure of the nebula remained unchanged. For example, the characteristic "bay" in the south-eastern part of the nebula, which has already been mentioned repeatedly, is to be recognized in the photographs of 1899 just as clearly as in the photographs of 1942. An investigation of Mount Wilson and

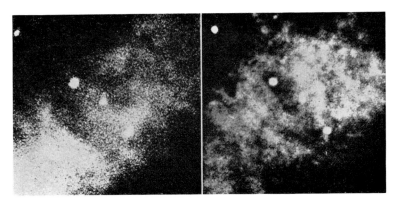

Fig. 100   Variability of details in the north-western part of the Crab nebula.[235]

Mount Palomar photographs of the Crab nebula obtained between 1921 and 1955, and also of other original negatives, yielded new and indubitable proofs of the presence of an amorphous mass in it which displays relatively rapid changes. Figure 100 may serve as an example; it shows the north-western part of the nebula photographed in 1924 by Hubble and in 1938 by Baade, using one and the same telescope, a 100-inch reflector. It is clearly seen that the dark band which extends parallel to the three bright stars has undergone a displacement by about 15″ in a north-western direction; this corresponds to a distance of 0.1 psc. Its structure has also changed considerably. In 1944 this band could not be observed any longer. A comparison with photographs taken in polarized light by Baade in 1955 (see Fig. 95) shows that a relatively bright and strongly polarized filament of amorphous mass penetrates the zone of the nebula represented in Figure 103, on which the three stars are projected. Changes of a similar kind may also be observed in other parts of the nebula. The characteristic rates of change to be observed in these cases are of the order of 10^9 cm/s.

Woltier, who photometrized the photographs of the Crab nebula obtained in various years (among them also Hubble's photograph, part of which is shown in Figure 100), came to the conclusion that individual details had changed their brightnesses by 50 per cent within 14 years.[163] This gives the impression that the amorphous mass of the nebula consists of two components. The one component is almost without structure, its brightness variations are insignificant with time, and the light it emits is almost free from polarization. The other component consists of rather bright strongly polarized details which display considerable changes in configuration and brightness. It is, of course, possible also that the first component possesses a complex structure of comparatively small scale, which cannot be observed, in particular because of the projection effect, and each detail of this structure is polarized.

In any case, an analysis of photographs of the Crab nebula demonstrates that it possesses a "striated" structure which is subject to rapid changes. In the framework of classical physics it was completely impossible to explain this structure and the characteristic rates of change. Only the new concepts as to the nature of the Crab nebula proved to afford an explanation of these remarkable effects.

§ 13   The Crab nebula's synchrotron radiation in the entire frequency range

In the previous section we discussed a series of decisive arguments derived from observations to prove that the optical radiation from the Crab nebula is of synchrotron nature and a natural continuation of its radio-frequency radiation. It is well known that the synchrotron radiation differs essentially from the thermal radiation and is determined mainly by the energy spectrum of the emitting relativistic electrons. Since the latter is as a rule a power function of the form $dN(E) = KE^{-\gamma} dE$ (where γ may vary along the spectrum) the spectral flux density must, as proved by theory, vary according to the same exponential law: $F_\nu \propto \nu^{-\alpha}$ where $\alpha = (\gamma - 1)/2$. The spectral index of an arbitrary source of synchrotron radiation is its most important characteristic parameter. Particularly interesting are the characteristic changes of the spectral index, for example, its discontinuities. Knowing details of the spectrum one may determine a series of important parameters of the source, for example, its age, the magnetic field strength and the like. As in the case of the Crab nebula the synchrotron spectrum is observed within an extremely wide frequency range and particularly valuable information may be obtained from a detailed investigation into it.

The calculation of the optical synchrotron radiation of the Crab nebula as it was carried out in § 12 was of merely informative character. It was the aim of the calculations to show in which way the synchrotron theory may yield a natural and obvious explanation of the optical emission from the amorphous mass. The fundamental quantity K obtained in this section, which characterizes the concentration of the relativistic electrons, is a mean value averaged over the whole volume of the nebula, and the spectral index was adopted without the necessary discussion. The previous investigations of the Crab nebula's continuous spectrum, which we discussed at the beginning of § 12, were very incomplete. Nevertheless, they permitted the conclusion that the spectral flux density F_ν decreases as the frequency increases (cf., for example, Fig. 92).

Among the investigations of the energy distribution in the continuous spectrum of the Crab nebula available at present, O'Dell's paper of 1962[236] is the best one. He used a photoelectrical method, the observations were made successively through twelve interference light filters, covering the spectral range from 3,200 to 8,440 Å. The spectral pass bands of the various light filters varied from 75 to 260 Å. The filters were chosen in such a way that no intense emission lines of the gaseous filaments' spectrum should fall into the pass bands. The results of the measurements were calibrated in absolute units, referring them to stars with well-known characteristics. The observations were made with several telescopes of small or medium sizes. In most cases the diaphragm was so broad that it "covered" the whole nebula. The influence of the background caused by the nocturnal sky was taken into account.

When these measurements were carried out, all possible errors were estimated. In particular, one of the sources of error lies in the fact that the radiation from the Crab nebula is relatively strongly polarized (see the previous section). If the apparatus used for the measurements (telescopes, photometers) has its own characteristic of polarization, an error will arise when polarized radiation is observed. Special investigations, however, showed that in the observations described this effect was negligibly small.

Since the Crab nebula is sufficiently far away from us (1,000 psc or even more) interstellar absorption, which causes a reddening of the object under investigation, may affect the results of observation. O'Dell studied especially the problem of light absorption in the direction of the Crab nebula; for this purpose he studied the reddening of eight early-type stars in the neighbourhood of the Crab nebula with the help of a photoelectrical method; he chose such stars whose distances could be determined. The results of these investigations are illustrated in Figure 101, which shows the absorption as a function of the distance for these eight stars. It follows from this graph that A_v is a linear function of r. This

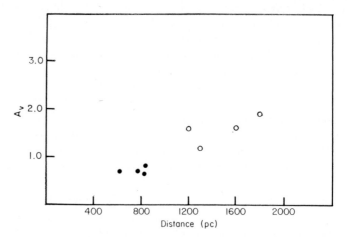

Fig. 101   Dependence of absorption on stellar distance in the direction of the Crab nebula.[236]

means that in this direction the absorbing substance, that is, the interstellar dust, has a more or less constant density up to $r = 2,000$ psc. As the distance of the Crab nebula $> 1,000$ psc, the absorption $A_v > 1.1$ magnitudes. If we assume that $r \sim 1,500$ psc (which is a probable and reasonable value, see below), $A_v = 1.6$ magnitudes. When interstellar absorption and the reddening of the light caused by it are taken into account the spectrum of the Crab nebula displays an essential change. Figure 102 illustrates the results of O'Dell's measurements. The lower row of dots represents the results of observations not corrected for interstellar absorption, $A_v = 1.1$ and 1.6 magnitudes. How important it is to take interstellar absorption into account may be seen from the fact that with $A_v = 1.1$ a spectral index of $\alpha = 1.2$ results from Figure 102, whereas with $A_v = 1.6$ we obtain $\alpha = 0.76$.

O'Dell's observations show that in the optical frequency range the spectral flux density decreases exponentially as the frequency increases, with a spectral index $\alpha \sim 1$. The accurate determination of the spectral index in this range depends on the applicability of the value of interstellar absorption of the light that comes to us from the Crab nebula.

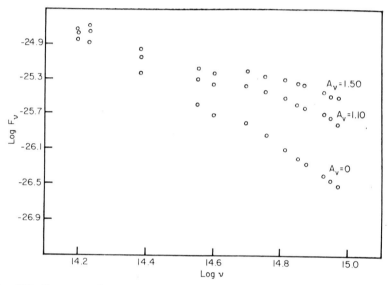

Fig. 102   Spectrum of amorphous mass in the Crab nebula in the optical frequency range.[236]

Observations in the infrared frequency range where the influence of absorption is insignificant are therefore particularly important for the investigation of the amorphous mass of this nebula. For example, near $\lambda = 2\,\mu$ and with $A_v = 1.6$ magnitudes the correction for interstellar absorption of the spectral density observed amounts to only 0.2 magnitudes, and with $A_v = 1.1$ to only 0.07. The infrared radiation from the Crab nebula was studied for the first time in the U.S.S.R. by P. V. Shcheglov in 1957[237] and V. I. Moroz in 1960 and 1962.[238,239] P. V. Shcheglov used an electron-optical converter with a filter as the radiation

receiver. The effective wavelength at which the observations were made
was about 9,000 Å. Much more valuable were the observations of V. I.
Moroz, who studied the Crab nebula's radiation at much lower frequencies.
The observations were carried out with the help of a photoelectrical
photometer with a sulphur photo-resistor, covering the spectral range
from 1 to 2.5 μ, with the 122-cm reflector of the Crimean Astrophysical
Observatory and the 125-cm reflector of the southern base of the State
Astronomical Institute imeni Shternberg. In the procedure of observations the telescope was directed at the centre of the nebula, then to a
part of the sky close by the nebula, then again to its centre and so on.
From time to time the telescope was directed to a star near the nebula
which served as an "intermediate standard." It must be noted that the
absolute energy distribution in the spectral range of 1 to 2.5 μ has not
been investigated for a single star, apart from the sun. Therefore, in
order to determine the absolute value of the flux from the Crab nebula,
stars of the spectral classes dG_1 to dG_4, i.e., stars similar to the sun, were
chosen as "intermediate standards." The results of Moroz' observations
are compiled in Table 25. The first column of this table gives the
effective wavelengths, the second the logarithms of the spectral flux
densities and the third the probable errors.

TABLE 25

λ_e	$\log F_\nu$ (W/m$^2 \cdot$c/s)	$\Delta \log F_\nu$
1.26	-25.22	± 0.10
1.78	-24.90	± 0.10
1.90	-24.86	± 0.15

As already stressed above, the problem of determining the spectral
index of optical synchrotron radiation from the Crab nebula is essentially
a problem of determining the interstellar absorption of the light from this
object. Apart from O'Dell's photoelectrical determination, the interstellar absorption in this region of the sky was also studied by E. S.
Brodskaya.[240] With the help of a photographic method she determined
$B - V$ and the spectral classes of about a hundred early-type stars in
an area of 2° × 2° around the Crab nebula, and found that $A_\nu \sim r$ up to
$r = 1.8$ kpsc. An analogous result was also obtained by O'Dell. Brodskaya, however, obtained a much smaller value for the interstellar absorption than O'Dell. For the distance of 1,000 psc the total light absorption

in this direction amounts, according to [240], to only 0.7 magnitudes; Moroz took the arithmetical mean of O'Dell's and Brodskaya's results: $A_v = 0.9$. To us, however, it seems that Brodskaya's value of the light absorption is too low. Perhaps there exist some systematic errors in her results. Though the number of stars used by O'Dell was much smaller than in Brodskaya's studies, the photoelectrical observations of the American investigator are obviously more reliable. But we must stress that this important problem has not yet been fully elucidated. New precision observations are therefore very desirable.

Figure 103 shows the results of observations of the spectral flux density of the radiation at various frequencies obtained by V. I. Moroz and O'Dell, for the spectral range of 0.3 μ to 2.5 μ. The lowest row of dots corresponds to observations not corrected for interstellar absorption. The upper two rows of dots were obtained on the supposition that $A_v = 0.9$ and $A_v = 1.59$ magnitudes. It is obvious that a neglection of interstellar absorption causes an apparent inflection of the spectral curve which, of course, does not correspond to reality. In spite of the considerable spread of the points the linear character of the function $F_v(v)$ is conserved in both the cases $A_v = 0.9$ and $A_v = 1.59$. Assuming $A_v = 0.9$ magnitudes, V. I. Moroz obtains a spectral index of 1.5 ± 0.2 for the synchrotron radiation from the Crab nebula in the range of $\lambda = 0.3$ μ to 2.5 μ. This value of α seems to us to be much too high (see later).

Since the spectral density of the synchrotron radiation flux from the Crab nebula varies exponentially, i.e., relatively slowly as the frequency increases, it must be expected that radiation of this nebula may be discovered at very high frequencies. Radiation in the range of $\lambda = 2,900$ Å cannot pass through the earth's atmosphere and can therefore be discovered only by means of the methods of rocket astronomy. In the spectral range $912 < \lambda < 2,900$ Å the flux is strongly attenuated by interstellar absorption. In the spectral ranges $\lambda = 912$ Å and up to 50–100 Å the radiation must be absorbed almost completely by the interstellar neutral hydrogen, but from 30–50 Å onwards the interstellar medium (other than the earth's atmosphere) is transparent for the radiation. It is therefore possible, with the help of the methods of rocket (extra-atmospherical) astronomy, to investigate the X-ray emission of the Crab nebula.

It is well known that, beginning with 1948, X-ray astronomy yielded outstanding results in the investigation of the sun. High-quality spectrograms of the sun, covering a wavelength range up to 15 Å, were obtained in particular in 1965. But only in 1962 X-ray sources, far away from the earth's atmosphere, were discovered for the first time. These observations which represent a landmark in astronomy were carried out by a group of investigators, among them Giacconi, Gursky, Paolini and

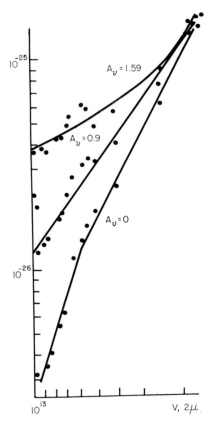

FIG. 103   Spectrum of the amorphous mass of the Crab nebula in the optical and the infrared ranges.[239]

Rossi.[241] Geiger counters with an effective surface of 60 cm² were used as the X-ray indicators. The sensitivity of the counters was a hundred times higher than that of the devices previously used in solar investigations. The counters were provided with two mica windows which, with regard to the spectral transmissivity of the gas with which the counters were filled, were designed for a pass band of 2–8 Å. The device had a very low resolving power with respect to the co-ordinates. Nevertheless, an X-ray source with the co-ordinates $16^h < \alpha < 17^h$, $\delta \approx -40°$, could be discovered with certainty.

In April 1963 a group of investigators of the Marine Laboratory in Washington under the guidance of Friedman, the initiator of extra-atmospherical astronomy, made analogous observations, but with the help of a much better apparatus.[242] The X-ray "telescope" with pro-portional photon counters of an area of 65 cm^2 used for these observa-tions had an already passable directivity, namely 10° referred to half the sensitivity. The first radio-telescopes possessed about the same directivity as those used in the forties, operating in the metre band. The counters were provided with thin beryllium windows and were sensitive in the range from 1.5 to 8 Å. During this experiment (carried out with the help of a small rocket of the type "Aerobee") a strong X-ray source was discovered in the constellation Scorpius, with the co-ordinates $\alpha = 16^h15^m$, $\delta = -15°$; the angular dimensions of the source were less than 5°. In addition to this, one discovered X-rays emitted from a celestial region surrounding the Crab nebula. The source could be localized with an accuracy of $\pm 2°$. From the pulse counting rate trans-mitted by the telemeter and the given spectral characteristic of the counters the spectral flux density could only be obtained when definite assumption was made on the relative spectral distribution of the radiation from the source. Thus, for example, on the assumption of a "plane" spectrum, the X-ray flux from the Crab nebula, calculated for a spectral interval of 1 Å, will be $2.0 \cdot 10^{-9}$ erg·cm^{-2}·s^{-1}. If, however, the spectral energy distribution corresponds to that of an absolutely black body at a tempera-ture of $2 \cdot 10^7$ °K, the flux will be equal to $1.5 \cdot 10^{-8}$ erg·cm^{-2}·s^{-1}.

The discovery of a quite considerable X-ray flux from the Crab nebula is of essential significance not only for the elucidation of the Crab nebula's nature but also for astrophysics as a whole. It was therefore natural that the discovery of the scientists of the Marine Laboratory attracted attention. First of all it seemed necessary to determine the source's co-ordinates more precisely, as their initial determination had been very rough. Though it was very probable that the X-ray source in Taurus was identical with the Crab nebula, it was necessary to have a proof. There arose yet another problem that urgently required a solution: which object was to be considered as the X-ray source, the Crab nebula itself or

the star which, in 1054, exploded as a supernova?   It seemed quite natural
to assume that the ex-supernova was a powerful X-ray source.   But up to
the present we do not know what this star became after it had exploded.
For many years one discussed the hypothesis that after the explosion
the star went over to a neutron state of very high surface temperature
($\sim 10^7 \,°$K).   Such an object (if it cannot cool down) must be a very powerful X-ray source.   Many, if not most, of the investigators were at that
time of the opinion that the X-ray source discovered recently in Taurus was
a neutron star (cf., for example, [243]).   In this connection we must take into
consideration that at present we know already several X-ray sources which
are not identical with the remnants of supernovae and are, possibly,
neutron stars.   On the other hand, the X-ray range of the spectrum is
very far from the optical range.   It was therefore a quite natural assumption that the Crab nebula's synchrotron spectrum ended somewhere
between the optical and the X-ray spectrum.
    It seems that with this low resolving power that can only be
attained as yet in X-ray astronomy, the problem of whether it is the star
or the nebula that emits the radiation cannot be solved in the near future.
In order to prove that the star is this source one has to ascertain that the
angular dimensions of the source are in any case smaller than 10–20″.
Nevertheless, there is a lucky circumstance which helps us in answering
this question quickly and unambiguously.   The author of this book based
his considerations on the analogy between radio-astronomical observations
(without interferometers) and X-ray observations.   Previously, together
with P. I. Bakulin, we suggested a study of the intensity distributions
within sources with the help of eclipses caused by the moon.[244]   Such
eclipses (for the given source which lies near the ecliptic) occur about once
every nine years.   This method proved to be very suitable (see § 11).
Analogous observations may be carried out also in X-ray astronomy.
If at a suitable moment during such an eclipse a rocket is started which is
carrying an X-ray telescope, one can determine the angular dimensions
of the source when the radiation flux is recorded continuously.   If it is,
for example, a point source, the flux must drop to zero at the moment
when the source is eclipsed; if it is an extended source, the flux will decrease more or less steadily.   Precisely on July 7th, 1964, the Crab
nebula must have been eclipsed by the moon.   In the early spring of
1963 we suggested to Friedman to observe such an eclipse and at the same
time we intended to organize analogous observations in our own country
where the eclipse was to be observed on August 4th, 1965.   For various

reasons these observations could not be carried out in our country. As regards the American investigators, they were extraordinarily successful.[245]

On July 7th, 1964, at 22ʰ42ᵐ30ˢ universal time, an "Aerobee" rocket was launched from the White Sands base in Arizona. The moon moved over the nebula with a velocity of 0′.5 per minute. As the largest dimension of the Crab nebula is equal to about 6′ (see § 10), the total eclipse must have taken about 12 minutes. But according to its ballistic data it could stay for only 5 minutes above the dense layers of the atmosphere (higher than 100 km). Thus the observations were planned in such a way

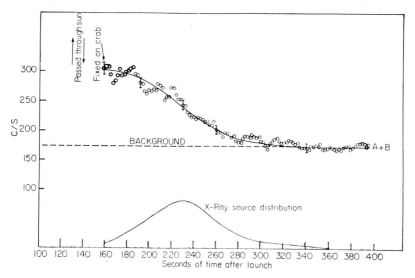

Fɪɢ. 104   Results of observations of X-ray emission of the Crab nebula during its eclipse by the moon.[245]

that only the eclipse of the central part of the nebula of a width of about 2′ was observed. Two X-ray telescopes with Geiger counters on board the rocket were directed all the time towards the Crab nebula. The telescopes differed in the thickness of the windows which were made of plastic. Therefore their spectral characteristics of sensitivity were different.

The time dependence of the photon counting rate obtained in this experiment is shown in Figure 104. We also see in it the position of the rim of the moon (dashed line) relative to the Crab nebula at various moments of time. First of all we see from Figure 104 that the X-ray flux decreases steadily as the eclipse progresses. This convincingly disproves the hypothesis that the star is the X-ray source. An analysis of the flight diagram of the rocket excludes the possibility of explaining the reduction in flux by the variation of X-ray absorption in the atmosphere. During these observations the rocket was at such heights (up to 221.4 km) that this effect was quite insignificant. A differentiation of the "curve of eclipse" may yield the X-ray intensity distribution in the area of the nebula.

The angular dimensions of the radio-frequency emitting area were found to be $\sim 1'$, i.e., much smaller than the dimensions of the amorphous mass of the Crab nebula observed at optical wavelengths. The centre of gravity of the X-ray source is displaced relative to the geometrical centre of the nebula in a north-western direction and coincides with the brightest part of the amorphous mass observed in the optical frequency range. In Figure 105, the zone of X-ray emission of the nebula is marked by a circle.

In this way it was proved that it was not the star that emitted but the nebula itself. But we still have to prove that this X-ray emission is due to a synchrotron mechanism. We cannot, for example, exclude *a priori* the possibility that a very hot plasma is the source of this radiation. In this case the emission mechanism is thermal and the X-ray quanta are produced in free–free transitions. Initially it was Friedman and co-workers who supported this interpretation. Calculations based on the simple theory of free–free radiation led to the conclusion that, if the observed X-ray flux was brought about by this mechanism, the product $N_e N_i$ must be $\sim 6 \cdot 10^5$ cm^{-6}, where N_i is the proton concentration. Hence it follows that the hypothetical hot plasma must display a very high density ($N_e \sim 400$ cm^{-3}) and its total mass must be $\sim 0.3 M_\odot$.[246] In this way the old model of the Crab nebula's amorphous mass "emerged" rather unexpectedly, a model which was still suggested by Minkowski (see § 12). An attempt at treating the X-ray emission of the Crab nebula as a thermal emission of a very hot plasma seems to us quite useless. We may, as an example, consider a simple argument against this interpretation. In § 11 we mentioned that the angular dimension of the zone emitting polarized radiation in the centimetre band is small, $\sim 1'$ (see Fig. 94), the centre of this zone coinciding with the brightness maximum of the Crab nebula in the optical range. The zone emitting polarized centimetre radio-waves is thus virtually identical with the zone emitting X-rays (see Fig. 108).   But if there $N_e \sim 400$ cm^{-3}, the radio-frequency radiation must be depolarized because of the Faraday rotation.

In fact, if we apply Equation (11.3) to the Faraday rotation in which we substitute for H the value of $3 \cdot 10^{-4}$ Oe, $N_e = 400$ cm^{-3}, $\nu = 10^{10}$

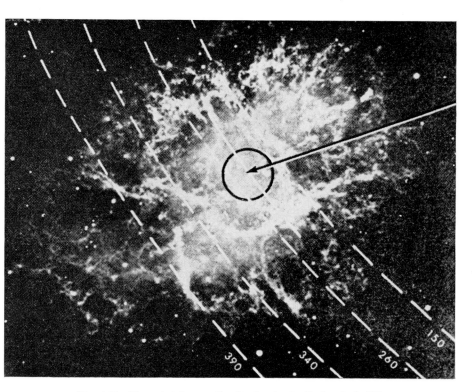

FIG. 105   X-ray brightness distribution in the Crab nebula.[245]

s^{-1} and $l = 10^{18}$ cm, we obtain a value of $\Psi \sim 50$ rad for the angle through which the plane of polarization is rotated, i.e., there cannot be any linear polarization.   In § 11 we have estimated the upper limit of N_e in the Crab nebula on the basis of polarization measurements and we obtained a value of ~ 1 cm^{-3} which obviously disagrees with the interpretation of the American investigators.

Initially they refused the possibility of interpreting the X-ray emission of the Crab nebula as the result of a synchrotron mechanism, first of all because they over-estimated the reliability of their spectral measurements. As already mentioned above, they worked with two counters having different spectral transmission characteristics. One of them, owing to the smaller thickness of the window, was sensitive to much longer waves than the other. Since the synchrotron spectrum must grow as the frequency increases, the "long-wave counter" must have yielded the higher pulses. On the other hand, the pulse counting rate of both

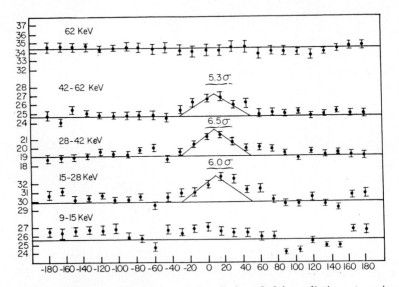

Fig. 106 Results of observations of the Crab nebula's radiation at various frequencies in the X-ray range.[274]

counters was virtually the same. From these facts the American investigators derived the conclusion that the spectral flux density of X-ray emission has a maximum of about 3 Å and resembles the curve for an absolutely black body at $T = 10^7\,^\circ$K. Later on, however, Friedman and co-workers discovered a systematic error in their spectral measurements and calculations.[246] According to later measurements, carried out during the rocket flight of November 25th, 1964, the observed X-ray emission could be interpreted equally well as either synchrotron radiation with a spectral index of $\alpha = 1.1$, the radiation of an absolutely black body at $T = 5 \cdot 10^6$ °K, or the free–free emission of an optically thin layer of plasma of $T = 10^7$ °K. In this case the X-ray flux in the spectral range between 1.5 Å and 8 Å is equal to $1.1 \cdot 10^{-8}$ erg/cm$^2 \cdot$s. If we assume that the spectral flux density of this radiation is $F_\nu \propto \nu^{-1.1}$, we obtain for $\lambda = 3$ Å ($\nu = 10^{18}$ s^{-1}), $F_\nu = 10^{26}$ erg/cm$^2 \cdot$s. We adopt this value in the following considerations.

The hypothesis on the synchrotron nature of X-ray emission of the Crab nebula obtained a final proof by Clark who, with the help of balloons, made very important observations of the much harder radiation emitted by this object.[247] He used calibrated scintillation counters with an effective area of 97 cm^2. As usual in such observations, the field of vision was determined by means of a collimator and was $\pm 10°$ in one direction and $\pm 55°$ in the other. The observations were made in the channels of $h\nu = 9$–15 keV, 15–28 keV, 28–42 keV, 42–62 keV, and > 62 keV. Figure 106 shows the results of observations of the passages of the Crab nebula through the "radiation pattern" of X-ray receivers. On the ordinate the pulse counting rates are plotted and on the abscissa the angle between the direction to the Crab nebula and the axis of the X-ray telescopes. We see at once that, except for the last channel for the hardest quanta with energies > 62 keV, the X-ray emission from the Crab nebula was observed in all cases. After a careful consideration of X-ray absorption in the atmosphere it could be shown that

$$F_\nu = F_{\nu_0} \left(\frac{\nu}{\nu_0}\right)^{-2}$$

where

$$F_{\nu_0} = (2.4 \pm 0.6) \cdot 10^{-27} \text{ erg/cm}^2 \text{ s} \cdot \text{c/s}$$
$$\nu_0 = 7.2 \cdot 10^{18} \text{ c/s}$$

It was shown in this way that in the spectral range between $\nu_1 = 3 \cdot 10^{18}$ c/s and $\nu_2 = 10^{19}$ c/s the radiation decreases according to a spectral law, with a spectral index $\alpha = 2$. The absence of an observable radiation in the channel $h\nu > 62$ keV permits the determination of the upper limit of the spectral flux density in this shortest-wave range of the spectrum. At $\nu = 2 \cdot 10^{19}$ c/s ($h\nu \sim 80$ keV) one obtains $F_\nu < 1.2 \cdot 10^{-28}$ erg/cm^2 s$\cdot$c/s. The spectral index of the X-ray emission in the range from 10^{19} to $2 \cdot 10^{19}$ c/s was found to be higher than 4.

If the radiation measured by Clark had been of thermal nature its temperature must have been $\sim 6 \cdot 10^7$ °K, and in the case of an optically thin layer of gas $T_e = 2 \cdot 10^8\,°K$.   These results are in contradiction with the temperatures obtained under the same suppositions from an analysis of softer X-rays.   A natural explanation of the results of observing the Crab nebula's X-ray emission in the wide spectral range from 0.3 to 8 Å is possible only if we assume that this radiation is produced in a synchrotron mechanism.

Let us now consider how the results of observations of the X-ray emission of the Crab nebula and the above results of radio, infrared and optical observations fit together.   For this purpose we determine the "mean" spectral index of the synchrotron radiation emitted by the Crab nebula between the infrared and the X-ray ranges of the spectrum. The choice of these two spectral ranges is determined by the fact that the influence of interstellar absorption is minimal.   According to V. I. Moroz' observations $F_\nu = 1.4 \cdot 10^{-25}$ W/m²·c/s at $\nu = 1.57 \cdot 10^{14}$ c/s ($\lambda = 1.90\,\mu$), whereas in the X-ray range, at $\nu = 7.2 \cdot 10^{18}$ c/s, $F_\nu = 2.4 \cdot 10^{-30}$ W/m²·c/s.   Hence results a spectral index $\alpha = 1.0$.   We must note, however, that in the X-ray range α increases with the frequency. As we have good reason to assume that the spectral index varies smoothly in a wide frequency range, it is a natural conclusion that for frequencies $10^{14} < \nu < 10^{18}$ c/s (e.g., in the optical and ultraviolet ranges) $\alpha < 1$ and must be close to 0.8.   This is an independent method of estimating the spectral index of the Crab nebula in the optical frequency range, where the results of direct measurements are affected by the influence of interstellar light absorption.

The difficult problem of the source of ionization of the gaseous filaments in the Crab nebula is connected with its ultraviolet and X-ray emission.   If there did not exist a foreign source of ionization, the plasma in the filaments would be neutralized in a time given by $\tau_r \sim (N_e\sigma_r)^{-1}$, where σ_r is the recombination coefficient which, with $T_e \sim 17{,}000\,°K$ (see § 5), is equal to about $2 \cdot 10^{-13}$ cm³/s, and $N_e \sim 10^3$ cm³ is the electron concentration in the filaments.   Hence follows that $\tau_r \sim 5 \cdot 10^9$ s or ~ 150 years.   In the beginning, when the nature of the amorphous mass in the Crab nebula was still unknown, it was assumed that the ultraviolet emission of the central hot star, the ex-supernova, was the source of ionization.[162]   Later on, when the synchrotron nature of the optical emission from the amorphous mass had been recognized, Woltier stated the hypothesis that the source of ionization of the filaments was the ultraviolet and X-ray emission of the latter, being a natural continuation of the optical continuous spectrum.[163]   The spectral density of the synchrotron radiation decreases exponentially as the frequency rises, i.e., it decreases relatively slowly. Therefore, long before the X-ray emission had been discovered, a sufficiently high emissivity in the ultraviolet range was in any case to be expected. Let us consider this important problem in greater detail.

According to [163] the synchrotron emissivity of the Crab nebula, calculated per unit interval of frequency, is given by

$$I(\nu) = I(\nu_0)\left(\frac{\nu}{\nu_0}\right)^{-\gamma} = 4.85 \cdot 10^{21}\left(\frac{\nu}{\nu_0}\right)^{-\gamma} \tag{13.1}$$

where $\nu_0 = 7.06 \cdot 10^{14}$ at $\lambda = 4{,}250$ Å. If we assume that the mean radius of the shell forming the filaments is $R = 0.8$ psc and take into consideration that the hard radiation is produced mainly inside the shell, we obtain for the flux of ionizing quanta with energies $h\nu_1 > 13.54$ eV that hit the shell the following expression:

$$F_{L_c} = \frac{N_{L_c}}{4\pi R^2} = \frac{4.85 \cdot 10^{21}}{h}\left(\frac{\nu_i}{\nu_0}\right)^{-\gamma}\int_{\nu_i}^{\infty}\left(\frac{\nu}{\nu_0}\right)^{-\alpha}\frac{d\nu}{\nu}$$

$$= 3.5 \cdot 10^9 \text{ photons/cm}^2 \cdot \text{s} \tag{13.2}$$

Let us now consider the ionization equilibrium in the filaments for any arbitrary element, which is established in the field of the hard radiation of the amorphous mass. The condition of the ionization equilibrium reads as follows:

$$N_A\int_{\nu_i}^{\infty}\frac{\sigma_A(\nu)F(\nu)}{4\pi r^2 h\nu}\,d\nu = \frac{N_A I(\nu_0)(\nu_i/\nu_0)^{-\gamma}}{4\pi h r^2}\int_1^{\infty}\sigma_A(y)y^{-(\gamma+1)}\,dy$$

$$= \sigma_{2A}N_A^+ N_e \tag{13.3}$$

where $\sigma_A(\nu)$ is the photo-ionization cross section per atom, and σ_{rA} is the recombination coefficient. Substituting the numerical values of the coefficients and giving r in psc we shall have:

$$\frac{N_A^+}{N_A} = \frac{1.11 \cdot 10^{10}(\nu_A/\nu_0)^{-\gamma}}{\sigma_{rA}(T_e) \cdot N_e}\int_1^{\infty}\sigma_A(y)y^{-(\gamma+1)}\,dy \tag{13.4}$$

The effective photo-ionization cross sections for various elements are given in Table 25. The recombination factor σ_{rA} is equal to

$$2.24 \cdot 10^{-13}\left(\frac{T_e}{10{,}000}\right) - 0.7$$

for protons and equal to

$$2.16 \cdot 10^{-13} \left(\frac{T_e}{10,000} \right) - 0.8$$

for O II ions. For ions with the charge Z the value of σ_{rA} must be multiplied by Z^2.

TABLE 26

A	$\sigma_A(\nu)$
H I	$6.3 \cdot 10^{-18} \, (\nu/\nu_{\mathrm{H}})^{-3}$
He I	$8.0 \cdot 10^{-18} \, (\nu/\nu_{\mathrm{He\,I}})^{-2.3}$
He II	$1.6 \cdot 10^{-18} \, (\nu/\nu_{\mathrm{He\,II}})^{-3}$
O I	$4 \cdot 10^{-18} \, (\nu/\nu_{\mathrm{O\,I}} < 1.3)$
	$12 \cdot 10^{-18} \, (1.3 < \nu/\nu_{\mathrm{O\,I}} < 2.5)$
	$12 \cdot 10^{-18} \, (\nu/2.5\nu_{\mathrm{O\,I}})^{-3}$
O II	$8.1 \cdot 10^{-18} \, (\nu/\nu_{\mathrm{O\,II}})^{-3}$

Solving Equation (13.4) for the various ions, we shall have:

$$\frac{N_{\mathrm{H\,II}}}{N_{\mathrm{H\,I}}} = 31.5 \cdot R^{-2}(t_e)^{0.3} x^{-1} (4.66)^{-\gamma} (\gamma + 3) \simeq 57$$

$$\frac{N_{\mathrm{He\,II}}}{N_{\mathrm{He\,I}}} = 40.1 \cdot R^{-2}(t_e)^{0.3} x^{-1} (8.44)^{-\gamma} (\gamma + 2.3)^{-1} \simeq 58$$

$$\frac{N_{\mathrm{He\,III}}}{N_{\mathrm{He\,II}}} = 1.98 \cdot R^{-2}(t_e)^{0.3} x^{-1} (1.86)^{-\gamma} (\gamma + 3)^{-1} \simeq 1.3$$

$$\frac{N_{\mathrm{O\,II}}}{N_{\mathrm{O\,I}}} = 20.3 \cdot R^{-2}(t_e)^{0.3} x^{-1} (4.66)^{-\gamma}$$

$$\times \left[\frac{1 + 2(1.3)^{\gamma} - 3(2.5)^{-\gamma}}{\gamma} + \frac{47 \cdot (2.5)^{-(\gamma + 3)}}{\gamma + 3} \right] = 270$$

$$\frac{N_{\mathrm{O\,III}}}{N_{\mathrm{O\,II}}} = 10.1 \cdot R^{-2}(t_e)^{0.3} x^{-1} (12.03)^{-\gamma} (\gamma + 3) \simeq 5.5$$

(13.5)

where

$$(t_e) = \frac{T_e}{10,000}, \qquad x = 10^{-4} N_e (t_e)^{-1/2}$$

The numerical values of N_A^+/N_A in the right-hand side of Equation (13.5) are obtained under the supposition that $T_e = 17,000\,^\circ\text{K}$, $N_e = 10^3\,\text{cm}^{-3}$, $R = 0.8$ psc and $\gamma = 0.8$.

From Equation (13.5) it follows that the hard synchrotron radiation of the inner regions of the Crab nebula is quite sufficient to guarantee the high degree of ionization of the gas in the filaments. When calculating the ionization the filaments were assumed to be transparent for the hard radiation of the amorphous mass. Let us check the validity of this assumption. The thickness of bright filaments may be assumed as $\sim 3 \cdot 10^{16}$ cm (this corresponds to about 2″, see § 10). Assuming $N_i \sim 10^3$ cm^{-3} (where N_i is the concentration of the hydrogen ions) we obtain a value of $N_{\text{N I}} \sim 20$ cm^{-3} for the concentration of neutral hydrogen atoms, the optical thickness at the absorption edge is therefore obtained as $\tau_{\nu_{\text{H}}} = l\sigma_{\nu_{\text{H}}} N_{\text{H I}} \simeq 3.5$. At $\lambda \sim 500$ Å (this is close to the absorption edge of helium), $\tau_\nu \sim 0.6$. At $\lambda \sim 500$ Å, which includes the absorption by helium, and the abundance of helium in the filaments may be about the same as that of hydrogen (see § 10), absorption by He$^+$ ions whose abundance is very high (cf. Equation 13.5) will then also become effective. We may draw the conclusion that up to $\lambda \sim 100$ Å the optical thickness of bright filaments may be of the order of several units. This, however, indicates that at the outer periphery of the filaments the ionization will be much lower. This fact is likely to be the explanation of the presence of a rather bright O I line ($\lambda = 6,300$) in the spectra of filaments. In fact, if there were no absorption, the oxygen ionization would be almost complete, i.e., O II/O I ~ 270. At such a high degree of ionization, the line $\lambda = 6,300$ would display a very low intensity.

We are thus led to the conclusion that the lines O I and O II must be emitted in different parts of the filaments. It must be expected that $\lambda = 6,300$ is emitted only in the outer periphery of bright filaments. It would be interesting to verify this conclusion of the theory by way of taking photographs of the Crab nebula through a narrow-band interference filter ($\Delta\lambda \approx 50$ Å) centred to $\lambda = 6,300$ Å.

These calculations show us that the ionization of the filaments can be explained entirely by the ultraviolet and X-ray synchrotron emission of the amorphous mass. We must, however, note that the high intensity of the forbidden lines, compared to the intensity of the Hβ line, makes the filaments' spectrum dissimilar to the spectrum of usual gas nebulae which are ionized and excited by the ultraviolet radiation from hot stars. As to its shape the spectrum of the filaments is rather similar to the spectra of remnants of supernovae of the type II (see § 5). From this several authors derived the conclusion that the mechanism of ionization and excitation of the filaments must be an impact mechanism.[163] The collisions with electrons (and also with relativistic particles moving through the filaments) may of course play a certain part. On the basis of various hypotheses on the possible concentrations and energies of "super-thermal" particles, the ionization observed in the filaments may be formally explained. There is, however, an essential difference between the conditions in nebulae formed after the explosion of a type II supernova and those in the filaments of the Crab nebula. In the latter there exists a "foreign" source of hard photon radiation whose power is sufficiently high to explain the ionization in the filaments, whereas the former do not possess anything like it. As regards the relative weakness of the H lines in the filaments of the Crab nebula, this may be explained by the relatively low abundance of hydrogen.

In paper [248] it was attempted to prove that the power of hard synchrotron radiation of the amorphous mass should be insufficient to ionize the filaments. But the calculations carried out in this paper are based on the arbitrary supposition that the spectral index of the synchrotron radiation in the range of $\lambda < 912$ Å is equal to 2, whereas, actually, it is known to be smaller than unity and very likely close to 0.8 (see above). This causes an error in the number L_c of quanta emitted per second which corresponds to a factor of about 20. According to [248] the correct value of $N_{L_c} \approx 3.5 \cdot 10^{47}$ s^{-1}, whereas the number of hydrogen recombinations on all levels and in all filaments is of the order of 10^{46} s^{-1} (this value is obtained from the observed intensity of the Hβ line). An analysis of photographs of the Crab nebula may show that the filamentary system as a whole "screens" 3–10 per cent of the entire surface of the nebula. If we assume that the optical thickness of the filaments for L_c quanta is ~ 1 (the reasons for this were given above) we find that the number of these quanta absorbed in the filaments is virtually equal to the total number of recombinations. This simple estimation shows clearly that the ionization of the gas in the filaments is mainly due to photo-ionization by the hard synchrotron radiation of the amorphous mass.

Woltier drew attention to an interesting peculiarity of the spectra of individual condensations of the filaments. The theoretical intensity ratio of the forbidden lines O III and O II depends on the state of ionization, the electron concentration N_e and the temperature T_e:

$$\frac{I_{\lambda\,5,007+4,959}}{I_{\lambda\,3,727}} = 0.40\,e^{0.97/t_e} \cdot \frac{N_{\mathrm{O\,III}}}{N_{\mathrm{O\,II}}} = \frac{4.0\cdot(t_e)e^{0.3(0.97)/t_e}}{R^2 x} \cdot \frac{(12.03)^{-\gamma}}{\gamma+3}$$

$$(13.6)$$

where Equation (13.5) has been used for $N_{\mathrm{O\,III}}/N_{\mathrm{O\,II}}$.

This ratio is a very weak function of the electron temperature but depends strongly on N_e and R. If for each condensation the intensity ratio of the lines [O III] and [O II] is multiplied by R^2, the quantity obtained (let us denote it by Q) must be a function of N_e alone. In fact, however, there exists a marked correlation between Q and R: Q increases as R increases. Since this correlation is physically senseless, Woltier concluded that the values of the radii vectors of the individual condensations must have been determined incorrectly. The latter are determined from the radial velocities of the condensations and the angular distance to the centre of the nebula, on the assumption that the distance of the Crab nebula is a known quantity. Since it is obvious that no doubts may subsist as to the measured radial velocities and angular distances, Woltier assumes that, in order to remove the apparent correlation between Q and R, the value adopted so far for the distance of the Crab nebula should be multiplied by 1.5 to 2. If this is true the Crab nebula must possess the form of an *elongated* spheroid (i.e., a spheroid in which two axes are equally long while the third one is longer). Baade's estimate of the distance to the Crab nebula (1,130 psc, cf. § 10) was, however, based on the assumption that the Crab nebula represents a *flattened* spheroid (two axes equal, the third shorter). If, as suggested by Woltier, the Crab nebula has the form of an elongated spheroid, the linear velocity of expansion along the major axis will be at least 1.5 times the observed radial velocity of the filaments projected onto the central part of the nebula, which corresponds to a motion in the direction of one of the minor axes. Baade, however, assumed that these two velocities were equal and, on this assumption, he obtained the distance given above from measurements of the proper motions at the major-axis edges of the nebula. Adopting the model of the elongated spheroid we obtain a value of at least 1,700 psc for the distance to the Crab nebula; this distance may, however, even amount to about 2,000 psc.

There exists yet another important argument which, quite independently, speaks in favour of the necessity of increasing the distance obtained by Baade to at least 1.5-fold. In § 3 it was shown that the visual magnitude of the supernova of 1054 was -5. With a distance of 1,130 psc, without taking absorption into account, a value of -15.35 is obtained for the absolute magnitude of this supernova. If absorption is taken into account and, according to O'Dell (see above), a value of $A_v = 1.1$ magnitudes is chosen for interstellar absorption, the absolute magnitude of the supernova of 1054 is obtained as -16.45, that is, 2.4 less than the mean absolute magnitude of a type I supernova (see Table 2 from which it follows that the dispersion in absolute magnitude of type I supernovae at maximum is small). If, however, the distance of this supernova is 1.5 times greater, the modulus rises to 0.87 and, as the absorption in this region is a linear function of the distance, the absolute magnitude will be equal to -18.9, which corresponds precisely to the mean value of the absolute magnitudes of type I supernovae at maximum.

The model of the elongated ellipsoid is also preferable for other reasons. According to this model, substance was ejected during the outburst in two opposite directions (in all probability parallel and antiparallel to the axis of rotation). We observe a great number of such remnants in radio galaxies. In this case the scale of the phenomenon is much larger than in the case of supernovae. With outbursts of a much smaller scale, in the case of ordinary novae, the ejected shells are often observed in the form of two "pole caps."[71] We see that a similar image can be obtained with phenomena occurring on a much larger scale and supernova outbursts will hardly be an exception. As regards the model of the "spheroid flattened at the poles" which was used by Baade, it is devoid of any physical significance, for such a compression may only be explained by a sufficiently rapid rotation of the nebula. If it rotated about the minor axis (in this model) this rotation must in any case occur at a speed lower than 100 km/s as this follows from spectroscopic observations; a full rotation of the nebula would therefore take more than 40,000 years, not to mention the moment such a rotation would require, which is several million times the moment of rotation of the exploded star.

We thus have good reason to increase the distance to the Crab nebula from the value of 1,130 psc adopted hitherto to a value of about 1,700 psc. This increase of the distance by a factor of g, where $g \sim 1.5$, entails a series of grave consequences. First of all, the extent of interstellar light absorption increases; i.e., A_v becomes equal to about 1.6 magnitudes. Above, where we adopted this value of A_v without proof, we obtained a value of $\alpha = 0.8$ for the spectral index of the Crab nebula's synchrotron radiation in the optical frequency range. This value of α may now be considered as being sufficiently well established.

If this nebula is an elongated ellipsoid of revolution, its two minor axes, which are perpendicular to the direction of vision, are increased g-fold while the third axis (in the direction of vision) remains unchanged. As a result of this the nebula's volume has grown by a factor of $g^2 = 2.25$. The same factor describes the increase in mass of the gaseous filaments (if N_e is determined from the intensity ratio of the O II lines, $\lambda\,3{,}727$: $\lambda\,3{,}729$). The two velocity components of the filaments must increase g-fold and the mean square velocity is increased by a factor of $(2g^2 + 1)/3$. The kinetic energy of the filaments grows by a factor of $(2g^4 + g^2)/3$ or, with $g = 1.5$, to about fourfold. The emissivity of the Crab nebula rises g^2-fold throughout the spectrum. The quantity K, which determines the mean concentration of the relativistic particles and their energy density, remains unchanged since the dimensions of the nebula in the direction of vision are the same. Therefore, with a given surface brightness, the volume luminosity, the main observational quantity which enters Equation (6.7) of the synchrotron theory, remains unchanged. For the same reason the calculated value of H remains unchanged. The total energy of the relativistic particles and the magnetic field increases, owing to the increase in volume of the nebula, to the g^2-fold value. Consequently, the ratio between the kinetic energy of the filaments and the energy of the magnetic field and the relativistic particles remains unchanged.

As the problem of the spectral index of the synchrotron radiation of the Crab nebula in the optical frequency range has been elucidated (which was essentially connected with a revision of the assumptions on the distance of the Crab nebula), we shall now discuss the whole spectrum of synchrotron radiation of this object in the wavelength range from ~ 10 m to 0.3 Å. This spectrum, as constructed after all the publications of observations available at present, is shown in Figure 107. This spectrum is characterized by the following specific features: (a) In the range of $5 \cdot 10^7 < \nu < 3 \cdot 10^{10}$ c/s the spectral index is equal to $\alpha_1 = 0.28$; (b) in the optical and the near infrared ranges ($2 \cdot 10^{14}$ to 10^{15} c/s) the spectral index is $\alpha_2 \sim 0.8$ (if the distance of the Crab nebula is $\sim 1{,}700$ psc,

11+s.

see above); (c) in the millimetre range, beginning with $\nu \sim 3 \cdot 10^{10}$ c/s, the spectral flux density begins to increase with the frequency so that the spectral index assumes negative values, $\alpha_3 \approx -0.7$; (d) the X-ray range of the spectrum is tightly connected with the optical range, but it must be taken into account that, beginning with $\nu \sim 10^{16}$ c/s, the spectral index grows, reaching a value $\alpha_4 \sim 2$ at about $\nu \sim 10^{18}$ c/s and for still higher frequencies $\alpha_5 > 4$.

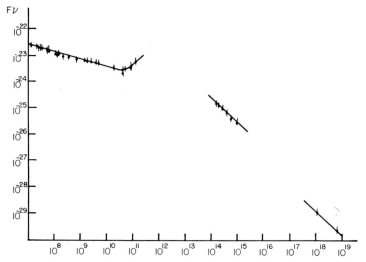

FIG. 107   Synchrotron spectrum of the Crab nebula in the whole frequency range.

The characteristic feature of the Crab nebula's synchrotron spectrum which, in our opinion, is most important, is the fact that the difference $\alpha_2 - \alpha_1 \approx 0.5$. It is well known from the theory of the synchrotron radiation that, if in a given zone with a constant magnetic field ($H_\perp = $ const) relativistic electrons are continuously injected which possess an initial energy spectrum $dN(E) = KE^- \, dE$, this spectrum, owing to the losses to synchrotron radiation, will assume the form $K'E^{-(\gamma+1)}$, i.e., it becomes steeper.[249]   If the injection time is finite and equal to t_1, it is obvious that the spectrum is only "transformed" for relativistic electrons whose energies are higher than E_1; E_1 is determined by the condition that electrons with this energy, when moving in a magnetic field H, lose an energy similar to E_1 because of synchrotron radiation.   It is obvious that the energy spectrum of electrons with $E < E_1$ remains unchanged whereas that of electrons with $E > E_1$ becomes steeper.   The "threshold" energy of the relativistic electrons E_1 is determined by the formula (derived in [250])

$$E_1 = \frac{8.35 \cdot 10^6}{H_\perp^2 t_1} \text{ eV} \qquad (13.7)$$

where t_1 is the time in years during which continuous injection has taken place.

In the range of $E = E_1$ electrons are "accumulated" which, previously, had higher energies.   Since the spectral index $\alpha = (\gamma - 1)/2$, an increase of γ by unity will, for electrons with $E > E_1$, correspond to an increase of the spectral index by 0.5 in a higher frequency range. Between the spectral ranges with $\alpha = \alpha_1$ and $\alpha = \alpha_1 + 0.5$ an intermediate range must exist in which the spectral curve will possess either a maximum or an inflection point.

Precisely this spectrum is observed in the case of the Crab nebula. If the "discontinuity" of the spectrum due to the change of the spectral index by 0.5 occurs at the frequency ν_1, it follows from Equation (13.7) that

$$H_\perp \approx 700 \nu_1^{-\frac{1}{3}} t_1^{-\frac{2}{3}} \qquad (13.8)$$

Assuming for our case that $t_1 \sim 900$ years and $\nu_1 \sim 10^{12}$ c/s, we find that $H_\perp \approx 7.5 \cdot 10^{-4}$ Oe.   This value of $H_\perp$ was also used in the calculations of the synchrotron radiation carried out in the previous sections. The magnetic field in the Crab nebula was first estimated by S. B. Pikel'ner[251] with the help of this method.   At that time (1957), however, the observational data on the spectrum of the Crab nebula was very scanty.   Note that this estimate of H depends very slightly on the value chosen for ν_1.   Of greatest importance, however, is the conclusion that the injection of relativistic particles in the Crab nebula has been taking place all the time, in particular at the present time.   The initial energy spectrum of the relativistic electrons, which are continuously injected into the Crab nebula, has the form

$$dN_1(E) = \frac{K_1 \, dE}{E^{1.6}} \qquad (13.9)$$

where $10^8 < E < 10^{13}$ eV.   With $E > 10^{13}$ eV the initial energy spectrum becomes somewhat steeper; this results in an increase of the spectral index of the Crab nebula's synchrotron radiation at the transition to the X-ray range of the spectrum. The value of $K_1 = K$ where K is obtained from an analysis of the relatively long-wave synchrotron radiation caused by relativistic electrons which, for the present, have conserved their initial energy spectrum. According to Equation (11.1), $K = 9.6 \cdot 10^{-9}$. Hence follows that the total energy of the relativistic electrons which have been injected into the Crab nebula during its time of existence must be equal to

$$\mathscr{E}_{\text{rel.el.}} = v \int_{E_1}^{E_2} \frac{K_1}{E^{0.6}} \, dE = v K_1 E_2^{0.4} = 5 \cdot 10^{-8} v \text{ erg}$$

where $E_2 \sim 3 \cdot 10^{12}$ eV. Assuming a value of $v \sim 10^{55}$ cm^3 for the volume of the nebula, we find that $\mathscr{E}_{\text{rel.el.}} \approx 2.5 \cdot 10^{48}$ erg. Let us now determine the total energy of all relativistic electrons which at present exist in the Crab nebula. In § 11 we determined the energy density of the relativistic electrons whose $E < 1.5 \cdot 10^9$ eV, and in § 13 that for the relativistic electrons with $E > 3 \cdot 10^{11}$ eV. An analogous estimate may also be obtained for $W_{\text{rel.el.}}$ with $1.5 \cdot 10^9 < E < 3 \cdot 10^{11}$ eV. The total energy density of all relativistic electrons is equal to $\sim 7.5 \cdot 10^{-9}$ erg/cm^3; this is one-quarter of the magnetic energy density with $H_\perp = 7.5 \cdot 10^{-4}$ Oe.

The energy of the relativistic electrons injected into the Crab nebula for the time of its existence is therefore six to seven times higher than that of the relativistic electrons it contains at present. From this we may conclude that, by way of a synchrotron mechanism, the nebula emitted an amount of $4.2 \cdot 10^{-8} \cdot v \approx 2.5 \cdot 10^{48}$ erg. It is interesting to compare this value with the synchrotron emissivity of the Crab nebula in the entire frequency range. Integrating the curve of Figure 107 we find that $\int F_\nu \, d\nu = 2.5 \cdot 10^{-7}$ erg/cm$^2 \cdot$s. Assuming that $R = 1{,}700$ psc we obtain a value of $L \sim 9 \cdot 10^{37}$ erg/s for the total synchrotron emissivity of the nebula. Note that the optical emissivity in the range $7{,}600 < \lambda > 3{,}200$ Å amounts to about one-tenth of the bolometric value. Thus, if the injection occurred all the time at a constant rate, $2.4 \cdot 10^{48}$ erg will have been emitted during a time of ~ 900 years $= 2.7 \cdot 10^{10}$ s; this value agrees with the above estimate obtained in an independent way. It must be stressed that this conclusion does not depend on the value chosen for the distance of the Crab nebula since the quantity L and the nebula's volume v (which, with constant K, determine the total energy of all relativistic electrons injected into it) depend likewise on r.

It must not be assumed that, simultaneously with the injection of relativistic electrons, relativistic protons or any other nuclei are injected into the Crab nebula, the total energy of the latter exceeding the energy of the relativistic electrons injected by a factor of k.   It is well known that in the primary cosmic radiation the energy of the proton and nuclear component is about a hundred times higher than the energy of the electron component (see § 16).   Some authors assumed that the situation in the Crab nebula may be similar.[252]   But if besides the relativistic electrons, relativistic protons and nuclei also were injected into the Crab nebula, they must, first of all, have remained in the nebula.

   In § 19 we shall show that the magnetic field in the Crab nebula is of "intrinsic" origin and cannot be amplified by interstellar fields.   With such a structure of the lines of force it is virtually impossible that relativistic particles should gradually "leak" out of the nebular region and fly away into interstellar space.   If their pressure is high enough, they may only deform the system of the magnetic lines of force and even "scatter" them.

   We must also take into consideration that the heavy relativistic particles injected into the nebula and retained in it will virtually not lose any energy to synchrotron radiation as their masses are too great.   Their energy will therefore grow steadily and at present it should have reached

$$Kk \int_{E_1}^{E_2} E^{-0.6} \, dE = 2.5kKE_2^{0.4} = k5 \cdot 10^{-8} \ \text{erg/cm}^3$$

this value is obtained under the assumption that the energy spectrum of the heavy nuclei injected equals that of the relativistic electrons.   As at present the mean magnetic energy density in the nebula is $W_m \sim 3.3 \cdot 10^{-8}$ erg/cm^3, we see at once that k cannot exceed unity, as otherwise the field would have been strongly distorted by the relativistic particles. We shall now determine more accurately the upper limit of k and, at the same time, consider the interesting problem of explaining the secular acceleration of the Crab nebula's filaments.

   In § 10 we discussed the conclusion first obtained by Baade according to which the filaments in the Crab nebula move at an acceleration of $g = 0.0011$ cm/s^2.   As the acceleration is proportional to the major axis of the filamentary system, and as this axis proved to be 1.5 times longer than assumed by Baade, we obtain $g = 0.00165$ cm/s^2. S. B. Pikel'ner suggested for the first time that this acceleration of the filaments might be caused by the pressure of the magnetic fields and relativistic particles present in the Crab nebula.[251]   Let us estimate this effect quantitatively.   We denote the total mass of the system of the gaseous filaments by M_1; the condition that the pressure of magnetic field and relativistic particles is equal to the force acting on the filaments will then read

$$M_1 g = \left[\frac{H^2}{8\pi} + (1 + k)P_e \right] 4\pi R^2 \qquad (13.10)$$

where R is the characteristic dimension of the nebula and H the magnetic field strength at the periphery of the nebula, in the region of its gas shell consisting of the filaments. From the fact that the radio-frequency radiation from the Crab nebula at a distance of 3′ from its centre has dropped to one-tenth of the maximum (see § 11) we may conclude that the product $k \cdot H_1^{(\gamma + 1)/2}$ will also drop to 30 per cent. Hence it follows that H at the periphery of the nebula is about one-third of H in the central part and we shall assume a value of $3 \cdot 10^{-4}$ Oe for it. We assume further that $P_e \sim 2.5 \cdot 10^{-9}$ erg/cm³ (this, too, is one-third of the value in the central part of the nebula since $P_e \sim H$) and that the effective radius of the filamentary system is $R = 3.5 \cdot 10^{18}$ cm; we then obtain, with $k = 0$, $M_1 \approx 5 \cdot 10^{32}$ g or $\sim 0.25 M_\odot$. With $k = 1$, M_1 would exceed the solar mass, and this is impossible since the supernova of 1054 was of type I. In this way we come to the conclusion that in the Crab nebula some particular mechanism must be effective which mainly accelerates the electrons up to relativistic velocities; the power of this mechanism should vary but slightly with time.

The differences in the values of H and, perhaps, even in the energy spectrum of the relativistic electrons in the various parts of the nebula, may cause differences in the spectra of synchrotron radiation. It has been already stressed in § 11 that the angular dimensions of the Crab nebula at radio frequencies (referred to the half-power points) are definitely greater than those of the optical range; in other words, the brightness gradient in the latter is greater. This provides a natural explanation for the difference of the spectral indices of the two forms of radiation. Since the volume luminosity is $\varepsilon_\nu \propto H$ (cf. § 6), a higher value of α will correspond to a stronger dependence on H; with $\alpha = 0.28$, $\varepsilon_\nu \propto H^{2.95}$ and $\alpha = 0.8$, $\varepsilon_\nu \propto H^{3.7}$. In this way one can explain the small dimensions of the zone emitting X-rays for which $\alpha \sim 2$. The different values of H in the various parts of the nebula may also have other consequences.

As already mentioned in § 11, V. I. Slysh recently stated a very interesting hypothesis on a new possibility of explaining the observed decrease of the degree of polarization of the radio emission of the Crab nebula accompanying an increase in wavelength.[254] Since, according to observations, the source of polarized radio-frequency radiation possesses angular dimensions of 2″ and virtually coincides with the zone emitting polarized optical synchrotron radiation (see § 11), it is quite natural to assume that the polarized radio-frequency and optical radiations are emitted from the same inner parts of the nebula. It is therefore very probable that both the radio-waves and the optical radiation are produced

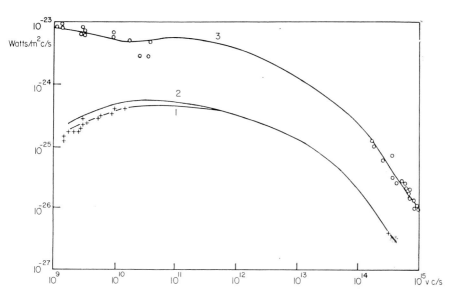

FIG. 108   Spectrum of the polarized radiation from the Crab nebula.[254]

by relativistic electrons moving in the same magnetic fields. Consequently, the polarized radio-frequency and optical radiations must be determined by one and the same energy spectrum of relativistic electrons. V. I. Slysh based his considerations on the bold assumption that there is no depolarization in the Crab nebula and in this way he developed the spectrum of the polarized radiation from the Crab nebula (cf. Fig. 108). This spectrum differs essentially from the integral spectrum of the nebula shown in the same figure. In the radio-frequency range the spectral index of the radiation is negative and, what is noteworthy, it is close to $-\frac{1}{3}$. This is precisely the value the spectral index of synchrotron radiation must possess if it is emitted by relativistic electrons whose energy spectrum displays a sharp "lower" cut-off at an energy E_0 for frequencies lower than

$$\nu_c = \frac{eH_\perp}{2\pi mc} \left(\frac{E_0}{mc^2}\right)^2$$

(see § 6). As assumed by V. I. Slysh, the sudden jump of the angle of position of the electrical vector at the transition from the optical range to the 3-cm band may be explained by some change in the process responsible for the production of the radiation.

It follows from the theory that for the low-frequency harmonics of the radiation caused by relativistic electrons (i.e., at $\nu < \nu_c$) the degree of polarization of the radiation of each relativistic electron diminishes to 50 per cent, whereas with $\nu \gg \nu_c$ it is equal to 100 per cent.[255] It is therefore quite natural to assume that the polarized radiation in the radio-frequency range consists of the low-frequency harmonics of the relativistic electrons' radiation; these electrons are responsible for the emission of the Crab nebula at higher frequencies (mainly in the visible range). This radiation is emitted in the central parts of the Crab nebula whereas the non-polarized radiation comes from its peripheral parts and is perhaps generated in the shell.

As shown in § 10, the optical emission of the Crab nebula consists of an almost completely polarized radiation of individual zones and a non-polarized background. The low-frequency harmonics of the relativistic electrons' radiation from these zones will, according to V. I. Slysh's hypothesis, also appear as polarized radio-frequency radiation of the Crab nebula. In this case the 10° rotation of the plane of polarization of the radio-frequency radiation is explained by a reduction of the degree of polarization accompanying the transition to the lower harmonics (see above), since the entire polarized radiation of the Crab nebula is the sum of the radiations of the individual parts of the nebula possessing a high degree of polarization. It must be assumed that the angle of position of the resulting electrical vector is very sensitive to changes of the degree of polarization of individual regions. As the transition to the lower harmonics in the individual regions does not occur at the same time (because of inevitable slight differences in the magnetic field strength and the spectrum of the relativistic electrons) the "weight" of the various regions will be different at lower frequencies and this gives rise to a rotation of the resulting electrical vector.

We have given here a relatively detailed description of V. I. Slysh's hypothesis which is very interesting and promising. In our opinion an important factor for this hypothesis must be the considerable difference between the magnetic field in the central part of the Crab nebula (from which chiefly polarized radio-frequency and optical radiations are emitted) and that in the peripheral parts. It may be supposed that the low-frequency "aggregation" at $\nu < 50$ Mc in the Crab nebula's integral spectrum (see Fig. 85) is "repeated" in some way for polarized radiation at the higher frequency of $\sim 5 \cdot 10^9$ c/s (see Fig. 101). If the relativistic electrons move in the given spatially variable magnetic field with conservation of the adiabatic invariant, we find that, as $E \propto H^{1/2}$, the maximum frequency of the synchrotron spectrum

$$\nu_c \sim \frac{eH}{2\pi mc} \left(\frac{E}{mc^2}\right)^2 \propto H^2$$

Therefore, if the central part of the nebula contains individual parts where the magnetic field is stronger by an order of magnitude than that in the peripheral parts, and more or less uniform, these parts may emit a polarized radiation of the spectral composition observed.

§ 14   The remnant star of the supernova of 1054 and its continued activity

The most important result of the investigations into the synchrotron radiation of the Crab nebula is the proof that relativistic electrons of high and super-high energies are still produced at present. Let us recall the principal facts whose analysis forms a basis for the following conclusions:

(a) In a field of $H_\perp \sim 7.5 \cdot 10^{-4}$ Oe, which must be assumed to explain the discontinuity observed in the spectrum of the Crab nebula's synchrotron radiation, the time within which an electron loses half its energy in the form of radiative losses is given by the expression

$$t_{1/2} = \frac{8.35 \cdot 10^{-3}}{H_\perp^2 E} \simeq 70 \text{ years} \tag{14.1}$$

where E is given in beV. This period of time is essentially shorter than the time of existence of the nebula. Consequently, all the relativistic electrons which are responsible for the optical emission of the Crab nebula must be "renewed" every 50–100 years.

11*

(b) Since the X-ray emission of the Crab nebula must also be of synchrotron origin, the value of $t_{1/2}$ will yet be smaller for it. For example, in the case of electrons emitting synchrotron radiation in the range of 50–60 keV which was observed by Clark (cf. § 13), $E \sim 3 \cdot 10^{13}$ eV and $t_{1/2} \sim 0.5$ years.

From (a) and (b) it immediately follows that some "foreign mechanism" must be effective in the Crab nebula, which provides its permanent "supply" of relativistic electrons. From the character of the synchrotron spectrum of the nebula (see Fig. 10 and the discussion in § 13) it follows that the "primary" energy spectrum of the relativistic electrons injected displays a slope corresponding to $\gamma \approx 1.6$.

If in the optical frequency range the Crab nebula's radiation is caused by relativistic electrons which have been accumulated there in the course of 30 years, the emission in the X-ray range is due to "fresh" relativistic electrons which were produced a few weeks ago. Any possible power fluctuations of the injection mechanism will therefore be smoothed considerably for the "optical" relativistic electrons, whereas the X-ray emissivity may vary according to the power fluctuations of the injection mechanism, provided, of course, that their characteristic time exceeds several months. It would be very interesting to carry out systematic long-time observations of the X-ray flux from the Crab nebula in order to discover possible variations of the flux in this frequency range. Such observations could be made from a specially designed artificial satellite.

In the previous section it was shown that the power of the injection mechanism effective in the Crab nebula must be more or less constant and equal to the power of its synchrotron emission, i.e., $\sim 10^{38}$ erg/s. There arises the question of the source of such an injection. The possibility of an injection into the entire volume of the nebula must be discounted, as in this case the mechanism of relativistic particle acceleration would display quite an unusual character. Since these losses to synchrotron radiation are proportional to the square energy of a relativistic electron, for their compensation it must, first of all, be assumed that the energy gain per unit time is proportional to E^δ, where $\delta > 2$. Such a mechanism is, however, unknown in physics. Moreover, the action of such a mechanism in the nebula would result in a secular increase of the number of high-energy relativistic electrons which, in its turn, would radically influence their synchrotron spectrum so that it would be essentially different from that which is actually observed.

Previously, some authors[256] assumed that the relativistic electrons in the Crab nebula might be secondary particles. According to this hypothesis they might be produced in collisions between relativistic protons (or any other heavy nuclei) and nuclei of ions of the plasma constituting the Crab nebula. It is, however, easy to see that this hypothesis cannot withstand criticism. The total amount of energy of the relativistic electrons injected in this way per second will be equal to

$$n_{\text{rel.prot.}} n_0 \sigma c v E = 10^{38} \text{ erg/s} \tag{14.2}$$

where $n_{\text{rel.prot.}}$ denotes the concentration of the relativistic protons with a mean energy of $\sim 20\bar{E}$ ($\bar{E}$ being the mean energy of the injected electrons), $\sigma \sim 3 \cdot 10^{-26} \text{ cm}^2$ is the collision cross section of the nuclei, $v \sim 3 \cdot 10^{55} \text{ cm}^3$ is the effective volume of the nebula and n_0 is the concentration of the gas. The right-hand side of Equation (14.2) gives the observed value of the total synchrotron emissivity of the Crab nebula. Assuming that $\bar{E} \sim 10^{10}$ eV, we obtain a value of ~ 0.3 for the product $n_{\text{rel.prot.}} n_0$, which is quite impossible. If, for example, $n_{\text{rel.prot.}} \sim 10^{-7} \text{ cm}^{-3}$ (which corresponds to an energy density of the relativistic protons of $\sim 3 \cdot 10^{-8} \text{ erg/cm}^3$, which is equal to the energy density of the magnetic field, see the preceding section), $n_0 \sim 3 \cdot 10^6 \text{ cm}^{-3}$, a value which is absurdly high.

The inapplicability of the hypothesis on the secondary nature of the relativistic electrons in the Crab nebula was proven by direct observations. The fact is that in every nuclear collision besides the relativistic electrons and positrons, gamma quanta are also produced whose energy is about the same as that of the relativistic electrons and positrons. In 1960 Cocconi developed the hypothesis that the Crab nebula may be a source of a measurable flux of very hard gamma quanta.[257]

From 1960 onwards, A. Ye. Chudakov and co-workers studied the possibility of fluxes of super-high photons from various cosmic sources, in particular from the Crab nebula.[258] Though the above calculations show that it cannot be expected that secondary relativistic electrons and positrons are generated in the whole volume of the nebula, the possibility cannot be excluded that such a process occurs in a sufficiently small region (for example, in the neighbourhood of the ex-supernova, see below) from which, as we may assume, relativistic protons of high gas density are continuously injected.

The observations of A. Ye. Chudakov's group were carried out within a period of four years. The method of these observations was based on the registration of extensive atmospheric showers in a small solid angle (of the order of several thousand steradians) by way of recording the Cherenkov radiation produced by them in the atmosphere. The observations were made with the help of a telescope system shown in Figure 109. As we see from this diagram, the system consists of four telescopes, each representing a system of three paraboloids with parallel optical axes. A photoelectric multiplier is arranged in the focus of each of the paraboloids and the signals of all these multipliers are fed through h-f cables to the counting unit. The showers are recorded with the help of a coincidence method. All the devices used were high-power instruments so that it was possible to record flashes of Cherenkov radiation induced by showers of a relatively low energy of about $2 \cdot 10^{12}$ initial eV.

Fig. 109 Photograph of the installation in order to observe the radiation from the Crab nebula.[258]

The results of these interesting observations were negative: it was not possible to detect any measurable effect when the telescope was directed towards the Crab nebula. The showers recorded were all due to the isotropic background. Thus in [258] the conclusion was drawn that the photon flux from the Crab nebula was weaker than $5 \cdot 10^{-11}$ photons/ cm$^2 \cdot$s for photons with energies $h\nu > 5 \cdot 10^{12}$ eV. This result is at least a thousand times smaller than the value expected on the supposition that the relativistic electrons in the Crab nebula are produced in secondary processes.

So we cannot imagine that the relativistic electrons are injected into the entire volume of the nebula by virtue of some kind of mechanism. We must therefore assume that there exists some object in the Crab nebula which acts as a relativistic electron generator of extremely high power and which may be regarded as "foreign" with respect to the Crab nebula. The physical conditions in this object (density of matter, temperature, magnetic field) must be quite different from the conditions in the Crab nebula so that the mechanism of electron acceleration up to relativistic velocities may be highly specific. It is a natural assumption that this object is identical with the ex-supernova star plus its immediate environment.

The observational results support the assumption that the Crab nebula contains, mathematically speaking, a "singularity" of small dimensions. First of all we shall discuss the surprising metamorphoses observed by Baade, which occur in the central part of the Crab nebula (see § 12). The surface brightness of the moving "plaits" in the central part of the Crab nebula may be roughly estimated in the following way. According to a communication by Baade, the integral stellar magnitude of the "plait" is usually 1 magnitude below that of the little star close to it, i.e., it is about 17; its angular dimensions amount to about 5 × 5 seconds of arc (see Fig. 99). Hence it may be derived that the total radiation from the "plait" is a thousand times weaker than that from the nebula as a whole, whereas the surface brightness is about equal to the mean brightness of the nebula from an area of a radius of 1″ surrounding the central star. As the thickness of the "plait" is about 1″ its volume luminosity will be about one hundred times higher than the mean volume luminosity of the central part of the amorphous mass.

From observations of the Crab nebula in polarized light it follows that the magnetic field in this part of it is directed along the "plait" axis; its velocity is therefore perpendicular to the direction of the magnetic field. Now we can imagine that the "plait" was formed in the following way: Owing to the effect of some external cause the lines of force of the magnetic field were rapidly compressed. This magnetically denser zone was then propagated in a direction perpendicular to that of the perturbing forces, as a magneto-hydrodynamic wave. Owing to the local intensification of the magnetic field the volume luminosity of the relativistic electrons contained in this zone increased considerably. According to Equation (6.13), with $\gamma = 2.6$, it is necessary for ε_v to increase 100-fold so that the field intensity increases 3.5-fold, i.e., relatively insignificant. We must take into consideration that the relativistic electrons contained in the region of the "plait" move along helical trajectories around the lines of force and cannot escape the "plait" during its time of existence ($\sim 10^7$ s). Only moving along the plait axis, which has a length of $\sim 2\cdot 10^{17}$ cm, they may escape at its ends; the pitch of their helical trajectories is, however, small, which follows from the adiabatic invariant. The relativistic electrons which are responsible for the optical emission of the "plait" cannot lose an essential part of their energy during the lifetime of this formation, which amounts to several months. In the "normal" parts of the nebula $t_{1/2} = 60$ years, with $H_\perp = 7.5\cdot 10^{-4}$ Oe. If the field strength is increased 3.5-fold, $t_{1/2}$ will be ~ 10 years. But why does such a "plait" disappear? The only natural explanation is a dissolution of the magnetic perturbation as the wave is propagated.

On the assumption that the motion of the "plait" may be considered as the propagation of a single pulse tranversely to the magnetic field, we find from the usual condition

$$\frac{H^2}{8\pi} = \frac{\rho V_A^2}{2}$$

where V_A is the propagation velocity of the wave ($\sim 3\cdot 10^9$ cm/s) and ρ is the density of the surrounding medium, with $H \sim 3\cdot 10^{-3}$ Oe, $\rho \sim 8\cdot 10^{-26}$ g/cm^3; it follows from this estimate that $N_e \sim 5\cdot 10^{-2}$ cm^{-3} which is in agreement with the estimate of N_e obtained from polarization observations discussed in § 13.

We may now ask the reason for this rapid pinch of the magnetic lines of force that gave rise to the formation of the "plait" and its movement. The most probable explanation seems to assume that a great number of relativistic particles was ejected from a relatively small region surrounding the ex-supernova. It is well known that a sudden appearance of a great number of relativistic charged particles will "expel" the surrounding magnetic field. A good example for such a process is the "Argus" experiment, as the result of which a "void" of several hundred kilometres in diameter was formed in the magnetic field of the earth and maintained for some time. But, when the pressure of the relativistic particles become similar to the pressure of the magnetic field, their free flight ceases and they begin to move in the direction of the magnetic field.

Let us now consider the case where a cloud of relativistic particles is ejected from some small region in the central part of the Crab nebula. Such periodically repeated ejections are indeed the source of the particle injection. As these ejections occur, on the average, every $\sim 5 \cdot 10^6$ s, the total energy of the relativistic electrons contained in one ejection will be equal to $E_b = 5 \cdot 10^6 \cdot 10^{38} \sim 5 \cdot 10^{44}$ erg. From the condition

$$\frac{E_b}{\frac{4}{3}\pi R_1^3} = \frac{H^2}{8\pi}$$

we may estimate the radius of the region in which the relativistic particles "swept out" the initial non-perturbed magnetic field whose intensity may be assumed as $\sim 10^{-3}$ Oe. We obtain $R_1 \sim 1.4 \cdot 10^{17}$ cm which, with a distance of the Crab nebula of about 1,700 psc, corresponds to about 6″. This is precisely the distance at which the "plait" always appears (cf. § 12).

The picture of the "plait" formation sketched above is, of course, very rough. It is, nevertheless, able immediately to give an explanation of the fundamental peculiarities observed with these remarkable formations (magnitude and direction of the motion, why they never appear in the immediate proximity of the central star, and the like). Remember that such characteristic formations which resemble the "plaits" also appear east of the central star (see Fig. 99). This fact is also explained easily by our hypothesis.

In the inner region of the nebula surrounding the central star there usually exists a "void" of the magnetic field which is expelled by the injected clouds of relativistic particles. The relativistic electrons which, under the conditions of free flight, move along straight lines, will therefore virtually not emit radiation. Thus it is not insignificant that the brightness of the amorphous mass of the Crab nebula is small in this area. It is, obviously, due to a projection of more peripheral parts of the nebula. After the pressure of the relativistic particles has come into equilibrium with the magnetic pressure, these particles, moving along the lines of force in a channel whose width amounts to about $3 \cdot 10^{17}$ cm, "escape" into the nebula and mix there with the relativistic particles already present. At the same time the magnetic field in the central part begins to "regenerate" rather quickly to be "swept out" again by the following portion of relativistic particles injected into the central region.

In this way we may imagine the injection of relativistic particles into the Crab nebula, according to an analysis of the metamorphoses observed

328 The Crab nebula [Ch. III

in its central region. As already mentioned above, it is natural to connect these periodically repeated ejections of clouds of relativistic particles with a continued activity of the ex-supernova. What can we say about this star, on the basis of the observational data available at present? It is well known that two stars exist in the central part of the Crab nebula whose mutual angular distance amounts to 4".9. According to Baade, these stars have almost the same visual magnitude, $m_{\mathrm{ph}} = 15.9$.[160] The northern star has a colour index of $+0.80$, the southern star's colour index is equal to $+0.41$. The colour indices alone do not, therefore, indicate that one of these objects has an anomalously high temperature of its emitting surface. It is interesting that none of the faint stars in this part of the nebula, up to $m = 20$, displays any anomaly in colour which might indicate a high temperature. We must, however, bear in mind that owing to the interstellar absorption the colour index must be lower and, consequently, the colour temperature must be higher. The corrections for interstellar absorption of the colour indices of these stars are equal to $+0.14$ and $+0.53$ for the southern and the northern stars, respectively. From this we can estimate the spectral classes of these stars as F1 and G4.

These photometrical observations were completed by Minkowski's spectrographical observations.[162] It must be noted that it is an extremely difficult task to obtain slit spectrograms of these stars. The fact is that these faint objects are projected onto the very bright nebula. A reliable result may only be obtained from very good images when a sufficiently narrow slit of the spectrograph can be used so as to improve the contrast of the stellar spectra against the continuous spectrum of the nebula.

The spectrum of the northern star indicates that the temperature of its photosphere is considerably lower than that of the southern star. One may recognize weak absorption lines. It is, however, difficult to obtain an accurate spectral classification as the contrast against the nebular background is poor and, moreover, emission lines are superimposed. It can, however, be proved that the spectral class is somewhere between early F and early G. The spectrum of the southern star is purely continuous, absorption lines were not discovered in it. A comparison of the energy distributions in the continuous spectra of the southern and the northern stars shows that the former is of a later spectral type than the latter subclass B. This result does not contradict Baade's estimate given above. It must be mentioned that the spectrum of the little southern star does not range so far into the ultraviolet as that of such hot stars as ex-novae, pseudonovae and the like.

At that time Minkowski shared the prevailing preconceived opinion that the luminosity of the Crab nebula was of the same origin as that of the planetary nebulae, i.e., it was due to the presence of a "central" star, which possessed a very high surface temperature. He therefore tried in every way to show that the southernmost of the two stars positioned in the central part of the Crab nebula was this hot "nucleus" of it. But an analysis of the very scanty observational material in no way led to the conclusion that this star was very hot. Recently a brief communication was published, according to which Kraft, who was the first after Minkowski to obtain a spectrogram of the southern star, discovered in its spectrum the Fraunhofer lines H and K of ionized calcium; this would permit its classification as an ordinary F-type star.[259] Unfortunately, Kraft has never published his observations and we do not know to what extent the report contained in [259] is reliable.

And yet this star does possess an interesting peculiarity which attracts our attention. According to Duncan's observations the proper motion of the southern star is given by $\mu_\alpha = -0''.019$, $\mu_\delta = 0''.000$, whereas the neighbouring northern star's motion is defined by $\mu_\alpha = 0''.000$, $\mu_\delta = 0''.000$.[158] Old observations made by A. N. Deych and V. I. Lavdovski in Pulkovo are in agreement with Duncan's results, as they yielded for the southern star $\mu_\alpha = -0''.018$, $\mu_\delta = 0''.003$, and for the northern star $\mu_\alpha = 0''.000$, $\mu_\delta = 0''.002$.[159] The probable error of these observations does not exceed $\pm 0''.003$.

It should also be noted that from the old and insufficiently accurate observations by van der Maan, Baade found a value of $\mu_\alpha = -0''.010$ for the proper motion of the southern star,[160] which is lower by almost 50 per cent. This result, however, deviates essentially from the above three results obtained in independent measurements and its value is insignificant. It is interesting that the proper motion of the entire system of filaments in the Crab nebula is, according to [158], similar in magnitude and of the same sign as the values given above: $\mu_\alpha = -0''.022$, $\mu_\delta = +0''.007$.

If the southern star is located in the Crab nebula, we obtain the relatively high value of ~ 150 km/s for its tangential velocity, and ~ 190 km/s for its probable spatial velocity, which is six to seven times higher than the velocity dispersion of main-sequence stars of the spectral class F. In the case of sub-dwarfs the dispersion of velocities reaches ~ 150 km/s.[261] An F-type sub-dwarf of an absolute magnitude $+5$ located in the Crab nebula should, however, possess a visual magnitude of

18.5 (which has already been corrected for light absorption) and this is 2.5 magnitudes below the actual magnitude of the southern star in the central part of the Crab nebula. In general, pre-outburst supernovae of the type I are hardly ever found among the sub-dwarfs as this would be in contradiction with the observed position of supernovae of this type in the spiral galaxies (most of them appear at the edges of the disc).

It might also be assumed that this star is projected by chance on the Crab nebula. It is, however, easily proved that the probability that a star assumes such a position relative to the nebula is very small. The fact is that the "physical centre" of the Crab nebula, i.e., the zone containing the powerful energy source whose activity has continued to the present time, has been determined quite accurately. As this follows from the considerations of the problem of "plait" formation (see above), it will in any case be located in the neighbourhood of the southern star, within a radius of 3″. On the other hand, according to data of stellar statistics, the number of stars of magnitude up to 16 positioned in the region of the galactic equator amount to 10^4 per square degree; hence we can estimate the probability of finding such a star inside a circular area of a radius of 3″: $2 \cdot 10^{-2}$. It must still be added that the star we are interested in belongs to the spectral class F. It is easily proved that stars of this spectral class, possessing a photovisual magnitude of 15.5, may only be found at distances equal to the distance of the Crab nebula (taking interstellar light absorption into account, $A_v \approx 1.5$ magnitudes). The probability for F-type stars being found by chance within the region of the physical centre of the Crab nebula will *a priori* be as low as $\sim 10^{-3}$, i.e., low enough. We can therefore assume with high probability that the southernmost star in the central part of the nebula is connected with the genetics of the latter. On the other hand, on the basis of the scanty observational data, we may conclude that this star is not so unusual that it may be regarded as an ex-supernova. Minkowski's spectrogram which, admittedly, is of very poor quality, seems to indicate that this star cannot be very hot. If Kraft's observational results mentioned above are correct, we are concerned with an ordinary F-type star. It is very difficult to imagine that a star which has survived such a catastrophe has not undergone radical changes.

In view of this situation the author of the present book recently developed the hypothesis that the star observed is one of the components of a binary system whose other component exploded as a supernova and at present cannot be observed by optical means.[262] An argument in favour of this hypothesis is the anomalously high spatial velocity of this star. One may attempt to explain such a high velocity by the "sling effect" (cf. § 4). Let us consider the following simplified model of the phenomenon: We assume that the ex-supernova has been the component of a system of close binaries of similar masses. We further assume that after the outburst the system did not disintegrate, i.e., the motion remained elliptic, only the parameters had changed considerably. We shall suppose that the observed spatial velocity of the southern star in the Crab nebula resembles the velocity of the centre of gravity of the system after the explosion of one of its components. The theory developed in § 4 is perfectly suited to treat our problem. For definiteness we assume that the pre-outburst mass ratio of the two components was $M_2/M_1 = 0.8$ and the initial orbit was circular. The further analysis will be based on Tables 5–7. We see from these tables that if the star has lost more than 50 per cent of its mass in the explosion (i.e., $q < 0.5$), the velocity of the centre of gravity of the system after the explosion (relative to the "old" centre of gravity) will, principally, consist of the initial orbital velocity. For example, if $q = 0.3$ (i.e., the star has lost 70 per cent of its initial mass in the explosion) the velocity of motion of the centre of gravity after the explosion will amount to ~ 0.5 of the initial orbital velocity. Hence it follows that, if we want to explain the observed high spatial velocity of the star in the centre of the Crab nebula by the "sling effect," the initial orbital angular velocity must have been very high, $\sim 300–400$ km/s. When each component had a mass of $\sim 1 M_\odot$, the distance between them must have been about $3–4 R_\odot$, i.e., this must have been a system of very close binaries with a period of revolution of about 24 hours.

It follows from Table 5 that, if the mass was lost rapidly enough (in our case within several hours), the orbit may have assumed a purely elliptical shape. For example, if $\tau_c = 0.2$ (i.e., a time of mass losses of the exploding star ~ 0.2 of the period) and $q = 0.1$ the major semi-axis of the orbit after the outburst will become twenty-one times larger than the radius of the initial circular orbit. The period of revolution will in this case rise a hundredfold, i.e., it will then be of the order of several months.

The observed high spatial velocity of the star in the centre of the Crab nebula may therefore be explained by the assumption that the star which exploded as a type I supernova had a pre-outburst mass similar to the solar mass of which it lost at least 80–90 per cent during the outburst, within a time of several hours. It is quite natural to assume a relatively small initial mass of the exploded star as the supernovae of type I pertain to the galactic population II. The assumption that the star loses 80–90 per cent of its mass in the explosion is, however, not so obvious. But it must be borne in mind that a mass loss may be due not only to ejection of gases but also to powerful neutral emission. Here, however, we are concerned with the fundamental problem of the cause and the mechanism of supernova outbursts which has not yet been touched upon. This problem, which is still far from being solved, will be considered in § 18. But it must be mentioned right now that the modern theories and hypotheses do not assume such great mass losses for supernovae. At this point our own hypothesis meets with serious difficulties.

If we assume that an essential part of the mass of the exploding star was ejected in the form of gas (and not by neutral emission), we must expect that the mass of the Crab nebula's filaments must amount to $\sim 1 M_\odot$, whereas the value obtained in present estimates for the mass of the filaments amounts to only one-tenth of this (see § 10). This difficulty, however, does not seem insurmountable to us. We may, for example, assume that a great part of the mass of the filaments consists of cold, non-emitting gas (e.g., of neutral helium and hydrogen of a low degree of ionization). Such an assumption may be based on the rather intense emission of the filaments in the [O I] lines, indicating that the outer parts of the filaments may consist of neutral gas. We saw already (cf. § 13) that an estimate of the total mass of the Crab nebula's filaments, from the acceleration observed, depends relatively strongly on the value assumed for H in their peripheral zones. In particular, if the field strength is there increased two- to three-fold, the mass of the filaments is obtained as $\sim 1 M_\odot$. There is yet another difficulty: the law of conservation of momentum requires that the velocity of the centre of gravity of the gas shell, ejected in the outburst, must be opposite to the velocity of the star. But according to previous observations made by Duncan, as already mentioned above, the residual proper motion of the Crab nebula's filamentary system is given by $\mu_\alpha = -0''.022$, $\mu_\delta = 0.000$, i.e., almost equal in magnitude and of equal direction to the proper motion of the southern of the two stars located in the centre of the Crab nebula.[158] It must, however, be mentioned that a displacement is superimposed upon the suggested proper motion of the Crab nebula's filamentary system, which exceeds the latter by at least an order of magnitude (see Fig. 66). The determination of the proper motion of the filamentary system as a certain differential effect is therefore a very difficult problem, while the principal effect is not at all determined.   If, in fact, ~ 80–90 per cent of the stellar mass were ejected in the outburst, the expected proper motion of the filamentary system must be very small and hardly detectable.

We have so far discussed the numerous difficulties with which our hypothesis meets.   At the same time it seems to be able (in principle) to explain some important effects following an analysis of the results of observations of the central part of the Crab nebula.   If the remnant of the supernova moves on a highly eccentric orbit within a period of several months, it may be expected that in the periastron of its orbit it will, so to speak, "dip" periodically into the atmosphere of the non-exploded star. This may be accompanied by high-energy processes in which a great number of relativistic particles are generated.   We have good reason to assume that after the outburst the supernova turns into an object of almost nuclear density whose dimensions are close to the Schwarzschild radius (cf. § 18).   Each particle that falls onto this star will therefore possess a velocity similar to the velocity of light.   If we assume that the continued activity of the nucleus of the Crab nebula is caused by an accretion of the gas compressed by the star (cf. § 19), the absorbed periodicity of about a hundred days of the metamorphoses in the central part of the Crab nebula described above may be explained by the orbital motion of the ex-supernova.   When the latter "dips" periodically into the atmosphere of the non-exploded component, powerful jets of gas are torn out of it, impinging on the ex-supernova and streaming around it. The process of this ejection will take a time of the order of several hours, then follows a relatively quiet period of two to three months.   In § 19 we shall calculate the possible power of the relativistic particles generated in this process.

To verify this hypothesis it would be very important to observe systematically the luminosity of the central star.   If this hypothesis is true, it may be expected that the star displays periodic flares of brightness, the duration of which should amount to several hours and the period to several months.

We cannot exclude the possibility that the "binary" or, in general, the multiplicity, is a fundamental property of all exploding objects.   It is well known that ordinary novae display periodic outbursts only because they are components of close binaries.[263]   Under certain conditions the normal evolution of such objects is impossible and a different type of instability arises.   It may be assumed that under particular conditions, which exist relatively rarely, the components of a system of close binaries may explode as supernovae. We, however, touched repeatedly on the problem of the cause of supernova outbursts which will be considered below.

There is yet another problem which is connected with the problem of the continued activity of the nucleus of the Crab nebula; it concerns an interesting singularity of the energy spectrum of the relativistic electrons in the Crab nebula. From the analysis of the spectrum of the synchrotron emission from the Crab nebula in the range of relatively low frequencies ($\nu < 50$ Mc) it follows that the energy spectrum of the emitting relativistic electrons displays a rather sharp cut-off at an energy of ~ 100 MeV (cf. § 13). What is the reason for this cut-off? Relativistic electrons of such energies cannot undergo any essential losses of energy in the nebula itself. In the case of $H \sim 10^{-3}$ Oe, for these electrons $t_{1/2} \sim 10^5$ years and, in order to undergo essential ionization losses, the relativistic electrons must, as can be shown, travel through a substantial layer of ~ 1 g/cm^2. The distance each relativistic electron travels within a time of $\sim 3 \cdot 10^{10}$ s amounts to $\sim 10^{21}$ cm so that, for the above thickness to be traversed, it has to move in a medium with a density of $\sim 10^{-21}$ g/cm^3. The mean density of the substance in the amorphous mass of the Crab nebula must in fact be lower by at least four orders of magnitude (see § 13).

Hence we may draw the conclusion that the discontinuity in the energy spectrum must be a characteristic feature of the injected electrons. One of the possible explanations for this cut-off and, in our opinion, also the most natural, consists in the assumption that in the injection zone the relativistic electrons pass through a layer of matter possessing a surface density of ~ 1 g/cm^2.

If we know the surface density we can determine the lower limit of the gas concentration in the injection zone. As the characteristic time between the appearances of two "plaits" amounts to $\sim 10^7$ s and must be equal to the period of time between two injections, each relativistic particle will travel a distance of $\sim 3 \cdot 10^{17}$ cm in this time. It is obvious that only a small fraction of this distance will lie in the injection zone. From the condition that

$$c\tau N_H \cdot m_H > l N_H m_H \sim 1 \text{ g/cm}^3$$

we find that $N_H > 2 \cdot 10^6$ cm^{-3} and hence follows a value of $\gtrsim 3 \cdot 10^{-18}$ g/cm^3 for the gas density in the injection zone. This estimate is in all probability much too low. We can therefore draw the conclusion that the injection of relativistic particles into the Crab nebula takes place in a relatively dense plasma where the gas concentration is at least 10^8 times higher than the particle concentration in the amorphous mass of the nebula and at least 10^5 times higher than the gas concentration in the filaments. This result, which has been obtained from an analysis of the spectrum of synchrotron radiation from the Crab nebula in the low-frequency range, is an independent argument in favour of the assumption that an injector of relativistic particles exists in the central part of the Crab nebula, where the physical conditions differ essentially from the "average" conditions.

It is very tempting to link this peculiar zone in the central part of the Crab nebula with the powerful source of low-frequency radio emission possessing small angular dimensions (see § 11). We must remember that from observations of the scintillations at a frequency of 38 Mc it follows that a source exists in the Crab nebula which has the angular dimensions $\lesssim 0''.1$, corresponding to linear dimensions of $\lesssim 10^{15}$ cm, with a brightness temperature of $\gtrsim 10^{14}\,°\mathrm{K}$. It is quite possible that this source varies its power in the course of time. This assumption is supported by, e.g., the fact that no scintillations are observed for several months between October and February (see Fig. 87). If the absence of scintillations between the end of May and the beginning of July finds a natural explanation in the influence of the super-corona of the sun through which the radio-waves of the Crab nebula are transmitted, their absence between October and February may be explained either by the absence of notable inhomogeneities in the electron density in the interplanetary plasma or by a sharp decrease of the flux from the source of small angular dimensions. We cannot decide which of these two possibilities is preferable since the observational data available are too scanty.

The greatest difficulties we meet when trying to link the activity centre in the Crab nebula with the source of low-frequency radio emission of small angular dimensions are due to the results of observations of nebular eclipses by the Moon, at relatively low frequencies (cf. § 11). According to these observations the source of the low-frequency radio emission is displaced by $1'.2$ relative to the centre of the Crab nebula. We can hardly doubt that this source is identical with the source emitting the scintillating flux. As already stressed in § 11, it seems quite improbable to us that this very small source is located at the periphery of the nebula in the range of a bright filament. We can imagine that a more attentive consideration of the conditions of propagation of long-wave radio-frequency radiation (with, e.g., refraction taken into account) would permit an elimination of this difficulty and enable us to allocate the small source in its "right place," namely the centre of the Crab nebula.

As already stressed in § 11, the mechanism of radio-wave emission of the source of small angular dimensions in the Crab nebula cannot be a synchrotron mechanism. It is a natural assumption that plasma oscillations, which are induced by currents of fast particles, should be the cause of this radio emission. It is well known that an analogous mechanism is responsible for the appearance of great outbursts of radio-frequency radiation in the sun.

If plasma oscillations are the mechanism of radio-wave emission we may, on the basis of the observable part of the radiation, estimate the electron concentration of the plasma traversed by the relativistic particles which excite the plasma oscillations; for this purpose we use the well-known relation

$$2\pi\nu_L = \sqrt{\frac{4\pi e^2 N_e}{m}} = 5.64\cdot 10^4 \sqrt{N_e}\ \text{s}^{-1}$$

which yields a value of $N_e \sim 10^7\ \text{cm}^{-3}$; this is almost equal to the electron density in the middle part of the solar corona. Let us now estimate the total emissivity of the source of small angular dimensions: $L = 4\pi R^2 F$, where F is the flux from this source integrated over the frequencies which may be obtained from Figure 84. If we carry out this calculation we obtain $L \sim 2\cdot 10^{32}$ erg/s which is ~ 0.005 per cent of the synchrotron radiation from the Crab nebula at all frequencies (see § 13). It is interesting to compare this value with the radio emissivity of a great solar eruption of type II, where the effective temperature of the sun in the metre band reaches $\sim 10^{12}\ ^\circ$K. Assuming a value of $\Delta\nu \sim 3$ Mc of the band width of the frequencies at which the radio emission of the eruption is concentrated, we obtain a power of $\sim 10^{21}$ erg/s. If we now take into consideration that the dimensions of the region in which the radio-waves are generated during a solar eruption are of the order of 10^{10} cm, the dimensions of the small source which has been assumed to emit by way of a plasma mechanism are smaller by five orders of magnitude. The power of generation in this source, per unit volume, will then be a thousand times weaker than in the zone of a solar eruption, i.e., relatively moderate. It must be borne in mind that radio-waves may be absorbed by the plasma whose oscillations generate them. In a first approximation we assumed (though completely arbitrarily) that self-absorption does not take place.

As the absorption coefficient of the radio-waves is given by

$$H_\nu \propto \nu^{-2} N_e^2 l \cdot T_e^{-3/2}$$

the plasma will be transparent with $\nu \sim 3 \cdot 10^7$ s^{-1}, $N_e \sim 10^7$ cm^{-3}, $l \sim 10^{15}$ cm and if its electron temperature is higher than $10^8\,^\circ$K. To such a high temperature the medium may be heated by the plasma waves which are excited by the high-energy currents of relativistic particles passing through it.

We should also like to draw attention to another curious fact: the low-frequency emissivity of the small source, which we assume to be caused by plasma oscillations, amounts to $\sim 10^{-6}$ of the power of the total energy flux of relativistic particles which are supposed to excite the plasma oscillations. Precisely this value must be equal to the "transformation coefficient" for the energy of the corpuscular currents converted into the energy of transverse electromagnetic waves (cf. [264]). It is possible that this may be used as an argument in favour of the concept developed above. They are, of course, preliminary for two reasons. We are just beginning an adequate investigation into the interesting phenomenon of the activity of remnants of supernovae many centuries after their outburst.

At present it is very important to obtain as much observational data as possible. First of all it is necessary to observe systematically, through large instruments, the central part of the Crab nebula, preferably in polarized light. Such observations enable us to improve and, perhaps, essentially complete the whole picture of the phenomena, the development and the dissipation of the "plaits." It is conceivable that the time is not far distant when we shall possess films in astronomy which will show us the development of individual details in the central part of the Crab nebula, similar to the films demonstrating the development of protuberances which are now obtained in a great number of solar observatories throughout the world. Systematic observations of the scintillations would be very important and it is desirable that they be made at various frequencies, in the range between 20 Mc and 50 Mc. A task of particular interest is the study of a possible variability in the source of small angular dimensions. Systematic observations of the X-ray flux from the Crab nebula in the quantum energy range of 30–60 keV should be extended over long periods of time, with the aim of detecting any possible variabilities in it. Finally we need new high-quality spectrophotographic and electro-photometrical

338 *The Crab nebula* [Ch. III

observations of the star in the centre of the Crab nebula which, we may assume, is genetically linked with the latter.

With these numerous observations the possible sources of information on the activity of the Crab nebula's nucleus are, of course, not exhausted. In this field completely unexpected discoveries may be made which will shed fresh light on the whole problem.

§ 15   The remnants of Tycho's and Kepler's supernovae

We have so far dealt with the investigations into the physical conditions in the Crab nebula, the remnant of the type I supernova whose outburst was observed in 1054. There arises, however, the question as to what extent the Crab nebula may be regarded as typical of this class of objects. In order to answer it we must analyze the observational data on other remnants of supernovae of this type. In our galaxy supernovae were observed in 1572 and 1604; their light curves identified them as pertaining to type I (see § 3). But it must be mentioned that, optically, the remnants of these supernovae are very faint objects. The information obtained from an analysis of astronomical observations is therefore rather scanty and can in no way be compared with the extensive information from observations of the Crab nebula at various frequencies. The situation is complicated further by the fact that we do not know the exact distances to the ex-supernovae. The most important problem is, we consider, the estimation of the distances from the observational data available.

After Baade had investigated the light curve of Kepler's nova (1604) and had shown that this curve is identical with the light curve of type I supernovae (cf. § 3), he started a search for a nebula at the point of the explosion.[59] If this nova in fact was a supernova of the type I, one must expect the existence of such a nebula (formed from the masses of gases ejected in the outburst) similar to the Crab nebula which, at present, is observed around the point where the supernova of 1054 exploded. The nova of 1604 was photographed in red light, since it made its appearance in the constellation Ophiuchus which is positioned in a celestial area where the interstellar light absorption is relatively high.

The filter used for this purpose had a pass band of 6,300–6,700 Å. Baade's observations were crowned with success: on June 18th, 1941, at the 100-inch telescope of the Mount Wilson Observatory, the nebula sought was discovered near the point where the nova had appeared in 1604.

The centre of the nebula proved to be displaced relative to the point of explosion by only $-2^{s}.1$ in α and $+1''$ in δ. The nebula presents itself as a configuration of bright nodes and filaments covering an area $40''$ in diameter (cf. Fig. 110). It is obvious that only the brightest filaments and nodes were observed; owing to interstellar absorption, Baade could not at first discover the fainter details. At the limit of resolution one

FIG. 110   Photograph of the nebular remnant of the supernova of 1604.[59]

could detect individual faint condensations which were spread over an area 80–$100''$ in diameter. The phenomenon as a whole reminds us a little of the nebula Cassiopeia A (cf. § 5).

As to its photovisual emission this nebula is a very faint object. Averaged over an area of $40''$ the surface brightness in the spectral range

$\lambda = 3,600\text{--}5,000$ Å amounts to only 25.2 magnitudes per square second, that is, 4 magnitudes weaker than in the Crab nebula. We must, however, take into consideration that the latter emits a very bright continuous spectrum. If we compare the brightness of the nebula around the supernova of 1604 with the filamentary system of the Crab nebula (disregarding the continuous spectrum of the latter) the difference will not be so great and may be completely explained by interstellar light absorption. According to Baade's estimate the integral photographic magnitude of the nebula is in fact equal to 19.0 and that of the filamentary system of the Crab nebula is ~ 13.5. On the other hand, the angular dimensions of the latter are 7.5 times larger. Hence it follows immediately that the surface brightness of the nebula discovered by Baade was only about one order of magnitude higher than the brightness of the filaments in the Crab nebula averaged over the whole disc.

It is interesting to mention that the structure of the nebula surrounding the supernova of 1604 in the photographic range of the spectrum is essentially different from the structure in red light. It is more uniform and does not show these bright condensations which, in the photographs obtained through red filters, are in marked contrast with the background. One of the most important results of Baade's observations was a definite indication as to the absence of any bright continuous spectrum of this nebula. Even a special photograph taken with a filter for the range $\lambda = 7,200\text{--}8,400$ Å (in this part of the spectrum there are virtually no emission lines) did not show any traces of the nebula. The image of the Crab nebula is quite different; it possesses a very bright "amorphous mass" which emits a bright continuous spectrum to be observed in photographs obtained with this red filter (see Fig. 63). The fundamental difference between the nebula surrounding the supernova of 1604 and the Crab nebula is therefore the absence of an optical emission with a continuous spectrum in the former. This is particularly important as the continuous spectrum in the Crab nebula is of synchrotron origin.

Baade's observations showed that, at the point where the supernova of 1604 exploded, there does not exist any suitable star which might be suspected of being an ex-supernova. In the very centre of the nebula there is in fact a star of magnitude 18.6 with a low colour index which indicates its high surface temperature. Of course, it cannot be excluded that this star is projected by chance to the point where the supernova of 1604 had exploded. Unfortunately, no attempts have been made since 1942 to study this star.

Soon after Baade had discovered the faint nebula at the point of the supernova outburst of 1604, Humeson tried to obtain its spectrum in the photographic range.[265]   He succeeded in discovering only one very weak line which may be interpreted as the [O III] line at $\lambda = 5,007$ Å, with a radial velocity of -200 km/s.   Since in red-light photographs the nebula looks considerably brighter it may be expected that in spectro-photographs taken in the range of longer waves more intense lines should be discovered.   In the middle of May 1942 Minkowski obtained two spectrograms in this range with different angles of position of the slit.[266]   In these spectrograms one clearly recognizes the two well-known lines of [N II], Hα and also [S II] λ 6,731 and [O I] λ 6,300 which are superimposed on the corresponding lines emitted by the nocturnal sky.   As to their form the spectra very much resemble the spectra of the Crab nebula's filaments.   In Figure 111 we see the spectra of the nebula around the supernova of 1604 and of the Crab nebula on one and the same scale.   This figure makes it obvious that the intensities of the Hα and the [N II] lines in these spectra are approximately equal.   The intensity of the [N II] lines relative to Hα is rather high compared to the spectrographs of the diffuse nebulae.   Since the intensity ratio of the lines [S II], [N II], and [O I] is more or less normal, Minkowski assumes that the hydrogen lines in the new nebula are relatively weak and links this with a possibly insufficient hydrogen abundance, a conclusion, which, in our opinion, is insufficiently established.

Compared with the spectrum of the Crab nebula, the [O III] line at $\lambda = 5,007$ Å in the spectrum of the new nebula is essentially weaker.   It is almost certain that this may be explained by interstellar absorption of light.   The intensity ratio of the lines [N II] and [O III] in the new nebula is about 4.5 times higher than in the Crab nebula.   Under the assumption that the difficulty is due only to interstellar light absorption, when it is taken into account that the two nebulae are observed at different zenith distances, Minkowski obtained a value of $CE = 1.6$ magnitudes for the colour excess between $\lambda = 5,000$ Å and $\lambda = 6,500$ Å. Hence follows a value of $A_v = 6.3$ magnitudes for the total absorption of light in the visual range!   Such a high value of A_v, though not totally exceptional, is a little surprising.   But we must not forget that we have tacitly assumed that the intensity ratio of the lines [N II] and [O III] emitted in the Crab nebula is not subject to absorption.   It is a matter of fact that, if for this nebula $A_v = 1.6$ (cf. § 13), the colour excess between $\lambda = 5,000$ Å and $\lambda = 6,500$ Å is equal to $CE = 0.37$ magnitudes.   In this case a value of $A_v = 8$ will obviously be too high for a nebula formed in the outburst of the supernova of 1604. It is quite possible that the [O III] lines, without absorption, are actually weaker than [N II].

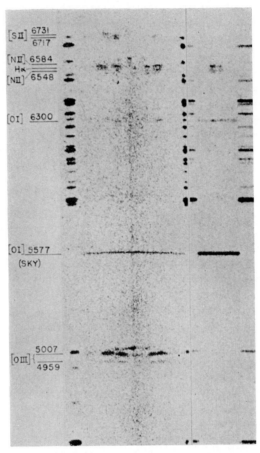

FIG. 111   Spectrum of the nebular remnants of the supernovae of 1604 and 1054.[266]

In another paper Minkowski tried to estimate the light absorption for the supernova of 1604, using the visual estimates of the stellar colour obtained by observers of the seventeenth century who compared the colour of the star with the colour of a planet in its neighbourhood.[14] The graph of Figure 6 shows the time dependence of the observed colour indices of two typical supernovae of types I and II, for the time elapsed after the maximum.   The circles indicate the colour estimates for the supernova of 1604 and the squares indicate the values for the supernova of

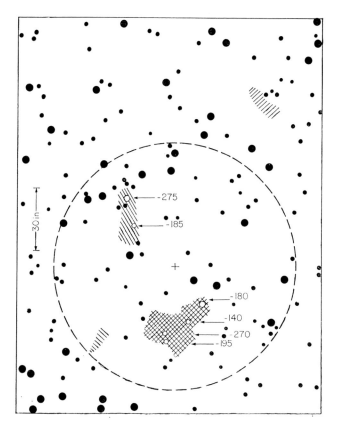

Fig. 112   Schematic representation of details in the nebular remnant of the supernova of 1604.[81]

1572.   Though these estimates are rather unreliable it is obvious that the colour index of the supernova of 1572 is 0.7 magnitudes higher than the "normal" index, and that of the supernova of 1604 is 1.1 magnitudes higher than that.   Assuming these abundant colour indices to be due to interstellar absorption, Minkowski obtained A_v values of 2.1 and 3.3 magnitudes, respectively, for these two supernovae.

Minkowski's measurements of the radial velocities for the lines emitted by the nebula which formed after the outburst of the supernova of 1604 yielded a value of about -200 km/s. From the N II line at $\lambda = 6{,}584$ Å one may draw the conclusion, admittedly not wholly verified, that over the extent of the nebula the radial velocity varies from -190 ± 30 km/s to -260 km/s.

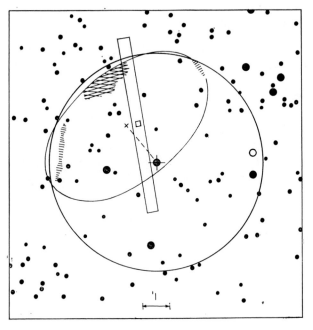

FIG. 113   Schematic representation of details in the nebular remnant of the supernova of 1572.[81]

In a later paper by Minkowski additional information is contained on the remnant of the supernova of 1604.[81] Unfortunately, it does not contain details of these investigations and reproductions of the original material. It seems that new gaseous filaments and condensations were discovered in the region of this outburst. Figure 112 gives a schematic representation of the arrangement of the individual details in this nebula.

The dashed circle indicates the accuracy of localization of the supernova's celestial position and the little circle marks the most probable point of the outburst.   Besides the nebula discovered by Baade (the grid-shaded area) we see another three faint parts.   The total area within which the nebular "patches" are observed can be placed in an ellipse with a major axis of 2'.5, possessing an angle of position of 55°.   Minkowski suggests that the velocity vectors of the nebular "patches" positioned at the periphery of the shell lie almost in the drawing plane.

The remnant of the supernova of 1572 is in its optical appearance a still fainter object than the remnant of the supernova of 1604.   It could be discovered only after the position of the supernova had been determined precisely by radio-astronomical observations.   According to [81] the very faint nebula which is to be observed at the point of explosion of the supernova of 1572 consists of two filaments, a long and a short one, and a very faint arc (see the schematic representation of Figure 113). It is possible that these details are at the periphery of the nebula.   The radial velocities of these details are close to zero.   But it must be mentioned that the radial velocities were only measured for a single line, Hα, and were rather inaccurate.   If the system of the filaments and the arc are arranged in an ellipse, the angular width of its major semi-axis must amount to about 7' and the angle of position to 130°.   Our attention is attracted by the fact that the centre of this ellipse does not coincide with the position of the stellar outburst determined on the basis of Tycho Brahe's observations.   The difference in right ascension reaches a value of 40ˢ, that is, more than 4'.   Such a great error is astonishingly high for Tycho Brahe's observations which possessed an extraordinarily high (for that time) accuracy of about 1'.

The conclusion as to the relatively small radial velocities of the filaments and nodes of the corresponding nebulae may have been the most important results of the optical observations of the remnants of Tycho's and Kepler's supernovae.   Minkowski assumed that this can be explained by their position at the periphery of the expanding shells, and that the velocity components in the image plane must be greater, e.g., several thousand kilometres per second.[81,266]   We can, however, hardly agree with that.   For example, if we assume a value of about 1,000 km/s for the velocity of expansion of the "arc" in the remnant of the supernova of 1572, whereas the radial velocity observed does not exceed 30 km/s, we are then forced to admit that the direction of motion of its individual elements deviates by at most 1–2° from the image plane.   It is, however, very unlikely that all the elements of such a relatively extended object as this arc would move almost absolutely parallel. It is also suspicious that the brighter emitting filaments which form the remnant of the supernova of 1604 display relatively low radial velocities of about 200 km/s. Minkowski also considers this case as being due to a fortuitous position of the filaments at "edges" relative to the terrestrial observer. Is that not too many coincidences? Minkowski, discussing this problem with the author of the present book, remarked that such an "edge" position (relative to the observer) of the filaments is quite natural as an optically thin expanding nebula will become brighter towards the periphery.[14] But the fact is that these faint remnants do not possess any regular shell; there exist only some more or less compact separate condensations and filaments moving with their own velocities. In any case, the effect of becoming brighter towards the edges of an optically thin shell cannot be attributed to the relatively large area with a diameter of 40″ and marked outer contours occupied by the nebula.[81] In this connection it should be noted that in the Crab nebula, even in its peripheral zone, radial velocities remain of the order of several hundred kilometres per second.

In this way we are led to the conclusion that the velocities of expansion of the filaments and the condensations of these two nebulae are relatively low, in any case much lower than in the Crab nebula where the expansion rate amounts to about 1,100 km/s. The initial velocities of the shells ejected in the outbursts must have been at least 1,000 km/s. We know from the example of the Crab nebula that at some stage of the expansion the filaments may display an accelerated motion. This can be explained by the effect of the pressures exerted by the magnetic field and the relativistic particles (cf. § 13). The only cause, however, which could explain the deceleration of an expanding shell is the resistance of the interstellar gaseous medium, the theory of which was considered in § 8. We must therefore assume that in the case of the remnants of the supernovae of 1572 and 1604 we observe slowed-down shells, in the first case the shell seems to be considerably slowed down.

Then, however, there arises another problem. The fact is that the angular dimensions of the shell, in particular in the case of the supernova of 1572, are very large while the time elapsed after the outburst is relatively short. To reduce an initial shell velocity of about 1,000 km/s to as low a value as about 200 km/s (and it is difficult to attribute a higher velocity to the shell of the supernova of 1572 since its radial velocity does not exceed 50 km/s) it is necessary that, with a density of the interstellar matter of $\sim 10^{-24}$ g/cm^3, the mass of the shell amounts to $\sim 10^{30}$ g or $5 \cdot 10^{-4} M_\odot$. If the interstellar medium possesses a density of $\sim 2 \cdot 10^{-23}$ g/cm^3 (this is the case when the exploding star is located in a cloud of interstellar gas with $N_0 \sim 10$ cm^{-3}) the mass of the shell must be $\sim 10^{-2} M_\odot$, i.e., likewise small. In this estimate it has been taken into account that the mean velocity of expansion of a strongly decelerated shell is equal to 2.5 times the present velocity of expansion, see Equation (8.11). Therefore, if $v_t \lesssim 2 \cdot 10^7$ cm/s, the radius of the shell of the supernova of 1572 will be equal to

$$R \leqslant 2.5 v_t (t - t_0) \lesssim 10^{18} \text{ cm}$$

On the other hand, the angular radius of the shell of this supernova amounts to $\sim 3'$. Hence follows a distance of the supernova of 1572 less than 370 psc! Note that this result is independent of the magnitude of the initial velocity of the shell. We have assumed only that it has been strongly decelerated and that its velocity of expansion is lower than 200 km/s.

Let us now consider the supernova of 1604. In this case the radial velocities of the condensations are known to be ~ 200 km/s. A rough estimate of the spatial velocity yields a value of ~ 400 km/s. If the initial velocity of the shell was $\sim 1,000$ km/s and if there was no acceleration, we may conclude that the process of effective deceleration has set in only recently. Then $R \simeq v_0 t \sim 10^{18}$ cm. With an angular dimension of $2'.5$ of the major semi-axis of the ellipse containing the condensations and nodes of the nebula, we obtain a value of about 1,000 psc for the distance of the supernova of 1604. Even with a density of the interstellar medium of $\sim 10^{-23}$ g/cm^3, the mass of the shell (which, under the conditions of a beginning deceleration must have been $\sim 4\pi R^3 \rho/3$) will be $\sim 4 \cdot 10^{31}$ g or $0.05 M_\odot$.

Let us now consider another extreme case: either the initial velocity was very high, for example, $5 \cdot 10^8$ cm/s (as assumed by Minkowski[14]), or, at a relatively early stage of development of the nebula, the shell ejected in the outburst was accelerated (due to the pressures exerted by the magnetic field and the relativistic particles) so that for a certain period of time the velocity was always higher than 10^8 cm/s. Since the present spatial velocity is hardly ever higher than 400 km (see above) the shell must have been strongly slowed down. In this case we can apply Equation (8.11):

$$R = 2.5 v_t \cdot t$$

hence we obtain $R \sim 10^{18}$ cm, $r \sim 1,000$ psc and, with $\rho \sim 10^{-23}$ g/cm^3, a shell mass $M \sim 0.05 M_\odot$, with $\rho \sim 10^{-24}$ g/cm^3 it will, correspondingly, be lower by one order of magnitude. We see that both estimates yield almost the same results.

If we interpret the weak nebulae now under observation at the point of the outbursts of the supernovae of 1572 and 1604, as shells decelerated in the surrounding interstellar medium, we reach the inescapable conclusion that the distances to them are not great, respectively 500 and 100 ps. With such distances, their absolute magnitude, disregarding interstellar absorption, will be -12.5. If interstellar absorption is taken into account, this estimate could be changed by one to two magnitudes, especially in the case of Kepler's supernova.

Assuming that these supernovae are "ordinary" type I supernovae, similar to those observed in other galaxies ($M_v \sim -18.3$) we must necessarily reach the conclusion that the nebulae observed in the region of the outbursts *are not decelerated shells*. Attention has already been drawn above to the similarity of the filaments and the "fragments" of the nebula near the supernova of 1604 to the nebula near Cassiopeia A. It is possible that the nebulae near Kepler's and Tycho's supernovae have no relation to shells ejected during the explosion, but are in fact interstellar gas compressed by relativistic particles and magnetic fields. We observe a precisely analogous situation at Cassiopeia A ("stationary condensations" see § 5). Such a situation naturally explains the low value of the radiation velocities of the optical remnants of the outbursts of Kepler's and Tycho's supernovae. Let us remember that with the "stationary" condensations of Cassiopeia A, the radiation velocities are also low.

If the weak nebulae observed in the region of Kepler's and Tycho's supernovae are not decelerated shells, it is of course impossible to determine the distances to them by the method used above. Thus, we can say that it is impossible to reach unequivocal conclusions about the distances to these objects using the methods of optical astronomy. Such conclusions can only be based on an analysis of radio-astronomical observations.

The radio emission of the remnants of the supernova of 1572 was first discovered in 1952 by Brown and Hazard with the large radio-telescope of the Jodrell Bank Observatory.[267] Whereas the radio emission of the Crab nebula had been discovered by chance, the discovery of the radio emission from the supernova of 1572 was the result of a planned search. The observations were made at a frequency of 158 Mc. The co-ordinates of the source were the following: $\alpha = 00^h 21^m 49^s \pm 2^s$, $\delta = +64°15' \pm 35'$

(1950), whereas the co-ordinates of the supernova found in the description of observations in the sixteenth century (see above) for that epoch were $\alpha = 00^\mathrm{h}22^\mathrm{m}02^\mathrm{s}$, $\delta = +63°52'$, with an accuracy of $\pm 2'$. The flux at this frequency is $F_\nu = 1.7 \cdot 10^{-24}$ W/m²·c/s, that is, approximately one-tenth of the flux from the Crab nebula. On this basis Brown and Hazard stated the hypothesis that the radio flux from the remnant of a supernova is proportional to the flux of the optical radiation at maximum. The latter is determined by the visual magnitude of the supernova at its brightness maximum. This hypothesis is, however, devoid of reliable foundations. Firstly, the various sources which are linked with the remnants of supernovae possess different spectral indices. Therefore, for example, if at a wavelength $\lambda = 1.9$ m the flux from the Crab nebula is ten times higher than the flux from the remnants of the supernova of 1572, it will be about twentyfold at $\lambda = 20$ cm. Secondly, owing to the expansion of the source, the radio flux must decrease with time, such that the rate of the decrease depends strongly on the spectral index (cf. § 7). For this reason it is hardly reasonable to establish a direct relationship between the radio flux from the remnants of the supernova in a certain epoch of its evolution and the luminosity of the supernova at maximum. On the other hand, the number of relativistic particles contained in the remnants of the outburst and responsible for its synchrotron radiation may, generally speaking, depend on the optical emissivity at maximum. But besides this outburst characteristic, the flux must still depend on the spectral index and the time after the outburst.

The discovery by Hanburry-Brown and Hazard was verified in 1955 at Cambridge.[268] Object number 34 in the Second Cambridge Catalogue of discrete radio sources has the following co-ordinates: $\alpha = 00^\mathrm{h}22^\mathrm{m}46^\mathrm{s} \pm 5^\mathrm{s}$, $\delta = +63°57' \pm 5'$ (1950). At a frequency of 81 Mc the spectral flux density was found to be equal to $F_\nu = 2.86 \cdot 10^{-24}$ W/m²·c/s. The Cambridge interference measurements showed that the source linked with the outburst of the supernova of 1572 possesses rather large angular dimensions of about $9'$. The first observations soon showed that the spectral index of this source was essentially higher than that of the Crab nebula.

At the position of the supernova of 1604 we find in the same Cambridge catalogue a relatively powerful source, registered under No. 1485. Its co-ordinates are the following: $\alpha = 17^\mathrm{h}26^\mathrm{m}24^\mathrm{s} \pm 15^\mathrm{s}$, $\delta = -21°22' \pm 15'$. The spectral density of the radio flux from this source at a frequency of 81 Mc is equal to $1.36 \cdot 10^{-24}$ W/m²·c/s.

In those days the observations described above played a great part in the development of radio-astronomy as they clearly demonstrated that all remnants of supernova are radio sources. On the other hand, the remnants of ordinary novae, even if they are relatively near to us and "young" (e.g., the Nova Persei of 1902, the Nova Aquilae of 1918 and the Nova Puppis of 1942), do not emit radio-frequency radiation of measurable strength. In any case it is certain that the flux from them is weaker than 10^{-26} W/m²·c/s. At the same time their visual magnitude at maximum reaches 0–1 magnitudes which is only 1.5–2 magnitudes less than that of the supernova of 1604. This interesting fact may indicate that there

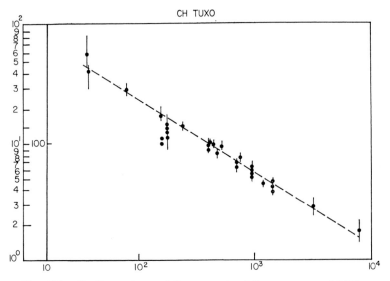

FIG. 114a   Radio-spectrum of the remnants of the supernova of 1572.

exists a qualitative difference between the outbursts of ordinary novae and supernovae, a conclusion which also results from other observational data (e.g., the absence of observable stars which are ex-supernovae whereas ordinary novae can be observed in both the pre- and the post-outburst states).

It is not necessary to give a detailed description of the great number of measurements of the fluxes from the remnants of the supernovae of 1572 and 1604 which were carried out after 1955 at various frequencies.

Figures 114a and 114b show graphs demonstrating the frequency dependence of the spectral flux densities of both sources. The plots were made on the basis of all observations published. From these graphs we may obtain the spectral indices of these sources. For the remnants of the supernova of 1572, $\alpha = 0.67$ [273a] and for that of 1604, $\alpha = 0.62$.[273b] As to the brightness distributions of these sources, the data available so far are rather scanty. In a first approximation we may admit that the source linked with the remnants of the supernova of 1572 has an almost round form and measures 6′ between the half-power points. It must,

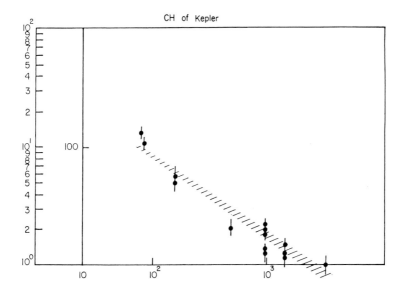

Fig. 114b   Radio-spectrum of the remnants of the supernova of 1604.

however, be remarked that this source seems to possess a complex structure. According to Lequeux' interference observations at a frequency of 1,420 Mc, the source might be a binary source.[94] One of its components has angular dimensions of $\sim 8''$, whereas the other component, whose flux is only half as intense as that of the former, has angular dimensions equal to 1.8″. This interesting result, however, requires a verification.

Yet the data are scantier for the brightness distribution in the area of the radio source linked with Kepler's supernova. Their angular dimensions are, in all probability, equal to about 3″,[270] which is in agreement with the angular dimensions of the nebula located in the area of this source. At the same time, individual observations yielded a value of ∼1″.5 (cf. [271,272]), whereas a single observation made at a frequency of 86 Mc during an eclipse of this source by the moon led to a value of ∼10″ which, obviously, is too high.[273] According to [272] the angular dimensions are smaller than 0.2°. In the following we shall assume that the angular dimensions of this source are 3″.

Just as in the case of the non-thermal radio sources, the problem of the polarization of the emission of these objects is interesting. The scanty data available are self-contradictory. In any case, if there exists a linear polarization, it is weak. Thus, for example, according to [274], the degree of polarization of the radio emission at a frequency of 1,410 Mc of the remnants of the supernova of 1572 is ∼2 per cent. According to [275], no polarization of the radio emission from this source could be discovered at the frequencies 1,420 and 1,670 Mc, whereas at a frequency of 300 Mc a degree of polarization of 2.7 per cent was observed, with an angle of position of the electrical vector of about 45°. Note that according to Minkowski the angle of position of the major axis of the elliptical remnant of this supernova amounts to about 130°. On the basis of the synchrotron theory we may therefore draw the conclusion that the magnetic field of this source tends to assume an orientation parallel to the major axis. But this conclusion must still be verified by new polarization observations.

The probable degree of polarization of the source linked with Kepler's supernova is yet smaller. According to [275] the degree of polarization of this source at a frequency of 3,000 Mc amounts to 0.8 per cent and the angle of position of the electrical vector is 117° ± 34°. At the same time no polarization was observed at the frequencies 1,420 and 1,670 Mc. It is interesting that independent observations at a frequency of 2,800 Mc yielded the same value of 0.8 ± 0.9 per cent for the degree of polarization and the same angle of position of the electrical vector.[276]

These are all the data available at present (end of 1965) on the various characteristic parameters of the radio emission from sources which are linked with the remnants of the supernovae of 1572 and 1604. Let us now turn to the theoretical interpretation of these observations. First of all, we shall estimate the number of relativistic electrons, their energy and the direction of the magnetic field in these two sources. For this purpose we use the usual fundamental formula of the synchrotron theory, Equation (6.7).

In estimating the distance to these supernovae, let us use formula (7.37) taking Cassiopeia A as the reference source. Assuming that the spectral index α for all sources is identical and equals 0.7 (the mean between the spectral index of Cassiopeia A and that of Tycho's and Kepler's supernovae) and taking into account the angular dimensions and surface brightness of the sources, we shall find that the distance to Tycho's supernova is ∼ 4,440 ps, while to Kepler's supernova it is twice as great. Since the power of the explosion of Cassiopeia A was about an order greater than those of Tycho's and Kepler's supernovae, the resulting distances should be decreased by 20–30 per cent (see formula 7.37). The distance to Tycho's supernovae finally appears to be ∼ 3,300 ps, and to Kepler's supernova ∼ 6,600 ps.

The analysis of the spectrum of the absorption line $\lambda = 21$ cm in their radio-spectrum is the direct radio-astronomical method of determining the distances to the remnants of supernovae. This was the method used when the distance to Cassiopeia A was first established (see § 6). Recently Menon and Williams have observed line $\lambda = 21$ cm in absorption in sources of radio emission, connected with the remnants of the outbursts of Tycho's and Kepler's supernovae. (T. K. Menon and D. R. W. Williams, *A.J.*, 71, No. 6, 1966.) The results of these observations are quite definite: the outline of the absorption line at the source associated with the supernova of 1572 is *double*, almost exactly the same as at Cassiopeia A (see Fig. 40). Since the angular distance of this source from Cassiopeia A is comparatively small (∼ 10°) the spiral structure of the galaxy in these directions is similar. This indicates that Tycho's supernova (as also Cassiopeia A) is situated behind the second sleeve of the spiral. Menon and Williams estimate the distance to this object as 3,500 ps.

The distance found by the direct method agrees completely with our estimate by the indirect radio-astronomical method. Thus, the distances to Tycho's and Kepler's supernovae are great, and their absolute values are approximately the same for supernovae of type I, flaring up in other galaxies. It is interesting to note that since the galactic latitude of Kepler's supernova is fairly high, bII $= -6°$, its distance from the galactic plane is very considerable, ∼ 600 ps. The expected density of the interstellar medium around this supernova must be insignificant, so it is not easy to understand the origin of the nebula observed there, if we treat the latter as "compressed" interstellar gas. On the other hand, at high

12*

galactic latitudes, clouds of interstellar gas have recently been discovered, moving at fairly high speeds.

Taking the distance to Tycho's supernova as 3,300 ps, using the basic formula of the synchrotron theory (6.7) we shall find that $KH_\perp^{1.6} = 9.1 \cdot 10^{-19} H_\perp \approx 6 \cdot 10^{-5}$. In the calculation it was taken that $\alpha = 0.6$, $U(\gamma) = 0.125$, and $T_b = 10^5$ ($\nu = 158\ Mc$). When $\mathbf{r} = 3,300$ ps, the radius of the nebula $R = 9 \cdot 10^{18}$ cm, the nebular volume $V = 2.7 \cdot 10^{57}$cc and its magnetic energy $W_m = VH^2/8\pi \approx 7 \cdot 10^{47}$ergs, i.e. almost the same as in the Crab Nebula. The source located at the point of Kepler's supernova has similar characteristics.

An important difference between the remnants of the supernovae of 1572 and 1604 and the Crab nebula is the fact that the former do not display any synchrotron emission of observable intensity in the optical part of the spectrum. This may very likely be explained by their steep spectrum. Let us estimate, for instance, the spectral flux density of optical synchrotron emission from the remnants of Tycho's supernova. In analogy to the Crab nebula it must be expected that for frequencies $\nu > \nu_1$ the spectral index of the synchrotron radiation will be higher by 0.5. For the remnants of the supernova of 1572 the value of ν_1 must be essentially higher than for the Crab nebula, since in the first case the age of the object t_1 and the field $H_\perp$ are lower. It follows from Equation (13.8) that

$$\nu_1 \propto H_\perp^3 t_1^{-2}$$

Since in the remnants of Tycho's (and also Kepler's) supernova $H_\perp$ is smaller by an order of magnitude than in the Crab nebula, and t_1 is 2.3 times smaller, with these objects ν_1 must be about 5,000-fold and equal to $\sim 5 \cdot 10^{15}$ c/s. The discontinuity in the synchrotron spectrum may therefore be expected only for the ultraviolet range. This indicates that one may extrapolate the synchrotron radiation flux density from the radio-frequency range to the optical range, using the spectral index of the radio-frequency range, $\alpha \approx 0.60$. It is, however, not impossible that the energy spectrum of the relativistic electrons injected possesses a peak at sufficiently high energies, as is the case with the Crab nebula (see Fig. 107). The estimate of the spectral flux density of synchrotron radiation emitted by the remnants of Tycho's and Kepler's supernovae will therefore be an upper limit.

At $\nu = 960$ Mc the spectral flux density of the remnants of the supernova of 1572 is equal to $57 \cdot 10^{-26}$ W/m²·c/s. Consequently, at $\nu = 7 \cdot 10^{14}$ c/s ($\lambda = 4{,}250$ A),

$$F_\nu = 57 \cdot 10^{-26} \left(\frac{9.6 \cdot 10^8}{7 \cdot 10^{14}}\right)^{0.61} = 1.5 \cdot 10^{-28} \text{ W/m}^2\cdot\text{c/s}$$

or ~1 per cent of that of the Crab nebula. The visual stellar magnitude of the optical source of synchrotron radiation positioned at the point of explosion of Tycho's supernova must therefore be weaker than 14 and, taking interstellar light absorption into account, weaker than 15. With an angular diameter of the source of 6' its surface brightness must be lower than that of a star of magnitude 10, per square degree, i.e., it would amount to at most 1 per cent of the background brightness of the nocturnal sky. An analogous result is also obtained for the remnants of Kepler's supernova. In this way the optical synchrotron radiation emitted by the remnants of Tycho's and Kepler's supernovae have an insignificant intensity and are difficult to observe. But it might be interesting to apply the modern contrast methods to these objects, methods which permit a separation of objects of low surface brightness from a bright background (cf., for example, [277]).

Let us finally consider the remnants of the other supernovae which have been observed in our galaxy for the last thousand years. In § 4 some information was given on the observations of a very bright star which exploded in 1230. It is very probable that this was a supernova which, as to its characteristic parameters, was similar to the supernovae of 1572 and 1604. Close to the point of explosion the radio source 3C 286 is located, a fact to which attention was drawn for the first time by Yu. P. Pskovskiy.[278] This source coincides with an optical object of magnitude 15 and small angular dimensions which, until recently, was considered as an extragalactic nebula.[279] But when the red shift of this object was measured, it was found to be unexpectedly small, namely ~30 km/s.[280] On the other hand, the red shift to be expected for a radio galaxy of magnitude 15 must amount to about 15,000 km/s. Yu. P. Pskovskiy therefore makes the justified assumption that this object belongs to our galaxy.[281] Since, according to [280], it spectrum is not an emission spectrum, the author of [281] suggests that what we observe is the spectrum of the star superimposed on a very faint nebula.

The angular dimensions of the source 3C 286 are equal to $1'.9$,[282] the spectral flux density at a frequency of 400 Mc is equal to $1.7 \cdot 10^{-25}$ W/m$^2 \cdot$c/s, whereas the spectral index is $\alpha = 0.64$.[283] Let us estimate the distance of this source under the assumption that, as to its nature, it resembles the remnants of Tycho's and Kepler's supernovae. The surface brightness of 3C 287 is only 1.4-fold of the sources linked with the remnants of the supernovae of 1572 and 1604. So it follows from Equation (15.5) that the distance of the source 3C 286 amounts to about 2,500 psc. If the visual magnitude of this star during its outburst was -3 (as is assumed in [281]), its absolute magnitude must amount to -15. It must, however, be taken into consideration that the estimate of the visual magnitude of the nova of 1230 is extremely uncertain. The object 3C 286, which is suspected to be the remnant of the supernova of 1230, deserves the attention of both optical and radio-astronomical research.

In § 4 we also described in detail the old observations of the unusually bright star that flared up in 1006.

Gardner and Milne have recently discovered in the region of the explosion of this star an extended ($\sim 40'$) source with low surface brightness. The co-ordinates of this source are: $\alpha 195° = 14^h 59.6, \delta = -41°42'$. As is shown by isophotes on wavelength 11 cm, this source has a shell structure. The degree of polarization of the individual component reaches 10 per cent, and the spectral index is $\alpha = 0.6$. It is quite possible that this source is the remnant of the supernova of 1006. Comparing it with the remnants of Kepler's and Tycho's supernovae, we may conclude that the distance to this source is $\sim 1,000$ ps, and its linear dimension $2R \sim 12$ ps. It would be interesting to discover at the point of this source a weak optical nebula of the type observed about the point of the outburst of the supernova of 1572.

CHAPTER IV

The connection with other problems and some theoretical questions

§ 16 Supernovae and the origin of cosmic radiation

The problem of the origin of the primary cosmic rays undoubtedly belongs to the most important problems of modern natural science. The cosmic rays, as we all know, were only discovered half a century ago. The progress of research into cosmic radiation was very slow in the first decades. For a relatively long time, because of its high penetrability, it was considered to be a hard gamma radiation. The discovery of the dependence of the intensity of cosmic rays on the geomagnetic latitude permitted the conclusion that at least an essential part of it consists of superhigh-energy charged particles. When penetrating into the earth's atmosphere they interact with the nuclei of the atmospheric elements in relatively high altitudes, thus producing secondary particles. It is these particles which we may observe at sea level and beneath the surface of the ground.

For many years only these secondary particles were studied by the various methods of experimental nuclear physics. In a marvellous laboratory nature itself produced particles of high and superhigh energies. The modern accelerators had not yet been developed at that time, but even now no accelerators are at our disposal which are capable of supplying particles of such energies as we may observe in cosmic radiation. In the history of nuclear physics the study of cosmic rays was of extraordinary importance; it is sufficient to indicate that the positrons and mesons were first discovered in the secondary cosmic radiation.

However, apart from the great importance of the investigation into the cosmic-radiation processes for nuclear physics, the fundamental problem is that of its origin. That it comes from the cosmos, as the name tells us, is an unsatisfactory answer. It was in fact necessary to find answers to the following fundamental problems: (a) What is the spatial distribution of cosmic rays in the universe? Are they localized in the solar system or do they exist in the galaxy and even in metagalactic space?   (b) Which cosmic objects are (or were) sources of cosmic rays? (c) What is the mechanism that accelerates the charged particles constituting the cosmic rays?   (d) In what way do the cosmic rays move through the universe?   (e) What part do they play in the universe?

From the very beginning we must admit that not even now are we able to answer any one of these questions exhaustively, although we know a great deal about the nature of the primary cosmic rays.

To find answers to the questions we asked, it was, first of all, necessary to study the nature of the primary cosmic rays observed around the earth.   This problem was not so easy, as the primary cosmic rays cannot be observed immediately at low altitudes above sea level.   The development of the technique of physical experiment at high altitudes (with the help of balloons) permitted in 1948 the solution of the most important problem of the chemical composition of the primary cosmic radiation.   Besides superhigh-energy protons (which constitute the principal component), it was found to consist of nuclei of all elements.   It must, however, be noted that the relative content of the various nuclei depends essentially on what is called "mean cosmic."   In Table 27 we have compiled some data on the chemical composition of cosmic radiation.

TABLE 27

Group of Nuclei	Z	A	Intensity $(\mathrm{cm}^{-2}\cdot\mathrm{sterad}^{-1}\cdot\mathrm{sec}^{-1})$	N/N_{H}	$(N/N_{\mathrm{H}})_{\mathrm{univ.}}$
p	1	1	0.13	680	6,830
α	2	4	$8.8\cdot10^{-3}$	46	1,040
L	3–5	10	$1.9\cdot10^{-4}$	1.0	10^{-5}
M	6–9	14	$5.7\cdot10^{-4}$	3.0	10
H	10	31	$1.9\cdot10^{-4}$	1.0	1
VH	20	51	$5.3\cdot10^{-5}$	0.28	0.05

In Table 27, according to the classification established, the nuclei are distributed in six groups.   Group L comprises the light nuclei (lithium, beryllium, boron); group M, the medium-weight nuclei (C, N, O, F); group H, the heavy nuclei ($Z \geq 10$); and finally group VH (a subgroup of H), the very heavy nuclei.   The fifth column contains the relative concentrations of the nuclei contained in cosmic radiation, referred to group H. In the last column of the table we have compiled the relative abundances of the elements in the universe (referred to the same group H), borrowed from paper [135]. There is a striking characteristic difference between the relative nuclear abundances in cosmic radiation and, on the average, in the universe. The cosmic radiation is relatively rich in nuclei of group L, whereas these nuclei are actually rare in the universe. Another important peculiarity of the cosmic rays is the relatively high abundance of nuclei of the groups M, H and VH, compared to the protons and α-particles.

The most important peculiarity of the cosmic rays is their isotropy. This isotropy is a fact that essentially complicates the problem of the origin of the cosmic rays, as it renders the immediate identification of their cosmic sources impossible. The isotropy of the cosmic radiation is a consequence of the fact that the constituent particles do not move on rectilinear trajectories (like the light quanta) but along very complex curves. This character of motion is easy to understand if we take into consideration that throughout the universe there are magnetic fields of very different scales and directions. For example, the magnetic field in the arms of our own galaxy has an intensity H of about 10^{-5} Oe. The radius of the helical trajectory described by a charged relativistic particle will, in this field, be given by $r = E/(300H) \sim 3 \cdot 10^{12}$ cm if $E \sim 10^{10}$ eV. This value is very small compared to the smallest characteristic scales for interstellar matter. In a first approximation the relativistic particles will therefore move along the lines of force, following all their curves. One would think that virtually the total isotropy of the primary cosmic rays should exclude the possibility of answering the question of their origin. In fact, however, this is not so (see below).

An important characteristic of the primary cosmic radiation is its energy spectrum. The overwhelming majority of the cosmic rays whose energies are within the limits $2 \cdot 10^9 < E < 10^{15}$ eV have an exponential energy spectrum

$$dI_A = K_A E^{-\gamma} dE \qquad (16.1)$$

where I_A is the intensity of the cosmic rays pertaining to group A (e.g., M, H, etc.). The quantity γ has, within the limits of experimental error, the same value for all groups of cosmic rays and is close to 2.5 ± 0.2.

The intensity of the cosmic radiation depends on the geomagnetic latitude. Thus, for example, for a geomagnetic latitude of $58°$ the total intensity of the primary component amounts to ~ 0.3 particles per cm$^2 \cdot$ s $\cdot$ steradian (for energies $> 1.2 \cdot 10^9$ eV/nucleon).   Since the primary cosmic radiation is isotropic, the concentration of the relativistic particles on the earth will be given by

$$N(E > 1.5 \cdot 10^9 ab) = \frac{4\pi}{c} I(E > 1.5 \cdot 10^9 ab) \approx 10^{-10} \quad \text{cm}^{-3}$$

(16.2)

The energy density of the primary cosmic rays is determined by the expression

$$W_{\text{k.n.}} = \int_{E_1 = 1.5 \cdot 10^9}^{\infty} N(E) E dE \approx 1.2 \cdot 10^{-12} \frac{ap2}{\text{cm}^3} \sim \frac{ab}{\text{cm}^3} \quad (16.3)$$

It is an important fact that, beginning with about 58° of geomagnetic latitude, the intensity of cosmic radiation virtually does not increase as the distance to the magnetic pole decreases.   Hence we may conclude that, for some reason, protons with an energy below $1.2 \cdot 10^9$ eV do not reach the earth.   Investigations showed that this "high-latitude cut-off" is of magnetic nature, i.e., the low-energy particles do not reach the earth in the regions of the magnetic poles because of the action of some magnetic field which is external relative to the earth.   In all probability this field is of interplanetary origin and connected with the solar activity.   The sun itself is in this energy range a source of cosmic rays of variable power. In a period of minimal solar activity the high-latitude cut-off is much less effective.   We do not know, however, whether it disappears entirely. With this situation we cannot yet exclude the possibility that the energy spectrum of cosmic radiation, far away from the solar system, may show a "peak" in the low-energy range.   If this is the case, it may be explained by the conditions of generation of the relativistic particles in the sources.

    After the chemical composition of the primary cosmic rays had been determined, the first serious attempts were made to comprehend theo-retically the origin of the cosmic rays.   The possibility of their meta-galactic localization was rejected by most of the investigators on the grounds of energy considerations.   In the opposite case it was necessary to assume an energy density of about 10^{-12} erg/cm^3 for the cosmic radia-tion "smeared" over the whole universe; this value is by several orders of magnitude higher than the density of all other forms of energy (with the exception of the density of the rest energy of matter, ρc^2, which is at least a hundred times higher).   It is, however, possible that a "metagalactic" localization of cosmic radiation was rejected too hastily. At present (1965) the argument of a high-energy density does not hold good by itself. For example, an anomalously intense high-frequency cosmic radio emission has recently been discovered.[284] If it is interpreted as a "relic" from an early epoch of cosmic evolution (cf. [285]), it may be assumed that the volume density of energy of this radiation which fills the whole universe (and is described by a Planck curve with $T = 3°.5$) will amount to 10^{-12} erg/cm^3, i.e., it is of the same order as the energy density of cosmic radiation around the earth. We need additional and sufficiently weighty arguments to exclude the possibility of a galaxy entirely filled with relativistic protons and nuclei with an energy density of about 10^{-12} erg/cm^3.

If we exclude the possibility of a metagalactic localization of the primary cosmic radiation, only two possibilities are left: (a) The cosmic rays are localized in a relatively small region around the solar system. (b) They are localized in the galaxy. A weighty argument in favour of the first hypothesis is the undoubted fact that the sun in a period of high activity (for instance, in a sunspot period) is a source of primary cosmic rays. A detailed analysis, however, shows that the main part of cosmic rays cannot be of solar origin. Firstly, the energy spectrum of the solar cosmic rays is much steeper ($\gamma \gtrsim 5$). Secondly, the chemical composition of the solar-origin cosmic rays has been determined quite reliably in previous years. It is essentially different from the chemical composition of the observed cosmic rays by a much higher relative abundance of protons and the absence of nuclei of the group L. Thus, until 1949, the overwhelming majority of the investigators advocated the "galactic" conception of a localization of primary cosmic rays. According to this conception our stellar system contains certain objects (stars, nebulae) which are sources of relativistic particles with an exponential energy spectrum. In this case the problem of the origin of the cosmic rays was suitably split in two: (a) the problem of acceleration of charged particles in the sources up to relativistic energies and (b) the diffusion of the relativistic particles produced in this way in the interstellar magnetic fields. In a series of cases the second problem can be considered independently of the first.

An essential argument in favour of the galactic theory of origin of the primary cosmic rays consists in the fact that they contain a sufficiently high amount of nuclei of lithium, beryllium and boron, whose cosmic abundance is very low. The light nuclei in the primary component are

produced in nuclear interactions between the cosmic rays and interstellar gas. Their observable abundance is explained by the fact that,
before reaching the earth, the cosmic rays, traversing the interstellar
space or the sources, had to pass through a substantial layer of a surface
density of ~ 5–10 g/cm^2.[95] Note, however, that this fact alone does
not exclude the possibility of a metagalactic origin of the primary cosmic
radiation.

The central problem of the theory of origin of primary cosmic rays is
the problem of the sources where they are produced. One would think
that in the case of a total isotropy of the cosmic radiation this problem
would only be a subject of speculation. The development of radio-
astronomy, however, permitted a treatment of the problem with the
help of a quantitative analysis.

Before the era of radio-astronomy the problem of the origin of cosmic
rays was in a confused state. The fact is that this problem is, essentially,
an astronomical one, since the primary cosmic radiation is not of terrestrial
origin but generated in some astronomical objects. Consequently, one
cannot think of solving this problem without carefully taking the true
properties of the cosmic bodies into account. In this connection, however,
the investigators met with a fundamental difficulty. Up to the beginning
of the 1950's the primary cosmic rays could be observed only in the
immediate proximity of the earth. The possibility of observing them in
the depths of the universe seemed so fantastic that one would not even
think of it. In general, it stands to reason that as long as we do not possess
any methods for such observations, neither the problem of the origin of
cosmic radiation nor that of its spatial localization can be solved
unambiguously. One could of course develop purely theoretical hypotheses and analyze some mechanism of charged particle acceleration up to
relativistic energies, but without any observational data on the primary
cosmic rays at the points of their generation, the theories would remain
mere hypotheses.

Almost the greatest achievement of radio-astronomy was the discovery that it was possible to observe the primary cosmic rays far away
from the earth, in the depths of the galaxy and metagalaxy. This
became obvious after the development of the synchrotron theory of non-
thermal radio emission of our galaxy and other sources. According to this
theory the cosmic radio-waves in the galaxy are emitted by relativistic
electrons whose energies are between 10^7 and 10^{10} eV and which move
through the interstellar magnetic field. These electrons, however, are

none other than the electron component of the primary cosmic rays. Analyzing the radio emission of the galaxy, one may, with the help of the fundamental formulas of the synchrotron theory, determine the concentration of the relativistic electrons, their spatial distribution and their energy spectrum.   In this way one had discovered an actually unique possibility of studying the cosmic rays (at least their electron component) with the help of the methods of observational astronomy.   So the radio-astronomical theory of the origin of cosmic radiation was developed.[286a] Since then a very great number of papers have been published in which this theory was developed and investigated; they are reviewed in a monograph by V. L. Ginzburg and S. I. Syrovatskiy, entitled "The Origin of Cosmic Rays."[95]

It must be noted that, according to this theory, one may expect to find relativistic electrons and positrons in the primary cosmic radiation observed near the earth.   These particles may be produced in the interstellar medium, in collisions between relativistic protons and nuclei where pions are produced which then decay, producing relativistic electrons and positrons according to the mode $\pi \to \mu \to e$.

The theoretical prediction that the primary cosmic rays should contain relativistic electrons was verified only in 1961.[287,288]   Since then many investigations have been carried out in this direction.   According to the last measurements[289] the flux of the electron component in the primary cosmic rays is equal to

$$\frac{dI}{dE} = 11E^{-1.6} \, (\text{m}^2 \, \text{sterad} \cdot \text{beV})^{-1}$$

where E is given in beV.   The exponent of the differential energy spectrum has been determined with an accuracy of ± 0.5.   The spectrum refers to the energy range between 0.5 beV and 3 beV.   The flux of cosmic electrons amounts to about 1 per cent of the flux of cosmic rays with energies beyond 1 beV.   It is noteworthy that the relativistic positrons in cosmic radiation are much rarer than the electrons.[290]

The following four problems are of fundamental importance for the development of the radio-astronomical theory of the origin of cosmic radiation:

(i) the region of spatial localization of the electron component of cosmic rays.   It must be determined in radio-astronomical observations;

(ii) the lifetime of the relativistic particles in the galaxy.   This quantity cannot be obtained immediately from observations.   It can be estimated by way of studying the character of motion of the relativistic particles in the interstellar medium, on condition that problem (i) has been solved and the characteristic parameters of the interstellar medium are sufficiently well known;

(iii) the source of the relativistic electrons. Their characteristic parameters (first of all the power of injection of cosmic rays averaged with respect to time) must be obtained from radio-astronomical and optical observations;

(iv) a comprehension of the relationship between the electron–positron component and the nuclear component of primary cosmic rays.

The developed theory of the origin of cosmic rays can be considered as reliable if, after the above four problems have been solved, it can be shown that the power of the sources ("injectors") averaged with respect to the time the cosmic rays exist in our galaxy is equal to the total energy of the relativistic particles contained in it. This means that we consider the cosmic radiation in the galaxy as being in a state of dynamic equilibrium.

We shall consider here all the four problems stated above. From an analysis of the isophotes of the cosmic synchrotron radio emission one may in principle determine the spatial distribution of the relativistic electrons which are responsible for this radiation. In practice, however, this is a very difficult problem. Apart from the specific difficulties of radio-astronomical observations which are connected with the low resolving power of the radio-telescopes, and the presence of side leaves in the radiation patterns which distort the true intensity distribution, other and more serious difficulties arise. The fact is that our own position in the galaxy is near its equatorial plane so that, without additional suppositions, it is impossible to draw a picture of the spatial distribution of the emitting substances (in our case the relativistic electrons and the interstellar magnetic fields). An analogous difficulty is encountered in the investigation of the spiral structure of our own stellar system from analyses of optical and radio-astronomical observations.

In 1952, when investigating the isophotes of cosmic radio emission which were available at that time (cf., for example, [291]), we came to the conclusion that the radio-frequency emitting substances were contained in a galactic disc, surrounded by a largely extended quasi-spherical corona.[292] As we are inside this corona we are not able to calculate its radius with only the help of radio-astronomical observations. In a rather arbitrary way a value of 10,000 psc has been chosen for it; the true value may of course be much larger (but hardly smaller).   The volume of this corona $\sim 10^{68}$ cm^3 whereas the volume of the disc whose thickness is ~ 300–500 psc is smaller by about two orders of magnitude.   Besides the character of the isophotes a strong argument in favour of the existence of a radio-emitting corona around the galaxy is provided by an analysis of the isophotes of one of the nearest galaxies, the large spiral M 31 in Andromeda.   These isophotes indicate clearly the existence of an extended corona around M 31 which possesses a relatively rich structure (see Fig. 115).

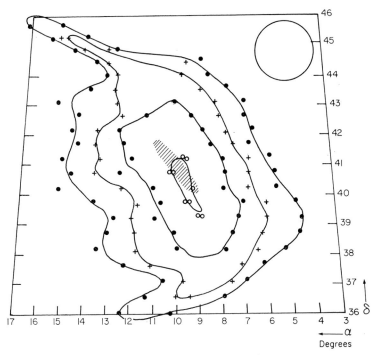

FIG. 115   Radio representation of M 31.

Recently, however, the existence of a corona surrounding our galaxy has been questioned.[292a]   The fact is that the old isophotes, on the basis of whose analysis one had realized the existence of a corona, are affected by the influence of the side leaves.   Taking this into account does not seem to permit the conclusion that the galaxy is surrounded by a radio-emitting corona. But this result requires an independent verification since a correct taking into account of the side leaves is a rather complex task. A much more important argument against the existence of a galactic corona are the recent observations of the brightness distribution of the so-called "normal" galaxies, carried out at the large Australian radio-telescope at Parkes.[293] In the three Sc-type galaxies NGC 253, NGC 4945 and NGC 5236 no coronae could be observed. In all three cases the dimensions of the radio-emitting regions were smaller than the optical ones and the radio emission was strongly concentrated at the edges of the corresponding galaxies. We must also take into consideration that the irregular galaxies NGC 55 and the Large Magellanic Cloud did not show any trace of a corona. It rather looks as if the radio-emitting coronae around the galaxies were less a rule than an exception. Among our nearest metagalactic neighbours M 31 is the only one that possesses a corona. So the question of whether our own galaxy has a corona still remains open, though this is very likely.† The problem of the spatial localization of the relativistic electrons which emit cosmic radio-waves is thus at present in an unsatisfactory state. The volume in which these electrons are localized may be either $\sim 10^{68}$ cm^3 (if our galaxy has a corona) or $\sim 10^{66}$ cm^3 if the radio-frequency radiation is almost entirely concentrated in the disc.

As problem (i) has no unambiguous solution, a certain indeterminacy also arises in problem (ii); let us consider two possibilities: (1) the cosmic rays are localized in the disc and (2) they are mainly localized in the galactic corona. The distribution of the radio-emitting substances in the disc is, obviously, not uniform but follows the spiral structure of the galaxy. This may be seen, e.g., in Figure 116 which shows the intensity of the radio emission of the disc as a function of the galactic longitude.[295] The distribution shows characteristic "steps" which correspond to the cases where the direction of observation coincides with a spiral arm. The thickness of a "radio-spiral" is, according to Mills,[295] equal to about 500 psc. The total extent of all spiral windings may be estimated as $\sim 3 \cdot 10^5$ psc. We shall consider this spiral as resembling a magnetic tube of force. Let us further assume that the relativistic particles (in particular the electrons) move along such a tube of force and may

† Recent observations with a new large cross aerial in Australia, at a frequency of ~ 400 Mc, led to the conclusion that the galaxies investigated at the Parkes Observatory do possess coronae (cf. [294]).

unimpededly stream out into the metagalactic space ("open model"). Since the lines of force do not run parallel along the tube but are strongly "twisted" and the velocity vector of the relativistic particles makes a certain angle with the direction of the magnetic field, the time the cosmic rays need to escape from our galaxy will amount to several millions of years. We must note that, moving through a medium with the mean concentration of the interstellar gas of ~ 1 cm^{-3}, these rays have to pass through a substance with a surface density of ~ 5 to 10 g/cm^2 which is sufficient to explain the abundance of lithium, beryllium and boron observed in the cosmic rays. On the other hand, such a picture of the motion of the cosmic rays in our galaxy requires their complete regeneration once in several millions of years.

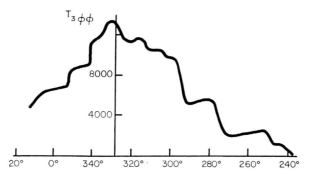

Fig. 116   Radio-frequency radiation intensity as a function of the galactic longitude.[295]

On the other hand, such a picture of motion of relativistic particles would imply anisotropy of cosmic radiation which is contrary to observation.

Let us now consider the image of the motion of relativistic particles under the supposition that they are mainly contained in a galactic corona whose density is low, in any case lower than 10^{-26} g/cm^3.[296] In this case, in order to explain the content of light elements observed in the cosmic rays, it must be assumed that the cosmic rays "wander" in the galaxy for at least several millions of years. This may be a motion along strongly twisted magnetic lines of force. A theory of such a galactic corona was developed in 1957 by the author of the present book together with S. B. Pikel'ner.[296]   Here we cannot enter into the details of this theory.

The two hypotheses on a possible spatial localization of the cosmic rays in the galaxy thus result in different estimates of the cosmic rays' lifetime. It is, however, essential to note that the ratio between lifetime and volume occupied by the system of relativistic particles (or, in the case of constant density of the latter, the ratio of the total energy of the relativistic particles contained in the galaxy and their lifetime) is almost the same for both models. On the other hand, if the cosmic rays in the galaxy are in dynamic equilibrium, the following simple relation must be fulfilled:

$$L_{c.r.}t = \mathcal{E}_{c.r.} \tag{16.4}$$

where $L_{c.r.}$ is the mean power of the sources (injectors) of cosmic rays in the galaxy, t is the lifetime of the latter, and $\mathcal{E}_{c.r.}$ is the total energy of the cosmic rays in the galaxy. Since for both models discussed above, $\mathcal{E}/t = $ const, $L_{c.r.}$ must be approximately the same for these models. In other words, the power $L_{c.r.}$ of the injectors is likewise almost independent of the nature of the model.

Which is the value of $L_{c.r.}$? It is obvious that, in order to determine the power of the injectors, one must, in particular, know the energy density $W_{c.r.}$ of the relativistic particles. When we may assume $W_{c.r.} \sim 10^{-12}$ erg/cm^3 for the relativistic protons and heavy nuclei (this is the value in the earth's neighbourhood, though the problem of the correctness of an extrapolation of this value to the whole galaxy is still unsolved), the value of $W_{c.r.}$ for relativistic electrons can be found from an analysis of radio-astronomical observations.

According to observations[297] the brightness temperature in the region of the galactic pole, at a wavelength of 75 cm, is $T_b = 25°$. We shall assume that two-thirds of this brightness is due to the disc whose effective extension R in this direction is equal to half its thickness, i.e., to ~ 250 psc. The fundamental formula of the synchrotron theory reads as follows:

$$\frac{2kT_b}{\lambda^2} = 1.3 \cdot 10^{-22} U(\gamma) K_e H_{\perp}^{(\gamma+1)/2} R\lambda^{(\gamma-1)/2} \tag{16.5}$$

Since the spectral index of the cosmic radio emission for relatively high frequencies may be assumed as being equal to 0.8,[298] $\gamma = 2.6$ and $U(\gamma) = 0.1$. From Equation (16.5) it follows that the mean value of K_e

in the solar neighbourhood, with $H_\perp = 10^{-5}$ Oe, will be equal to $6.5 \cdot 10^{-16}$. The concentration of the relativistic electrons with energies $E > 1$ beV is determined from the following equation:

$$N_e (> E_1) = \int_{E_1 = 1\,\text{beV}}^{\infty} K_e E^{-\gamma}\, dE = \frac{K_e}{\gamma - 1} E_1^{1-\gamma} = 7.5 \cdot 10^{-12}\ \text{cm}^{-3}$$

$$(16.6)$$

In the energy range below 1 beV the spectrum of the relativistic electrons becomes more sloping as the spectral index of the cosmic radio emission is lower at lower frequencies.[144] We can therefore assume that, with sufficiently high accuracy, the energy density of the relativistic electrons is equal to

$$W_\text{rel.el.} = 7.5 \cdot 10^{-12} \cdot 2 \cdot 10^9 = 1.5 \cdot 10^{-2}\ \text{eV/cm}^3 = 2.4 \cdot 10^{-14}\ \text{erg/cm}^3$$

whereas the energy density of all cosmic rays measured at the earth (mainly of relativistic protons and heavy nuclei) is of the order of 10^{-12} erg/cm^3, i.e., about forty times higher. Note that according to recent measurements at the earth $N_e\ (\geqslant 1\ \text{beV}) = 7 \cdot 10^{-13}\ \text{cm}^{-3}$ (see above), i.e., it is smaller by an order of magnitude than the value obtained in radio-astronomical observations. This deviation can be explained in several ways. First, we assumed that two-thirds of the total radio emission in the direction of the galactic pole was caused by the disc. The contribution of the corona may be essential but, irrespective of whether the corona exists or not, the galactic radio-emitting disc is a reality. Its contribution cannot be less than 30–40 per cent of the surface brightness observed in the region of the galactic poles. Accounting for a possible contribution from the corona will therefore permit a reduction of the value of N_e obtained from an analysis of radio-astronomical observations by at most 30 per cent. One might assume that $H_\perp$ is not equal to 10^{-5} Oe but, say, to $3 \cdot 10^{-5}$ Oe. This results in a reduction of $W_\text{rel.el.}$ by a factor of almost 9, and the deviation from the measurements near the earth has been avoided. But it must be mentioned that a value of $H_\perp = 3 \cdot 10^{-5}$ Oe is too high.

One could, finally, assume that the local value of N_e obtained in measurements near the earth is lower than the mean value. The relativistic electrons in the disc may possess a non-uniform "flocky" distribution, and the sun happens to be in a region of the disc where the concentration of the relativistic electrons is lower. This assumption seems the most

natural to us.   But one cannot exclude the possibility that in the solar
system there exist factors whose effects have not yet been recognized and
which may reduce the flux of galactic relativistic particles.   In any case
we assume that the value of N_e determined from radio-astronomical
observations is sufficiently reliable.   When we assume a disc volume of
$\sim 10^{66}$ cm^3 we obtain a value of $3 \cdot 10^{52}$ erg for the total energy of the
relativistic electrons contained in it.   On the other hand, the lifetime of
the relativistic electrons in the disc, determined by their escape from the
galactic spiral into the metagalactic space, amounts to $\sim 10^{14}$ s.   In
order to maintain dynamic equilibrium it is therefore necessary that the
mean power of the galactic sources of relativistic electrons be equal to
$\sim 3 \cdot 10^{38}$ erg/s.

The lifetime of the relativistic electrons in the disc may also be
estimated in another way.   Up to now we have assumed that the
relativistic electrons moving along the lines of force of a spiral arm are
freely discharged into the metagalactic space, as though through a nozzle.
We may, however, suppose that the free discharge from the spiral is
impeded by the formation of some magneto-turbulent "plug" which is
caused by a beam-type instability of the relativistic particles.   This
possibility was recently considered in paper [299].   Such an assumption is
necessary to explain the isotropy of the cosmic rays.   In this case the
time of residence of the relativistic particles in the disc may be determined
not by the escape time but by the time of loss to synchrotron radiation:

$$t_{1/2} = \frac{8.35 \cdot 10^{-3}}{H_\perp^2 E}$$

(where $t_{1/2}$ is given in years and E in beV).   We choose the values $E \sim$
$(1\text{--}2) \cdot 10^9$ eV (with $H_\perp = 10^{-5}$ Oe such electrons are responsible for an
emission of the disc in the metre and decimetre ranges) and $t_{1/2} \sim$
$(8\text{--}4) \cdot 10^7$ years.   If $t > t_{1/2}$ the power of the galactic sources of relativistic
particles must be equal to the power of the synchrotron emission of the
disc.   The latter may be estimated in the following way.   The emission
of the disc, per unit volume and per unit interval of frequency, is given by
the relation

$$\varepsilon_\nu = \frac{4\pi I \nu}{R} = \frac{8\pi k T_b}{R \lambda^2} \sim 10^{-38} \text{ erg/cm}^3 \cdot \text{s} \cdot \text{c/s} \qquad (16.7)$$

where T_b caused by the sources in the disc is chosen as equal to 15° at a
wavelength of $\lambda = 75$ cm.   Taking the radio spectrum of the galaxy into

account, we obtain $\varepsilon = \int \varepsilon_\nu \, d\nu \simeq 1.5 \cdot 10^{-29}$ erg/cm^3·s. The total syn-chrotron emissivity of the disc is obtained as $L = \varepsilon v = 1.5 \cdot 10^{-29} \cdot 10^{66} = 1.5 \cdot 10^{37}$ erg/s. It is obvious that the minimal value of the sources' emissivity $L_{\mathrm{c.r.}}$ is equal to L.

If our galaxy, besides the disc, also possesses a corona like the corona of M 31, it can be shown that the energy of the relativistic electrons will then increase to 10^{54} erg and the emissivity in the synchrotron radio-frequency range to $(1\text{–}2) \cdot 10^{38}$ erg/s. In this case the minimum power of the relativistic electron sources will therefore rise to $(1\text{–}2) \cdot 10^{38}$ erg/s.

But what can be said about the sources of cosmic rays and, in par-ticular, about the sources of the relativistic electrons? The most out-standing achievement of radio-astronomy was the discovery of sources of relativistic particles in the galaxy. These sources are the remnants of supernova explosions. In § 6 we calculated the total energy of the rel-ativistic electrons for a series of remnants of type II supernovae. For example, in the case of such an "old" object as the filamentary nebula in Cygnus, the energy of the relativistic electrons contained in it (on the assumption that the concentration of relativistic protons and heavy nuclei is low) was equal to $\sim 2.5 \cdot 10^{48}$ erg. Let us assume that the energy of the relativistic electrons contained in a "medium-age" object of this type is equal to $\sim 10^{48}$ erg. If the outburst frequency of supernovae of this type is about 1 per 200 years (see § 1 and also § 7) the mean power of injection will be $10^{48}/3 \cdot 10^9 \sim 3 \cdot 10^{38}$ erg/s. This is fully sufficient to maintain the galactic radio-frequency radiation at the level observed.

One may, however, suppose (though we have no direct proof) that the shells of supernovae, apart from the relativistic electrons, do also contain relativistic protons and heavy nuclei whose total energy is about a hundred times higher than the total energy of the relativistic electrons contained in it. The ratio of 100 : 1 has been chosen to explain the observed flux ratio of relativistic protons and electrons around the earth. According to the calculations carried out in § 6, the total energy of relativistic protons in the remnants of supernovae of the type II will in this case reach a value of $(1\text{–}2) \cdot 10^{49}$ erg and the total energy of relativistic electrons will drop to $(1\text{–}2) \cdot 10^{47}$ erg. In this case the mean power of injection of relativistic electrons will be $\sim (1\text{–}2) \cdot 10^{37}$ erg/s, which is sufficiently high to maintain the radio emission of the disc, on condition that the relativistic electrons cannot freely escape into the metagalactic space. If, however, our galaxy has an extended corona and its total synchrotron emissivity amounts to about $(1\text{–}2)\cdot 10^{38}$ erg/s, we see at once that the power of the relativistic particle injectors such as the remnants of type II supernovae is insufficiently high.

The power of injection of relativistic protons and heavy nuclei is equal to $10^{49}/3\cdot 10^9 \sim 3\cdot 10^{39}$ erg/s, a value which is too low for an "open" model.† If the whole volume of the galactic corona, which is $\sim 10^{68}$ cm^3, is filled with cosmic rays of an energy density of $\sim 10^{-12}$ erg/cm^3, their total energy in the galaxy will be equal to $\sim 10^{56}$ erg. In this case the power of the injectors, the type II supernovae, will be sufficient if the time of residence of the cosmic rays in the corona amounts to $\sim(1\text{–}2)\cdot 10^9$ years. With such a high value of t, there arises, however, the difficulty with the heavy nuclei in the primary cosmic rays which, with a mean density of the interstellar medium of $\sim 10^{-26}$ g/cm^3, must disintegrate in collisions with the nuclei of the interstellar gas. Note that the value of $\sim 10^{-26}$ g/cm^3 of the mean density of the interstellar medium is a minimum since it is obtained by "smearing" the interstellar gas in the disc over the volume of the galactic corona. One gets the impression that the outbursts of type II supernovae cannot be the main sources of relativistic protons and heavy nuclei in our galaxy.

The outburst of type I supernovae may also contribute essentially to it. As shown in § 13, the total energy of relativistic electrons in the Crab nebula, which are responsible for its synchrotron radiation, amounts to about 10^{48} erg for the whole spectrum. It is very important that this nebula does not contain a considerable amount of relativistic protons whose total energy would exceed the energy of the relativistic electrons (cf. § 13). If the Crab nebula is a typical object of this type, one may assume that the remnants of type I supernovae will inject only relativistic electrons into the interstellar medium. One could also doubt whether the remnants of type II supernovae do in fact contain chiefly relativistic protons. There do not exist any observational facts which would support this hypothesis. It was established, however, only in order to explain the flux ratio of relativistic protons and electrons observed at the earth. But one cannot exclude the possibility that, unlike the remnants of the type I supernovae, the remnants of type II may contain relativistic protons and heavy nuclei. We must, however, admit that this hypothesis is merely arbitrary. On the contrary, the relationship between the relativistic electrons observed in the sources that are remnants of super-

† The "open model," however, is in obvious contradiction to the observed isotropy of cosmic radiation and must therefore be rejected.

novae and those present in the galactic disc may now be the subject of quantitative investigations verified by observations.

Summing up, we may say that the outbursts of supernovae may quite well play the part of the injectors of relativistic electrons in our galaxy, in any case as regards its disc. Various authors, at various times, suggested that the radio-frequency radiation of the disc must be considered as the sum of radiations of extended discrete sources, the sufficiently expanded remnants of supernovae of the type II (cf., for example, [295]). In this connection the following may be mentioned. According to the estimates in § 7 our galaxy must contain several hundred (say, 500) objects of the type of the filamentary nebulae in Cygnus or younger ones. The power of the synchrotron radiation of the filamentary nebulae in Cygnus is easy to calculate from the flux and spectrum. It amounts to $\sim 10^{32}$ erg/s. The emissivity of all these objects must therefore be of the order of 10^{35} erg/s or about 1 per cent of the total radio emission of the disc. The contribution of the older sources is even smaller, since their luminosity drops rapidly as the expansion proceeds (cf. § 7). The main part of the synchrotron radiation in the disc is therefore due to relativistic electrons which are "deprived of individuality," as long ago they lost their connection with the nebular remnant of a supernova in which they had been generated. In individual regions of the disc, however, the concentration of the not yet fully "spread" remnants of supernovae of the type II may be considerable. This may be observed in the region of the galactic anti-centre, where the radio emission of the disc is concentrated in individual extended sources.[295]

It is interesting to consider in greater detail the relationship between the synchrotron radio emission of the Magellanic Clouds and the remnants of supernovae there to be observed. In the case of the Magellanic Clouds our calculation of the synchrotron radio emission is free from the indeterminacy which, in the case of our galaxy, is due to the fact that our own solar system is a part of it. At the same time these stellar systems which are nearest to us are very good objects of astronomical investigations.

According to [300] the radio flux from the Large Magellanic Cloud at a wavelength of 3.5 m is equal to $F_\nu = 2 \cdot 10^{-23}$ W/m²·c/s. With a spectral index assumed as $\alpha = 0.7$ and taking the distance of this galaxy into consideration (which is $\sim 50,000$ psc) we obtain a value of $\sim 3 \cdot 10^{36}$ erg/s for its synchrotron emissivity. Moreover, as we know the angular dimensions of the Large Magellanic Cloud, we can, with the help of the usual formulas of the synchrotron theory, determine the total energy of the relativistic electrons contained in it; we find a value of $\sim 10^{51}$ erg. In this calculation we assumed that $H_\perp \sim 10^{-5}$ Oe and that the galaxy has a "coplanar" structure with a thickness of about 1,000 psc.

At present we know three relatively young remnants of supernovae of the type II in the Large Magellanic Cloud; the age of these remnants was estimated not to exceed 20,000 years (cf. § 5). Hence we may conclude that the outburst frequency of the type II supernovae in this galaxy is about one per 5,000 years; this rate is by about 1.5 orders of magnitude lower than in our own stellar system. This might be explained by the relatively small mass of the Large Magellanic Cloud.

Since the total energy of the relativistic electrons in each of these remnants is of the order of 10^{48} erg (on condition that the amount of relativistic protons there is insignificant), the power of injection will be $\sim 5 \cdot 10^{36}$ erg/s which is fully sufficient to maintain the radio emission of the Large Magellanic Cloud at the observed level. It is, however, worth noting that if the relativistic protons in the remnants of type II supernovae observed in the Large Magellanic Cloud had an energy one hundred times higher than that of the relativistic electrons, the injection power of the latter would be insufficient.

In the past years another possibility of sources of relativistic particles in the galaxies has been discovered: explosions of nuclei. These explosions, whose powers vary within very wide limits, occur from time to time in the nuclei of normal and peculiar galaxies. We shall not discuss here this extremely interesting and important phenomenon whose investigation is at present only in its infancy. It seems that the concentration of radio sources in the central parts of certain normal galaxies, which we considered above, can be explained by the activity of their nuclei. If the sources of relativistic particles in peculiar galaxies (radio galaxies) are nuclear explosions, in the normal galaxies these sources are, obviously, periodically repeated nuclear explosions as well as supernova outbursts. The relative role played by these sources may be different in different objects. It may depend on the phase of activity of the nucleus. It is also possible that the relativistic particles in the spiral arms are replenished by the outbursts of supernovae (whose power is quite sufficient for this, see above) whereas the corona is formed by virtue of the nuclear activity and represents a rather variable formation.[301] All these problems are still unsolved and require further investigations on the basis of an analysis of astronomical facts and not of arbitrary assumptions. Irregular galaxies of the type of the Magellanic Clouds and NGC 55 have no nuclei. The only mechanism which may act as injector of relativistic electrons will therefore consist of the outbursts of supernovae.

We see that although radio-astronomy has given the problem of the origin of cosmic rays fresh impetus, there are still many problems, some of which are very important, awaiting a solution. In our opinion the basic problem of the sources of injection of the relativistic protons and heavy nuclei is in a particularly unsatisfactory position. The modern theories are in fact based on the arbitrary hypothesis that in explosions of supernovae and galactic nuclei, besides the relativistic electrons (which may be observed through their synchrotron radiation), non-observable relativistic protons, whose energies are about one hundred times higher than that of the former, are generated in some way. The validity of this assumption would be proved if the relativistic electrons contained in the cosmic rays were of secondary origin, i.e., they arose in collisions between nuclei and cosmic protons, α-particles and the like. This is, however, not the case. Firstly, as shown in [302], this assumption does not hold good under verification by quantitative calculation. Secondly, it is immediately disproved by experiments which show that in the cosmic rays the number of relativistic positrons is smaller than the number of relativistic electrons. But if the relativistic light particles were of secondary origin, the relativistic electrons and positrons would be observed in equal quantities. Thus there is no connection between the heavy and light components of cosmic rays which are established by experiments or observations.

In this situation it is of interest to consider any possible way of discovering the presence of relativistic nuclei in the sources of relativistic electrons. In this connection we shall consider the following experiment which is possible in principle and which might be carried out in the relatively near future. As already mentioned at the beginning of this section, a relatively high-frequency isotropic radio emission was recently discovered which seems to be a "relic" of a cosmological effect. The energy density of this radiation, which is emitted chiefly in the millimetre and sub-millimetre ranges, is $\sim 10^{-12}$ erg/cm^3 and constant in this large metagalactic region in which we are.

When relativistic electrons collide with such "cosmological" photons of the sub-millimetre range (inverse Compton effect), the energy of the latter rises by a factor of $(E/mc^2)^2$ so that they become X-ray quanta, provided the electron energy was ~ 1 beV. As shown in [303], the inverse Compton effect may be treated as a synchrotron radiation in the field of an electromagnetic wave, with an equivalent magnetic field of $H_{\text{equ.}} = 4\pi U$ where U is the electromagnetic energy density. With $U \sim 1$ eV/cm^3 we have $H_{\text{equ.}} \sim 5 \cdot 10^{-6}$ Oe. Let us now consider a sufficiently extended metagalactic source of synchrotron radiation with a low surface brightness in which $H_\perp$ is relatively low. Such a source is, for example, Centaurus A. According to [304], the field $H_\perp$ in this source amounts to $\sim 5 \cdot 10^{-6}$ Oe if the total energy of the relativistic protons is one hundred times the total energy of the relativistic electrons, and $H_\perp \sim 1.8 \cdot 10^{-6}$ Oe if the relativistic proton component is weak. It can be shown that in the first case the emissivity in the X-ray range caused by the inverse Compton effect will be precisely equal to the observed synchrotron emissivity in the radio-frequency range, whereas in the second case it would be six times higher. The radio flux from Centaurus A, integrated over all frequencies, is of the order of 10^{-11} erg/cm$^2 \cdot$s, whereas the lower limit of fluxes which can just be measured by the methods of modern rocket astronomy is a little higher than $3 \cdot 10^{-10}$ erg/cm$^2 \cdot$s. An increase in sensitivity of 1.5 to 2 orders of magnitude of the cosmic X-ray receivers would therefore enable us to determine the concentration of the relativistic electrons in the source Centaurus A; an analysis of the synchrotron radio emission would permit an independent determination of $H_\perp$. A comparison of the energy densities of the magnetic field and the relativistic electrons determined independently of one another would permit the conclusion as to whether the source contained a considerable quantity of relativistic protons and heavy nuclei. The above example concerns a metagalactic source, but this method, in principle, may also be applied to sufficiently extended remnants of type II supernovae, though in practice it would in this case be much more difficult to carry it out.

In the present state of the problem of the cosmic rays' origin we cannot exclude the possibility that relativistic protons and heavy nuclei are of metagalactic origin and are found throughout the universe, in a mean density of 10^{-12} eV/cm^3, whereas the relativistic electrons are generated in stellar systems, in the outbursts of supernovae and explosions of galactic nuclei. The relativistic protons may have been generated, for example, in the epoch of galactic formation and the stormy process of stellar birth. This "dualistic" hypothesis has in any case no less right to exist than the other hypotheses which are based on the assumption of a common generation of the "light" and "heavy" components of the cosmic rays in galactic sources. Another possibility presents itself in the assumption that stars with a very high activity are the injectors of cosmic rays.[305]

§ 17   The effects connected with a possible supernova outburst in the neighbourhood of the sun

As already mentioned repeatedly in this book, supernova outbursts in our galaxy are very rare events. It may be assumed that type II supernovae appear every 100–200 years, whereas the rate of type I supernovae is two to three times less. It is not impossible that "dwarf supernovae" such as were observed in 1572 and 1604 explode much more often, e.g., every year (cf. § 15).

It would be interesting to discuss the following problem: what is the probability that one of the solar-neighbourhood stars explodes as a supernova? The sun is at least $5 \cdot 10^9$ years old and in this time supernovae may have exploded in its nearest neighbourhood. Let us estimate first the probability of such an event and then consider the problem of the consequences of this, for the evolution of the solar system.

For definiteness, let us estimate this probability for outbursts of supernovae of the type II, under the assumption that one supernova of this type explodes somewhere in our galaxy, once in a hundred years.   As shown in § 7, these supernovae make their appearance in a very thin layer on either side of the galactic plane, i.e., a layer which is about 200 psc thick.   On the other hand, the galactic orbit of the sun is, as a whole, contained in this layer (and will remain in it for the future).   We shall consider a spherical region of radius R around the sun; the ratio between this volume and the volume of the whole galactic space in which type II supernovae explode will be given by

$$\frac{v}{V} = \frac{4R^3}{3r^2 d} \tag{17.1}$$

where r is the radius of the galactic disc in which supernovae of the type II appear and d is its thickness. This volume ratio represents the probability for the sun to be at a distance less than R away from a casual outburst of a supernova, where R must be smaller than d.

If, on the average, one supernova outburst occurs every 100 years we may expect a "nearby" outburst once in a period of time given by

$$t_1 = \frac{3r^2 d T}{4R^3} \tag{17.2}$$

Substituting $r = 10^4$ psc, $d = 200$ psc, $R = 10$ psc and $T = 100$ years, we find that $t_1 = 1.5 \cdot 10^9$ years. If $R = 20$ psc, $t_1 \sim 2 \cdot 10^8$ years. Note

13+s.

that t_1 may be several times less if a considerable part of the sun's galactic orbit lies in spiral arms where the type II supernovae explode predominantly.

This calculation shows that in the history of our solar system explosions of type II supernovae must have occurred thirty times at distances smaller than 20 psc and three to four times at distances smaller than 10 psc. If our ideas on the nature of objects of the types of the supernovae of 1572 and 1604 are right, there must have been five to six millions of outbursts of such stars at distances smaller than 20 psc.

The periodically repeated outbursts of supernovae in the immediate proximity of the sun may thus be considered as a regular process of evolution of our solar system. In 1957 attention was first drawn to this fact by V. I. Krasovski and the author of the present book.

We may now ask: what happens when one of the stars nearest to the sun explodes as a supernova? If such an outburst fell into an epoch where the earth was populated by rational beings, they must have observed, first of all, the appearance of an unusually bright star. If the outburst occurred at a distance of 10 psc, the star must have possessed a visual magnitude of -18. The light the earth would have received from this star must have been a thousand times brighter than that from the moon but a thousand times weaker than from the sun. Since the brightness temperature of a type II supernova at maximum amounts to about 40,000 °K, the radiation of this star would have been emitted mainly in the spectral range about 700–800 Å, that is, beyond the Lyman series. The entire hydrogen contained in a region with a radius of 30 parsec must have been ionized; only a few hundred thousand years after the explosion the interstellar hydrogen had again become neutral owing to recombination. The ionizing ultraviolet radiation flux at the earth must have reached a value of $\sim 10^3$ erg/cm^2 which is several hundred times the flux of this radiation from the sun. The upper layers of the atmosphere will therefore have been ionized tenfold. At the earth's surface, however, the ultraviolet radiation from the supernova could not have been noticed as it was entirely absorbed in the upper layers of the atmosphere.

The supernova must have been observable on the firmament for several years, and then it would no longer be seen with the unaided eye. A nebula had formed around the star and its filaments had undergone an expansion at an angular velocity of $\sim 2'$ per year. After 300 years the radius of this nebula must have reached $\sim 10°$ and the expansion rate will then have dropped as the ejected shell was slowed down by the interstellar medium.   After about 10^4 years the expanding nebula reached the solar system which, for the next 10,000 years, will have been inside the system of the gaseous filaments.   The nocturnal sky must have emitted the lines [O III], H, [O II] and the like, in which one could have observed the fantastic form of the filaments, extending through tens of degrees. The surface brightness of these filaments was similar to that of the Milky Way.

What effects are to be expected when the solar system is "suspended" for such a long time in a radio nebula, the remnant of a type II supernova?   The most important effect is an increased density of the primary cosmic rays, which has become higher by thirty times.   The mean energy density of the relativistic electrons in the region of the filamentary nebulae in Cygnus amounts to $\sim 10^{-11}$ erg/cm^3, and if there are relativistic protons and heavy nuclei their energy density will be $\sim 10^{-10}$ erg/cm^3 which is a hundred times higher than the present energy density of the cosmic rays around the earth.   Since the relativistic particles inside a radio nebula display a rather non-uniform distribution there must exist periods whose duration may be estimated as centuries, within which the energy density of the primary cosmic radiation around the earth may be several times higher than at present.

We may now enquire after the consequences of such a high density of primary cosmic rays around the earth which lasted 30,000 years.   First of all such a change in the cosmic conditions around the earth must have had serious biological (correctly, genetic) consequences for a series of species of animals and plants on our planet.   It is well known that the evolution of the species is controlled by natural selection, which occurs under the influence of the various physical conditions of the surrounding medium.   But in the analyses of this evolution it has not, until recently, been taken into account that the level of hard radiation might have changed with time.   The natural level of radio-activity in the lowest layer of the atmosphere and in water is, however, one of the causes of the so-called "spontaneous mutation," the sudden, jump-like changes of various biological characteristics of a given species which were passed on to the descendants.   An increase in the mutation rate by perhaps 100 per cent may entail serious genetic consequences for some species of plants and animals.   We know from radio-biology that the mutation rate increases when animals or plants are irradiated by a hard radiation.   But the various species react in different ways to such an irradiation.   Thus, for example, in the case of species with short cycles of reproduction, a

doubling of the mutation rate will in a series of cases require a hundredfold or even thousandfold radiation dose; for long-lived species, however,
doubling of the mutation rate may be the result of only a three- to tenfold
dose.

According to the data available the terrestrial mean radio-activity
of the lowest atmospheric layer amounts to 0.12 r (Roentgen) per year.
This radio-activity is by two-thirds due to "terrestrial" factors, first of all
the radio-activity of the earth's crust.   But 0.04 r per year are contributed
by cosmic radiation.

Hence it follows that if, for example, the cosmic rays' intensity were
a hundred times higher (which corresponds to the mean conditions inside
the filamentary nebulae in Cygnus) the mean level of radio-activity in the
lowest atmospheric layer would rise thirtyfold.   This may already have had
serious genetic consequences for various long-lived species.   The genetic
hazard is particularly high for highly organized and strongly specialized
species of animals with limited population.   For such species a continuously high level of ionization in the surrounding medium, maintained for
thousands of years, may entail catastrophic consequences.

In [306] a hypothesis was developed in which the well-known dying-
out of reptiles at the end of the Cretaceous period was explained by the
permanently raised level of cosmic radiation to its tenfold or even
hundredfold value.   This might have been the result of the explosion of a
solar-neighbourhood star as a supernova.   This hypothesis would have
been verified by a paleontological proof that these reptiles died out
everywhere on the earth after a time not exceeding 30,000 years.   At
present, as far as we know, there exists no reliable data on the duration
of the process of the universal dying-out of reptiles, in particular the
dinosaurs.   It would be desirable to interest specialists in the field of
paleontology in this problem.

A continuously raised level of hard radiation need not be fatal for all
species of animals.   It is quite possible that for a series of species such a
radiation might have been a favourable factor of evolution.   The high
level of radio-activity caused by the submersion of the solar system into a
remnant of a sufficiently nearby supernova might have been an important
factor of stimulation of life generation in lifeless substances.   Though the
investigation into the problem of the origin of terrestrial life has essentially
advanced in the past years, we are still far from understanding how life
came to our planet.   We can, for example, imagine that a high level of
radio-activity, caused by some cosmic events which took place in an epoch

some 10^9 years ago, may have stimulated the formation of highly complex compounds from simple organic compounds, and life on the earth
may have developed on the basis of these complexes. At present these
considerations are, of course, only hypothetical. But they show the great

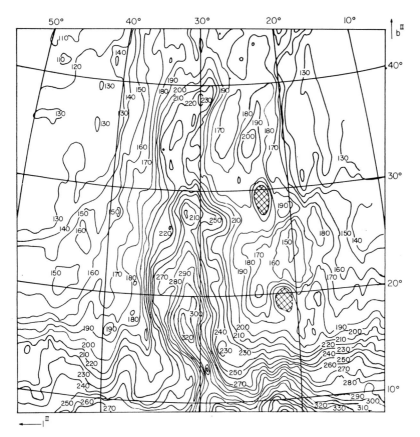

FIG. 117   Isophotes of radio-frequency radiation in the region of the galactic
"gulf".[307]

importance of such effects as supernova explosions for problems which,
at first sight, seem very remote from astrophysics.

In connection with the problem we have touched upon here, we
should like to discuss yet another interesting fact. For as long as more

than 15 years there has existed a not as yet explained detail in the observed image of the celestial distribution of cosmic radio-frequency radiation intensity.   It is well known that the intensity of cosmic radio emission is strongly concentrated towards the galactic equator and the

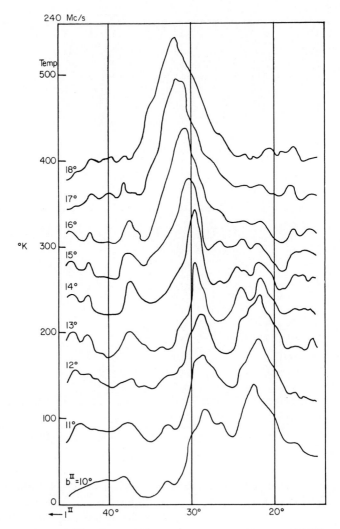

Fig. 118   Profile of isophotes in the region of the "gulf".[307]

nucleus. This tendency, however, disturbs the huge and rather intense "spur" of the radio-emission isophotes stretching across the heavens almost perpendicularly to the Milky Way. It begins in a zone of the Milky Way whose galactic longitude is $l^{\mathrm{II}} = 30°$ and extends almost to the galactic north pole and, describing a giant loop, it returns to the galactic equator. Figure 117 shows the isophotes of the celestial area near the galactic equator where this "spur" begins, for a frequency of

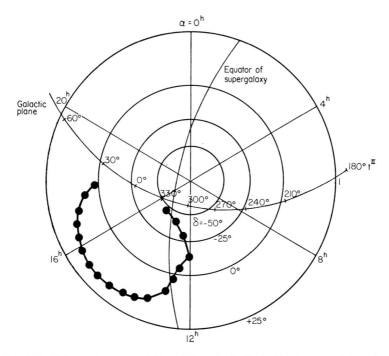

FIG. 119   Schematic representation of the galactic "gulf" in stereographic projection.[313]

240 Mc.[307] The width of the radio-telescopic pattern is $85' \times 60'$. The same picture has been provided with a new system of galactic coordinates. It is clearly seen that at $l^{\mathrm{II}} \sim 30°$ and $b^{\mathrm{II}} \sim 10°$ the isophotes run steeply upwards, almost perpendicularly, to the galactic equator. Figure 118 shows the sections ("profiles") of these isophotes for $b^{\mathrm{II}} =$ const, where this phenomenon is marked very clearly. The narrowness

of this detail attracts our attention, especially between the galactic latitudes of 11° and 16°. In individual cases (for instance, at $b^{II} = 20°$) the gradient of the brightness temperature is very high. As a rule this gradient is directed towards increasing longitudes. In individual areas this coarse detail of galactic radio emission shows a fine structure, i.e., several "combs" of the isophotes run almost parallel to one another.

Figure 117 shows only a part of this "spur." A systematic representation of it is given in Figure 119, in a stereo-photographic projection.[313b] It is clearly seen that the "spur" represents a small circle on the firmament whose diameter amounts to 111° ± 5°, and its centre is at $\alpha = 15^h00$, $\delta = -36° \pm 2°$. Observations made at different frequencies show that the radio-frequency radiation emitted by the "spur" is of non-thermal origin. It must still be indicated that polarization observations of the radio emission from the "spur" did not yield any positive results.[307] These observations were, however, carried out with the help of a radio-telescope with a relatively wide ($\sim 2°$) radiation pattern. The problem of a possible polarization of the radio emission from the "spur" is therefore still unsolved.

An important peculiarity of this coarse detail of the radio isophotes is the absence of any extended sources of optical radiation with which this detail could be identified. This problem was especially investigated in paper [308]. With the help of two high-power cameras which were provided with changeable interference and glass filters and centred on the basis of the nebular emission ([O II], λ 3,727, [O III], λ 5,007 and Hα), the area of the "spur" was photographed. The relative surface brightness in Hα rays was calibrated according to the filamentary nebulae in Cygnus. The results of these observations were, however, negative: in the area of the galactic "spur" not the slightest increase in the brightness of the sky could be observed. The fundamental characteristic parameters of the optical and the radio-frequency brightness of several nebulae which are remnants of outbursts of type II supernovae and those of the galactic "spur" are compiled in Table 28.

In the second, third and fourth columns of this table the intensity units are referred to the intensity of the Hα line in the nebula NGC 6960. In the fifth column the brightness temperatures of various sources are given which had been measured with a radio-telescope with a radiation pattern of 1.1°. The last column contains the ratios of the optical brightness in Hα and the radio-frequency brightness, the units being referred to this ratio for NGC 6960.

TABLE 28

Object	Hα λ 6,563	[O III] λ 5,007	[O II] λ 3,727	Tβ ν = 237 Mc	Hα/Tβ
Filamentary Nebulae:					
(a) NGC 6960	1.0	0.9	2.3	60°	1.0
(b) NGC 6992/5	0.7	1.5	6.0	36°	1.2
IC 443	0.7	0.3	8.0	300°	0.14
HB 9	0.2	—	—	80°	0.15
S 147	0.09	—	—	35°	0.15
"Spur":					
(a) $\alpha = 12^h10^m$, $\delta = 0°$	0.008	—	—	80°	0.006
(b) $\alpha = 13^h30^m$, $\delta = 20°$	0.003	—	—	80°	0.002
(c) $\alpha = 16^h40^m$, $\delta = 18°$	0.009	—	—	120°	0.004

We see from Table 28 that the ratio between the optical and the radio-frequency brightnesses for the "spur" is at least five hundred times less than for the filamentary nebulae in Cygnus and fifty times less than the ratio for the other remnants of type II supernovae. It must, however, be mentioned that English authors seem to have greatly over-estimated the sensitivity of their observations in Hα. Recently, with the help of an essentially improved method, P. V. Shcheglov and T. A. Lozinskaya showed that the upper limit of intensity of the line $\lambda = 3,727$ Å in the "spur" is only fifteen times less than the intensity of this line for NGC 6960.[309]

At various times hypotheses were propounded on the nature of the galactic "spur" described above. That by Brown, Davis and Hazard[310] is the most interesting. According to this hypothesis the "spur" is the remnant of a type II supernova which exploded 30,000 years ago in relatively close proximity to the sun. This hypothesis is illustrated by the schematic representation of Figure 120a. Figure 120b shows the brightness distribution to be expected for the shell of this supernova, under the assumption that, according to a very simple model, the radio emission per unit volume of the shell is constant.

If this interesting hypothesis is true, the brightness temperature of the sky inside the "spur" should be higher than outside the "spur" at the same galactic latitudes. The isophotes at 38 Mc[311] seem to indicate that inside the "spur" there are large "patches" of radio emission and the mean brightness temperature is higher. The same is, obviously, observed

13*

at a frequency of 158 Mc. But a more detailed analysis carried out in [307] did not lead to a definite result.

Since the brightness temperature of the "spur" is almost the same as that of the filamentary nebulae in Cygnus, the linear dimensions and the ages of the two objects must be similar, provided the interpretation suggested in [310] is correct. This conclusion follows from the theory developed in § 7. In this case the outburst of the supernova must have occurred about 50,000 years ago, at a distance of ∼30 psc from the sun. At this distance a type II supernova should, on the average, explode once per sixty millions of years (see above). Therefore, if the "spur" is the remnant of a type II supernova, we observe a very improbable event.

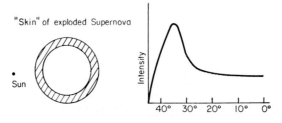

FIGS. 120a, b   Diagram illustrating the hypothesis of the outburst of a nearby supernova.[310]

An argument in favour of the hypothesis of the English radio-astronomers was provided by T. A. Lozinskaya's investigations; she showed that in the region of the "spur" a noticeable flaw in the clouds of inter-stellar hydrogen was observed, displaying small radial velocities.[312] This may be interpreted by assuming some correlation to exist between the solar-neighbourhood clouds of neutral hydrogen and the "spur." The latter may therefore be considered as being relatively near to the sun.

An argument against this hypothesis is the considerable difference (up to 25°) between the co-ordinates of the X-ray source and the centre of the small circle on which the radio emission of the "spur" is concentrated. We must, however, take into consideration that the diameter of the "spur" is ∼111° so that the position of the X-ray source is not so eccentric. It may also be supposed that, by virtue of the "sling effect" (cf. § 4), the ex-supernova has a very high proper velocity so that in the course of tens of thousands of years it has shifted considerably relative to the shell.

Another difficulty of this hypothesis consists in the necessity to admit an activity of the nucleus of the remnants of the type II supernova which has been maintained for tens of thousands of years.   Only future observations of the angular dimensions of the source in Scorpius may determine the chance of this hypothesis.

Unfortunately, the hypothesis by Brown, Davis and Hazard meets with very serious difficulties.   The fact mentioned above that there is no optical radiation of measurable brightness, though it is not a decisive argument against this hypothesis, will in any case indicate the unusualness of the "spur" if the latter is considered as the remnant of a supernova. The fact that the "spur's" emission band is so narrow (it reaches $\sim \frac{1}{50}$th of its diameter) distinguishes it from the bands observed at such relatively "old" objects as the filamentary nebulae in Cygnus and IC 443 (cf. Fig. 22).   There is yet another serious objection.   During a relatively thorough survey of the sky at high and medium galactic latitudes, at a frequency of 240 Mc, a broad and rather "blurred" radio-emission band of greater brightness was discovered in the constellation Cetus, which has the form of a small circle, 90° in diameter.[313]   The centre of this circle has the co-ordinates $\alpha = 23^h20^m \pm 10^m$, $\delta = 27° \pm 2°$.   It is quite obvious that the presence of two "spurs" in the radio-emission isophotes is an argument against the hypothesis of the explosion of a nearby supernova.   If the probability of a supernova outburst 50,000 years ago, at a distance of ~ 30 psc, is close to 10^{-3}, the probability of two supernova outbursts at such a short distance and within about the same period of time will be about 10^{-5} to 10^{-6}, i.e., vanishingly small.

We must, however, take into consideration that the "southern spur" which was discovered relatively recently in the constellation Cetus is far from being such a clearly marked formation as the "spur" in the northern part of the sky which has been known for a longer time.   It cannot be excluded that the "southern spur" is not even a real formation but merely a casual combination of isophotes at high galactic latitudes.

Very recently new observational data were obtained which seem to confirm the hypothesis of Brown, Davis and Hazard.[313a]   These observations were made when continuing the investigations of the "spur" at a frequency of 240 Mc, with a radio-telescope with a radiation pattern of $\sim 1°$,[307] which we discussed above: A large celestial area was investigated between $\alpha = 8^h$ and 16^h and $\delta = +18°$ and $-35°$.   When processing the results of the radio-astronomical observations a considerable number of details relatively bright in their radio-frequency radiation were discovered which are "filamentary" in their nature. Some of these bright bands ($T_b \approx 50°$) extend over almost 15°. Most of these filaments are concentrated in a celestial area inside the small circle formed by the "spur."

With the help of a stereographic projection which transferred the circle from the firmament to a plane the distribution of the "spur" and all "radio filaments" discussed above were investigated. It was proved that the main "ridge" of the isophotes which form the "spur" passes through the small circle 113° in diameter whose centre virtually coincides with the value given above. It is very interesting that almost all "filaments" are inside this small circle in an approximately concentric arrangement. The mean surface density inside the region bounded by the "spur" is considerably higher than outside the spur, which is an argument in favour of the hypothesis of a "shell" structure of this formation. It must be mentioned that the whole radio-frequency structure of the "spur" and the "filaments" contained in it strikingly resemble the optical structure of the filamentary nebulae in Cygnus. A very interesting new result is the high degree of polarization that was discovered in the outer parts of the "spur."

It must be mentioned, however, that the problem of the possible interpretation of the "spur" as the remnant of a nearby supernova is still unsolved at present. An alternative hypothesis on the nature of the "spur" is the assumption that it represents some coarse structural detail of the galactic corona connecting the latter with the disc. A very weighty argument in favour of this assumption is the distribution of the isophotes of radio emission from the Andromeda nebula shown in Figure 14, in which we see at least two large spurs stretching from the disc to the corona of this galaxy. The strong polarization observed of individual details of the spur speaks in our opinion rather in favour of the latter hypothesis than of that which considers this phenomenon as the shell of a supernova. For a total triumph of the latter it would be important to discover the emission, although very weak, in λ 3,727 or Hα connected with the "spur." It would be desirable to continue the investigations in this direction.

§ 18   The causes of supernova explosions

So far we have considered the phenomenon of supernova explosions mainly from the point of view of their consequences. A purely phenomenological description of the supernova is contained in the first two sections of this book.   The other sections deal with the highly interesting processes which take place in an expanding nebula, which is formed after an explosion of a supernova of type I or type II.   These processes play a great part in the dynamics of interstellar matter.   The investigation into the remnants of supernovae is also of fundamental significance for the theory of the origin of cosmic rays.   Section 16 has been devoted to this problem.

The pivotal question of the cause of the stellar explosions resulting in the appearance of supernovae has not yet been discussed.   Many problems connected with the analysis of the physical conditions in the remnants of supernovae may be investigated without knowing the mechanism of outburst.   It must also be stressed that the investigation of the remnants of outbursts yields the necessary parameters, without which it would be impossible to state the scientific problem of the cause and nature of such an explosion.   To these parameters belong the mass of the gaseous shell ejected, the kinetic energy of this shell and its chemical composition, the presence of a huge number of relativistic particles and their energy spectrum.

Photometrical and spectrographical investigations of supernovae permit the determination of the total radiative energy, the most important characteristic of the explosion, the initial velocities of the shells and their dependence on the type of supernova and several other important parameters.

So it seems quite natural to us that the problem of the cause of such explosions is dealt with at the end of this book.   In addition to this it is necessary to emphasize that this problem is very complex and cannot as yet be solved in a satisfactory way though there exist a great number of theoretical studies into it.   On the other hand, we must not say that we do not know anything about the cause of stellar explosions.   The outlines of the future complete theory become already apparent and certain results of the investigations are of great interest.   Our task does not include a review of all the numerous attempts at developing a theory of stellar explosions.   We focus our attention only on those which, in our opinion, help us to understand the causes of these magnificent cosmic catastrophes of supernova explosions.   So the compilation of the material will display a somewhat subjective character and this must not be forgotten in the following.

First we shall list the fundamental facts which are to be explained by the theory.

1. The theory has to account for the existence of at least two types of supernovae. As the supernovae of the type I are relatively old stars with a mass that is only a little greater than the solar mass, their age has been great enough. On the other hand, the stars with very great masses which explode as supernovae of the type II must be very young. It is quite possible that they have not yet had time to "settle" on the main sequence. It stands to reason that the mechanisms of explosion of the supernovae of the types I and II must be different. What is the reason for this difference?

2. If we assume that in the process of a type II supernova explosion a great part of the star's mass is ejected (so that we can speak of a "sling effect," cf. § 4) and that the speed of the masses ejected reaches 5,000–7,000 km/s, the nature of the explosion must be such that the kinetic energy per gram of substance of the exploding star $\sim (1$–$2)\cdot 10^{17}$ erg/g. With a stellar mass of approximately $30M_\odot$ the total energy of such an explosion must be of the order of 10^{51} to 10^{52} erg, and in the case of supernovae of the type III (cf. § 2), one to two orders higher.

3. The kinetic energy of the gases ejected during explosions of type I supernovae is considerably lower. Since, for example, the mass of the gaseous filaments of the Crab nebula is assumed to amount to $\sim 0.1M_\odot$ (cf. § 11) and the speed of ejection is assumed as 10^8 cm/s, we obtain a value of $\sim 10^{48}$ erg for the kinetic energy of the shell ejected. Note that the supernova of 1054 whose remnant is the Crab nebula was one of the most powerful objects of this type.

4. The two types of supernovae differ essentially in the following: Let us estimate the ratio of the energy of photon emission $\mathscr{E}_\phi$ of the supernova and the kinetic energy of the ejected shell, $\mathscr{E}_k$. We assume that the type II supernova has an absolute magnitude of -17.5 and the bolometric correction amounts to -3 (which corresponds to a colour temperature of 40,000°). Assuming an average light curve for this supernova (cf. Fig. 5) we find that $\sim 10^{50}$ erg and the ratio $\mathscr{E}_\phi/\mathscr{E}_k \sim 10^{-1}$ to 10^{-2}. For a supernova with $M = -18$, $\mathscr{E}_\phi$ is also $\sim 10^{50}$ erg, whereas $(\mathscr{E}_\phi/\mathscr{E}_k)_I \sim 10^2$. Thus we see that for supernovae of type I $(\mathscr{E}_\phi/\mathscr{E}_k)$ is a thousand times higher than for supernovae of type II. In other words, in the case of type I supernovae the "efficiency" with respect to emission is extraordinarily high. This must undoubtedly be connected with the explosion mechanism.

5. Both the remnants of type I supernovae and the remnants of type II supernovae contain a huge number of relativistic particles. Their

total energy is of the same order of magnitude as the magnetic field energies (10^{48} to 10^{49} erg). The generation of the relativistic particles is an essential attribute of the explosion. The theory has to explain the cause of the production of such a high quantity of relativistic particles.

6. The magnetic fields in the remnants of both type I and type II supernovae have relatively high intensities. In the case of the Crab nebula it is rather regular. In the case of type II supernovae the magnetic field and the relativistic particles moving in it display a shell structure, whereas in the Crab nebula (the only carefully investigated remnant of a type I supernova) the magnetic field is inside the system of expanding gaseous filaments. A theory will not be comprehensive if it does not explain the appearance of the magnetic field in the remnants of supernovae and its characteristic peculiarities.

7. In the case of the Crab nebula we have some proof of the continued activity of the nucleus, i.e., the ex-supernova. Though the outburst occurred almost 1,000 years ago, the nuclear power of relativistic particle generation amounts to at least 10^{37} erg/s and may be even higher (cf. § 14). This power is very high; it is sufficient to indicate that it amounts to at least 10 per cent of the radio-frequency synchrotron emissivity of our whole stellar system. It is therefore obvious that the problem of the exploded star's enormous activity, which has continued up to the present, is very significant. The problem of the continued activity of ex-supernovae is thus closely related to the fundamental problem of the cause of their explosions.

The most reasonable attempt at answering the first three questions the theory should be able to answer was, in our opinion, made by Hoyle and Fowler in paper [314] and the subsequent papers. First of all one has to find the source of this enormous amount of energy which is released by way of an explosion in the supernova outburst. It is commonly known that the energy source of stellar radiation in the case of main-sequence stars is the thermonuclear fusion reactions that occur in their interior. At present the theory of the "quiet" evolution of the stars is at a sufficiently high level and in agreement with the results of observations. But after the nuclear hydrogen fuel in the central zones has become exhausted, their evolution becomes much more complex. Today, we have not yet a theory at our disposal which answers definitely the question of what happens to the star in this final stage of its evolution. Individual details of the stellar evolution in this last stage can in fact be traced quite well. So we understand, for example, the mechanism of stellar transition from the main sequence in the Herzsprung–Russel diagram to the red giants. But we do not yet know definitely what will then happen to the star.

On the other hand, as early as the thirties, the theoretical astronomers were interested in the problem of the final phase of stellar evolution. We can sum up the fundamental theoretical results in the following way (this problem has been dealt with in detail by Ya. B. Zel'dovich and I. D. Novikov in the outstanding review articles[315,316]).

The main tendency of stellar evolution is the continuous consumption of the nuclear fuel. When virtually all the nuclear fuel has been used up in its central part, the equilibrium state of the star (more precisely, that of its theoretical model which is greatly simplified, in particular, without taking the rotation into account) will depend on its initial mass which is considered constant for the process of evolution. If the mass of this "idealized" star is smaller than $1.2M_\odot$ an equilibrium configuration is obtained in which the gas is in a degenerate state. The pressure gradient of the degenerate electron gas is then equal to the weight of the column of gas over it. The possibility of such a configuration existing was indicated for the first time by Fowler[317] and J. Frenkel.[318] A detailed theory has been developed by Chandrasekhar.[319] Stars which are described well enough by this model have been observed for a long time and are called the "white dwarfs."

For non-rotating stars with a mass of $1.2 < M < 2M_\odot$ a theory was developed by Oppenheimer and co-workers.[320,321] In this case the configuration with the degenerated gas is no longer in equilibrium. The star undergoes a sudden collapse and becomes a super-dense object, a so-called neutron star. It measures about 10 km in diameter and its mean density is of the order of nuclear density.

If, however, the mass of the star exceeds $2M_\odot$, the final state of stellar evolution must consist of an unlimited compression as there does not exist any equilibrium configuration, and a gravitational "self-contraction" of the star takes place. Energy cannot be emitted in any form and, at least in principle, the star can only be discovered through its gravitational interaction with other celestial bodies. Such a star may be denoted "congealed."

Therefore, according to the initial mass, the theory predicts three types of final stages of stellar evolution: (a) white dwarfs, (b) neutron stars and (c) collapsed or "congealed" stars. It is a peculiarity of astro-

physics at this stage of its development that in contrast to the white
dwarfs, neutron stars and collapsed stars have not yet been observed.
It is, however, not impossible that a great part of the galactic X-ray
sources discovered recently are neutron sources (cf. [322]).

⎰ Let us now discuss the problem of the supernova outbursts; first of
all we must stress that these outbursts are in all probability linked with
the final stage of stellar evolution as this was sketched above. It is quite
natural to assume that the huge amount of energy which is set free in a
supernova outburst is of nuclear origin. Since the energy is released in a
sudden explosion-like process, it is easily proved that all the nuclear fuel
of the star cannot possibly be used up in this explosion⎰ First of all, this
holds true for hydrogen. Although the energy generation is very high
in the case of a total fusion of hydrogen into helium (it amounts to $6 \cdot 10^{18}$ erg
per gram), ten times higher than in a type II supernova outburst, we know
that this reaction cannot be the cause of the explosion. The fact is that
even at an extremely high temperature the reaction $p + p \to d + \beta^{+} + \nu$
proceeds very slowly as it implies the β-decay. At high temperatures
helium transmutes into light elements through the Salpeter reaction
$3\,\mathrm{He}^4 \to \mathrm{C}^{12}$ and the subsequent reactions $\mathrm{C}^{12}(\alpha, \gamma)\mathrm{O}^{16}$ and $\mathrm{O}^{16}(\alpha, \gamma)\mathrm{Ne}^{20}$.
A relatively high rate of nuclear energy production may be achieved in
reactions of light elements with protons. These reactions occur relatively
rapidly even at a temperature of $10^8\,°\mathrm{K}$. In this way, however, each
nucleus of a light element may bind at least three to four protons, which
corresponds to an energy release of ~ 10–20 MeV per nucleus. For the
heavier nuclei produced by successive addition of protons, the presence
of the β-decay considerably slows down the reaction, for which reason the
decay loses its explosion-like character. As an example of a reaction
between light nuclei and protons we may consider, e.g., the following
chain reaction (Bethe cycle):

$$\mathrm{C}^{12}(p, \gamma)\mathrm{N}^{13}(p, \gamma)\mathrm{O}^{14}(\beta + \nu,\ 100\ \mathrm{s})\mathrm{N}^{14}(p, \gamma)\mathrm{O}^{15}\ (\beta + \gamma,\ 200\ \mathrm{s})\mathrm{N}^{15}(p, \alpha)\mathrm{C}^{12}$$
$$(18.1)$$

The time this sequence of reactions requires must be at least 300 s as
the chain contains two β-decays. If the explosion takes ~ 100 s, the
chain will break off at O^{15}; in this case the energy release will amount to
19 MeV per nucleus.

If the star has the same chemical composition as the sun, in each
gram of its substance $\sim 5 \cdot 10^{20}$ light nuclei will be contained. If we assume
that in the reactions described above the energy released per each light

nucleus amounts to 10–20 MeV, we obtain an energy output of $\sim 10^{16}$ erg/g of substance. Therefore, even if a star of solar mass explodes as a whole, the energy output due to this reaction would be of the order of 10^{49} erg, that is, by an order of magnitude lower than in the outburst of a type I supernova. If we suppose that, for some reason, the mass of the sun would be heated up to a temperature of $\sim 10^8$ °K, this would very probably result in an explosion, but the velocity of the gases ejected in this process would not exceed 500 km/s, which is by an order of magnitude lower than in the case of type II supernovae. Recall that in supernovae of this type the energy yield in an explosion must be at least $(1-2) \cdot 10^{17}$ erg/g.

In order to explain the catastrophic release of energy in a supernova explosion caused by nuclear reactions (and such reactions may only take place with light elements) it is a necessary supposition that the chemical composition of the mass of the exploding star differs essentially from that of the sun. It must be assumed that in these stars the abundance of the light elements relative to hydrogen is ten times higher than in the sun. This important result was obtained for the first time in [314].

At very high temperatures $\sim (2 \pm 0.5) \cdot 10^9$ °K the light nuclei display an explosive instability by virtue of the very fast reactions of the type $C^{12}(C^{12}, \alpha)Ne^{20}$, $C^{12}(C^{12}, p)Na^{23}$ and analogous reactions for O^{16} and other light nuclei. The characteristic time for these reactions is ~ 1 s and the energy yield per gram substance consisting of light nuclei is $\sim 5 \cdot 10^{17}$ erg/g. If a mass of this substance equal to $0.1 M_\odot$ explodes, an energy of $\sim 10^{50}$ erg is set free, which is in fairly good agreement with the energy of type I supernova explosions.

We may therefore draw the conclusion that the potential nuclear fuel responsible for the explosions of supernovae can only be a substance which is highly enriched in light elements. The usual cosmic "mixture," like the solar plasma, is, obviously, not suitable for this purpose. The question in which way this possibility is realized, is, however, still open. In other words, we do not know the natural processes which may raise the temperature of the stellar mass rapidly enough up to 10^8 to 19^9 degrees.

Hoyle and Fowler considered at first the final stage of evolution of a star of a relatively great mass, say, $M = 10 M_\odot$. One may assume that the results of this analysis will, to some extent, help us to understand the mechanism of explosion of type II supernovae. The substance in the interior of massive stars is non-degenerated as its density is relatively low. Qualitatively this may be understood in the following way: On the basis

of the virial theorem we may equate the gravitational energy of the star
and its thermal energy NkT. The gravitational energy per gram of
substance will be $\sim GM/R$. Since $R \sim (M/\rho)^{1/3}$, where ρ is the mean
stellar density, we obtain $\rho \sim (kT^3)/(G^3 M^2)$, i.e., ρ decreases rapidly as M
increases. The case is considered where the temperature in the central
part of the star is very high, $\sim 5 \cdot 10^9\,°\mathrm{K}$. At such extreme temperatures
the nuclear reactions can proceed at extraordinarily high rates. As the
result of a balance between the various modes of "direct" and "inverse"
nuclear reactions a temperature-dependent equilibrium will be established.
In this state a great quantity of the substance exists in the form of nuclei,
with a minimum value of the "packing factor." The calculations carried
out in [323] show that at $T = 3.8 \cdot 10^9\,°\mathrm{K}$ and a neutron/proton concentration ratio $n_n/n_p \sim 300$ most of the nuclei belong to the iron group.

The central part of such a star is surrounded by a shell whose temperature is considerably lower, e.g., below $1.5 \cdot 10^9\,°\mathrm{K}$. The chemical composition of this shell differs essentially from the chemical composition of
the nucleus. In the shell the light elements will prevail which represent
the potential nuclear fuel necessary for the star to explode. This potential
possibility is realized when in the process of evolution the star's nucleus
suffers a catastrophic collapse within the time of free fall, ~ 1 s. In this
process the mechanical equilibrium of the star is disturbed and its shell
begins to fall towards the nucleus. Within a very short period of time
(likewise ~ 1 s) the kinetic energy of the falling shell is converted into
thermal energy and the shell substance is very rapidly heated whereby the
conditions for nuclear explosion reactions with light elements are fulfilled.
In this connection it should be noted that the rate of nuclear reactions with
light elements depends very strongly on the temperature; this is due to the
presence of the factor $\exp(-85/T_9^{1/3})$ where T_9 is the temperature in units
of $10^9\,°\mathrm{K}$. Even a relatively small increase in the temperature will
therefore entail a catastrophic acceleration of these reactions.

It is essential that the collapse of the stellar nucleus must take place
within a period of time shorter than that the shell needs to alter its structure in a, so to speak, "quiet," quasi-equilibrium way, without explosion.
The time of the structural transformation is approximately equal to the
time of the characteristic hydrodynamic processes, which is of the order
of magnitude of the time a sonic wave needs to traverse the star.[315] The
sonic velocity in a star is $v_s = (\partial P/\partial \rho)^{1/2} \approx (P/\rho)^{1/2} = (GM/R)^{1/2}$. If we
assume, for example, $R \approx 3 \cdot 10^9$ cm (as the star has already approached
the end of its evolutionary track and has become a small body of very

high density) and $M \sim 10 M_{\odot}$, we obtain $v_s \sim 10^9$ cm/s and a value of $\tau_s \approx R/v_s \approx 3$ s for the time a sonic wave needs to pass through the star.

For the star's collapse to be a catastrophically fast process it is necessary that a mechanism be in action which prevents an essential increase in temperature during the compression. If the temperature of the nucleus were rapidly raised during the compression, the latter could in no way be catastrophic as the star would have time to regenerate its structure. Thus we need a "coolant" which removes the heat released in the compression from the nucleus of the star. This "coolant" must be extraordinarily effective as it has to withdraw $\sim 10^{18}$ erg/g·s. A necessary condition for the disturbance of a stable equilibrium or quasi-equilibrium configuration of the star represents the inequality (cf. [315])

$$\frac{d \ln P}{d \ln \rho} = \gamma \leqslant \frac{4}{3} \tag{18.2}$$

where P is the pressure, ρ is the density and γ the specific heat ratio. For a monatomic gas $\gamma = \frac{5}{3}$. If an essential part of the energy transferred to the gas is consumed in such processes as dissociation, ionization or production of neutrinos it is obvious that the temperature growth in the compression must be slowed down. In this case γ will be lower and may become smaller than $\frac{4}{3}$. We know that this situation exists, for example, in the sub-photospheric layers of the sun where, owing to the ionization of hydrogen, a convective instability arises. In this case the process of hydrogen ionization acts as a "coolant."

In the interiors of very hot stars the part of this "coolant" might be played by the process of very fast neutrino formation. But with these relatively low densities that occur in stellar interiors ($\rho \sim 10^7$ g/cm³, as there is no degeneracy), it can be shown that the neutrino radiation is too weak, only $\sim 10^{13}$ erg/g·s. It is easy to see that the losses due to photon radiation are even smaller. Nevertheless, there does exist a "coolant" in the star which is necessary for a catastrophically fast compression of the nucleus. The fact is that in a statistical equilibrium of nuclear matter, when its temperature is very high, the equilibrium conditions are sharply shifted from the iron-group elements to a neutron-α-particle mixture. Let us consider the reaction $Fe^{56} \rightleftharpoons 13\,He^4 + 4n$. Let us write this reaction in the general form

$$A \rightleftharpoons \alpha A_0 + \beta A_1$$
$$Z \rightleftharpoons \alpha Z_0 + \beta Z_1 \tag{18.3}$$

where (A, Z) is the symbol for an iron nucleus possessing the atomic weight A and the charge Z, (A_0, Z_0) and (A_1, Z_1) are its decay products, in our case the helium nuclei and the neutrons, with $\alpha = 13$ and $\beta = 4$. The equilibrium concentrations of the nucleus (A, Z) and the products of its disintegration are connected by the relation

$$n(A, Z) = n_0^\alpha n_1^\beta \frac{\omega(A, Z)}{\omega_0^\alpha \omega_1^\beta} \left(\frac{A}{A_0^\alpha A_1^\beta}\right)^{3/2} \left(\frac{2\pi\hbar^2}{M_0 kT}\right)^{3(\alpha+\beta-1)/2} \exp\left(\frac{Q}{kT}\right)$$

(18.4)

which is analogous to Saha's formula which is well known in astrophysics. In Equation (18.4) ω denotes the statistical weight, $M = 1/N_0$ is the atomic unit of mass, N_0 Avogadro's number and Q the energy which must be transferred to the nucleus (A, Z) to cause its disintegration into

$$\alpha(A_0, Z_0) + \beta(A_1, Z_1)$$

For the reaction

$$Fe^{56} \rightleftharpoons 13\ He^4 + 4n$$

in which we are interested we have numerically

$$n(56, 26) = \omega(56, 26) n_\alpha^{13} \cdot n_n^4 \cdot \frac{56^{3/2}}{2^{43}} \cdot \left(\frac{2\pi\hbar}{M_0 kT}\right)^{24} \exp\left(\frac{Q}{kT}\right)$$

(18.5)

where $\omega(56, 26) = 1.4$ and $Q = 124.4$. If we take into account that $n_n = 4n_\alpha/9$, we can show that the substance, as regards its mass, will consist half of iron nuclei and half of α-particles and neutrons, provided that the relation

$$\log \rho = 11.62 + 1.5 \log T_g - \frac{39.7}{T_g}$$

(18.6)

is satisfied; ρ is the total density of the substance, in g/cm^3. Figure 121 shows $\log \rho$ as a function of T_g. The points in the $\log \rho - T_g$ plane, on the left side of the curve, correspond to the equilibrium state of the substance when it consists almost entirely of iron, the points to the left of this curve correspond to a substance which is virtually free from iron nuclei and contains only α-particles and neutrons. The transition between these two domains occurs very rapidly, the width of the transition zone is $\Delta T_g = \pm 0.5$.

It is essential that the mean binding energy of a nucleon in an Fe^{56} nucleus is equal to 8.79 MeV, whereas the mean binding energy of a nucleon in the mixture $13\alpha + 4n$ is equal to 6.57 MeV. Thus, in order to split the iron nucleus into thirteen α-particles and four neutrons an energy of 2.22 MeV must be spent per nucleon ($= Q/56$) or $2 \cdot 10^{18}$ erg/g. This is much higher than the thermal energy per unit mass which, even at $T_g = 12$, amounts to only ~ 0.8 MeV per nucleon. Consequently, in order to "dissociate" the iron nucleus into α-particles and neutrons, one must have another energy source. Such an energy source can only be gravity.

Let us now consider the change in state of the substance in the central part of a star in the final stage of its evolution. Though the radiative energy losses at such high temperatures cannot cause the nuclear collapse, they accelerate principally the evolution. As a result, a point in the $\log \rho$–T_g graph, which corresponds to the momentary state of the star, will rapidly be shifted to the right (on curve II or III). Within a period of $\sim 10^7$ s this point reaches the transition zone (curve I) which separates the Fe^{56} domain from the He $+ n$ domain. Since the energy necessary for this phase transition is not available, the point begins to move upwards along the band edge, to the right.

In such a change of state of the star, it is inevitable that its mechanical equilibrium is disturbed. In the case of mechanical equilibrium the virial theorem

$$E_{\text{grav.}} = nE_{\text{therm.}}$$

must in fact be satisfied; the gravitational and the thermal energies refer to the star as a whole and the quantity n ($1 < n < 2$) takes the possible part played by light pressure into account. But we see from Figure 121 that the gravitational energy increases rapidly (as the mean density increases suddenly) whereas the thermal energy rises slowly. This indicates that under these conditions the virial theorem will no longer be satisfied from a definite moment on, so that the mechanical equilibrium of the star will be disturbed. This will inevitably entail a catastrophic collapse of the star which is accompanied by a fast increase in density while the temperature remains almost unchanged. This, according to Hoyle and Fowler, is in general outline the picture of the explosion of a massive star which we observe as the phenomenon of a type II supernova outburst. We see that, before it explodes, the star must have covered a long evolutionary track and during this process the chemical composition of its interior has undergone radical changes and is "potentially ready" for explosion. The immediate cause of the explosion is the collapse of the

star's nucleus and the fact that, induced by this compression, the layers
of the shell fall towards the star's centre.

Hoyle and Fowler also considered the problem of a possible explosion
of a star without such a sudden catastrophic compression of its nucleus
(collapse). The starting point of their analysis is a star in a state of
advanced evolution. Its central part is heated to a very high temperature but the "iron–helium" transition zone dividing the log ρ–T_g graph

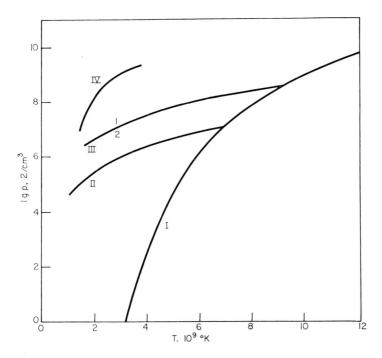

FIG. 121   Temperature dependence of density [314].

into two parts is not yet reached by any means. For the temperature
in the stellar interior to reach $\sim 2 \cdot 10^9 \, °\text{K}$ the mass of the star should
surpass Chandrasekhar's limit for white dwarfs

$$M \geqslant M_{\text{cr}} = \frac{5.80}{\mu_e^2} M_\odot \tag{18.7}$$

where μ_e is the mean molecular weight per electron (ratio of the nucleon concentration to the electron concentration). If $M < M_{cr.}$ an equilibrium configuration is possible in which the pressure of the degenerate gas compensates the gravitational force. According to the calculations carried out in [314], $\mu_e = 2.23$ so that $M = 1.16 M_\odot$. It should still be mentioned that M denotes the mass of the star when it has reached the considered (late) stage of evolution. Its initial mass may be higher since mass losses cannot be excluded, particularly in the red-giant state.

Since the temperature in the stellar interior is very high, the star, owing to the energy losses to neutrino radiation, will develop very rapidly, although not in a catastrophic way. The characteristic time of its evolution will under these conditions amount to $\sim 10^7$ s. This time is too short for the radiation from the stellar interior to diffuse to the outside, but it is considerably longer than the time of free fall of the stellar substance to the centre (collapse) so that the star throughout the process of this evolution will always be in a state of mechanical equilibrium.

At this time the chemical composition of the stellar interior undergoes essential changes. The greatest part of the substance inside the star consists of light elements whose nuclei are at high temperatures the potential explosive charge as has been shown. In the process of evolution described above the temperature of the stellar interior must, generally speaking, increase. The stellar nucleus will contract itself in order to compensate the energy losses caused by neutrino radiation. The gravitational force which increases in this process will compress the substance above the nucleus which results in a heating of the latter. Since the time of diffusion of radiation is high in comparison to the time of stellar evolution, the photons are in some way "locked" in it, which, in its turn, results in additional heating of the substance.

One would think that such a situation must inevitably result in a thermal explosion of the stellar interior. In fact, however, the situation is complicated by the fact that the star, with this way of heating, can regenerate its structure through expansion so that its interior is cooled down. It is well known that the stars possess the property of regulating the temperature of their interiors in this way ("negative specific heat" of normal stars; see, as regards this problem, paper [315]).

The characteristic time of change of stellar structure will be of the order of the characteristic time of the hydrodynamic processes (see above), i.e., much shorter than the time of stellar evolution. The question is whether there exist equilibrium configurations in which the star is larger than in its initial state. If such a configuration is possible, there will be no thermal explosion.

Calculations of stellar models show that such equilibrium configurations will exist whenever the stellar substance is non-degenerate. For precisely this reason, in order to explain the explosion of a star with a non-degenerate nucleus, we had to have recourse to the mechanism of a collapse in the presence of a powerful "coolant," i.e., a great number of iron nuclei in its interior. But the situation is quite different when the substance in the stellar interior consists of non-degenerate gas. The fact is that the pressure in such a gas depends first of all on the density and the chemical composition, whereas the temperature dependence is insignificant. This might mean that for an increase in temperature up to values where nuclear disintegration sets in, the light elements will, to a first approximation, not influence the stellar structure. In other words, the mechanism of thermal equilibrium self-regulation does not work. Hence Hoyle and Fowler draw the conclusion that a stellar explosion may be expected in the case where the substance which is potentially capable of exploding (i.e., which consists mainly of light elements) is in a degenerate state.

A structural analysis of stars with a polytropic index of 3,[314] enabled Hoyle and Fowler to conclude that explosions of stars, whose interiors consist of degenerate gas, may only occur within a relatively narrow mass interval. The width of this interval depends on the temperature T_b at which the explosion takes place. If $T_b = 1.5 \cdot 10^9 \,^\circ\mathrm{K}$, $1 < M/M_{\mathrm{cr}} < 1.1$ or $1.16 < M < 1.28 M_\odot$ if $T_b = 1.75 \cdot 10^9 \,^\circ\mathrm{K}$, the upper limit of the mass is increased to $1.5 M_\odot$. This narrow range of mass of the exploding degenerate stars provides, according to Hoyle and Fowler, an explanation for the fact that such explosions are so rare. It is, however, hardly possible to explain the low rate of supernova explosions in this way. For example, a consideration of other possible models of super-high-density stars, which differ from the simple model with the polytropic index 3, yields somewhat wider intervals of masses within which explosions may occur. It must not be forgotten that Hoyle and Fowler did in no way take account of such important characteristic parameters of the stars as their moment of rotation and the magnetism.

Since a great part of stellar matter is in a degenerate state, the central temperature must be very high, essentially higher than T_b. In the case of the model considered in [314] with $M = 1.28 M_\odot$, the central temperature is about $3.5 \cdot 10^9 \,^\circ\mathrm{K}$ and the central density is $\sim 2 \cdot 10^9 \, \mathrm{g/cm^3}$. In the log ρ–T_g diagram the point describing the state of this star is far to the left of the line separating the "iron" phase from the "helium" phase (Fig. 123, curve IV). From this it may be concluded that stars with relatively small masses explode when their inner zones suffer a collapse in the process of evolution and a neutron nucleus is formed. The mean density of the stellar model considered in [314] is equal to $\frac{1}{54}$ of the central density. The radius of the star may therefore be obtained from the simple relation

$$\frac{4\pi}{3} \bar{\rho} R^3 = 54M \qquad (18.8)$$

If we assume $M = 2.6 \cdot 10^{33}$ g and $\bar{\rho} = 2 \cdot 10^9$ g/cm^3, we find that $R = 2.5 \cdot 10^8$ cm or about 40 per cent of the earth's radius. According to a rather rough estimate the total energy released in the explosion of such a star amounts to $\sim 7 \cdot 10^{50}$ erg.

It is quite natural to assume that the mechanism of stellar explosion described above, for a star of a relatively small mass and in a late stage of evolution, corresponds to the phenomenon of an outburst of a type I supernova. It is, however, necessary once more to stress that the very interesting paper by Hoyle and Fowler does not yield an unambiguous solution to the problem of the cause of stellar explosion and the nature of the difference between supernovae of the types I and II. Too many simplifying assumptions have been made so that the model considered may be very remote from real exploding stars.

It is of cardinal significance to determine the chemical composition of the diffuse filaments of Cassiopeia A. Since in the explosion of a type II supernova we may assume that an essential, if not the greatest, part of the stellar mass is ejected, the chemical composition of the shell must correspond to the chemical composition of the interior of the exploded star. On the contrary, in the case of the Crab nebula the mass of the ejected shell is $\sim 0.1 M_\odot$, i.e., small compared to the mass of the exploded star. In this case the chemical composition of the shell is not characteristic as it may correspond to the composition of the outermost layers of the star, which need not be very different from the "normal" composition.

It should still be mentioned that in the case of the diffuse filaments in Cassiopeia A, owing to the "youth" of this object, it is in all probability the shell ejected in the explosion that is observed, and not the interstellar gas "swept together," whereas the "stationary" condensations consist of the interstellar gas "condensed" by a magnetic field.

We know that in the spectrum of the diffuse filaments of Cassiopeia A the Hα line is lacking, a fact which, in § 5, was explained by the influence of interstellar absorption of light.   But the spectrum absorbed does not of course exclude the fact that the filaments are anomalously poor in hydrogen.   It would be very interesting to try to obtain the spectrum of the filaments of Cassiopeia A in the near infrared ($\lambda \sim 1 \mu$).   The fact that this spectrum does not contain the P_γ line of the Paschen series, which is relatively slightly absorbed by interstellar dust, is a weighty argument in favour of the assumption that the interiors of supernovae are anomalously poor in hydrogen.

It follows from what has been said above that the temperatures of stars which explode as supernovae of the types I and II reach huge values, of the order of some 10^9 °K, within a relatively short period of time. Under these conditions, by virtue of fast nuclear reactions, the chemical composition of the stellar interior undergoes radical changes.   In particular, the explosion mechanism, the nuclear disintegration of light elements, requires an extremely high abundance of the latter.   It has already been mentioned that at temperatures of the order of 10^9 °K and very high gas densities, owing to the various types of fast "direct" and "inverse" nuclear processes, some equilibrium is established in the chemical composition of stellar matter.   For example, at $T = 3.8 \cdot 10^9$ °K and $n_0/n_p = 300$, most of the nuclei will belong to the iron group.

In the explosion itself, owing to the nuclear reactions of light elements, a great number of neutrons will be produced within a very short time. These neutrons will be captured by the nuclei of the iron group and will then decay so that heavier nuclei result. In this way (the so-called "r-process") a great many isotopes up to $A = 270$ may be formed within a short time as was shown by calculations.[326]   The possible formation of a considerable quantity of an isotope of the transuranium element, californium, Cf^{254}, is particularly interesting.

In 1956, Baade, Christy, Burbidge, Hoyle and Fowler developed an interesting hypothesis to explain the characteristic light curves of type I supernovae by means of the radio-active decay of Cf^{254}.[325,326]   As we know (cf. § 1), about a hundred days after the maximum, the brightness of supernovae of this type decreases by 0.0137 magnitudes per day.   In other words, the luminosity of a supernova is governed by a power law of decline

$$L = L_0 \exp(-t/\tau) \tag{18.9}$$

where $\tau \sim 70$ days. The rate of decline has doubled after a time of $t_{1/2} \sim 55$ days. The power law of decline is observed in both the photo-graphic and the visual ranges. It is worth noting that in the case of the type I supernova which exploded in IC 4182 the law of decline described by Equation (18.7) has been observed for a time longer than $10t_{1/2}$.

As early as 1950 Borst showed that this exponential decrease in flux observed with all type I supernovae may only be explained by radio-active decay.[327] He suggested the radio-isotope Be^7 with a half-life of about 55 days as being responsible for the exponential law of decline.

It must, however, be mentioned that apart from Be^7 also other iso-topes possess similar half-lives, for example, strontium 89 and californium 254.

The total amount of energy emitted in the explosion of a supernova of the type I may be estimated as 10^{49} to 10^{50} erg; in the last "exponential" stage of luminosity decrease $\sim 10^{48}$ erg are emitted. An analysis of the relative effectiveness of the isotopes of beryllium, strontium and cali-fornium permits the conclusion that Cf^{254} has the highest effectiveness. For example, a beryllium nucleus undergoes a β-decay where the energy yield per decay event is of the order of several hundred keV, whereas the Cf^{254} undergoes spontaneous fission where the total energy of the frag-ments is ~ 200 MeV. This indicates that the disintegration of 10^{30} g of the californium isotope yields an energy of $\sim 10^{48}$ erg, that is as much as a type I supernova emits on the exponential part of its light curve.

Californium 254 was synthesized for the first time on earth during the explosion of the American thermonuclear bomb in November 1952, where uranium was exposed to a very high neutron flux. But this is nothing more than an r-process which is assumed to take place very violently in a supernova, during the first seconds after its explosion.

Besides Cf^{254} and the isotopes Be^7 and Sr^{89} rejected above, other isotopes also exist which have suitable half-lives. In [328] the possibility of explaining the light curves of type I supernovae by the decay of nuclei of the isotope Fe^{59} was studied. To explain the energy observed to be set free in the "exponential phase" of the light curve, the necessary quantity of Fe^{59} would, according to calculations carried out in [328], be equal to $0.1M_\odot$, whereas according to [326] only $0.005M_\odot$ of this isotope may be produced in the outburst of a type I supernova.

More suitable for such an explanation of the light curve are certain isotopes of the transuranium elements which are produced during the explosion of a type I supernova in an r-process. As shown in [314], some of these isotopes possess suitable half-lives between ~ 10 days and 1 year. To these belong Cf^{256}, Cf^{258}, Fm^{260} and isotopes with $Z \geqslant 102$. But we must take into consideration that the synthesis of heavy nuclei by way of the r-process is limited. This limitation is due to the fact that the capture of a neutron by a nucleus whose atomic weight exceeds a definite high value induces a fission. For this reason the r-process occurs somewhere in the atomic weight interval $270 > A > 255$, just before the next neutron shell is filled, when the number of neutrons in the nucleus is $N = 184$ and $A = 280$.[329]

An analysis shows that in the r-process about ten nuclei with even atomic weights A are produced, which are stable against the β-decay. Precisely these nuclei suffer spontaneous fission. Only four of these nuclides have half-lives in the interval of 30–100 days, among them Cf^{254}. To obtain an energy of 10^{48} erg as is emitted in the exponential phase of the light curve of a type I supernova, a mass of $6 \cdot 10^{-4} M_{\odot}$ of these nuclei is necessary. If we assume that 25 per cent of the whole energy released falls to the share of Cf^{254}, a total of $1.5 \cdot 10^{-4} M_{\odot}$ of this isotope must be produced in the r-process. On the other hand, according to [326], Cf^{254} amounts to only 1 per cent of all nuclei produced in the r-process. Hence we may conclude that the total amount of substance which, in the explosion of a type I supernova, passes through an r-process amounts to about $1.5 \cdot 10^{-2}$ or about 1 per cent of the mass of the exploded star.

Thus, besides Cf^{254}, other nuclei with different half-lives may also contribute to the emission of the supernova in the post-maximum state. This may result in certain differences in the light curves of the type I supernovae as this is observed.

In the radio-active decay, energy is produced mainly in the form of kinetic energy of the fragments, the "splinters" of the decaying nucleus. As far as we know, no one has yet considered the problem in which way this energy is converted into radiant energy, emitted in the visible part of the spectrum, where the change with time of the optical quantum flux corresponds almost precisely to the power law of the fragments' kinetic energy yield in spontaneous nuclear fission. We shall enter here into details of this important problem.

First of all, the efficiency of the conversion of the fragments' kinetic energy into the energy of optical-frequency quanta must be high enough. Otherwise the mass of the substance of the exploded star which has undergone an r-process would be extremely high. Let us now consider the deceleration of a fission fragment of a heavy nucleus in the plasma in which this process takes place. The charge of this fragment is denoted by Z. With fragment energies $E_{\text{kin}} \sim 100\text{--}200$ MeV the losses will be mainly due to ionization. Per unit time a fragment will lose the energy (cf. [95])

$$-\left(\frac{dE}{dt}\right) = 7.62 \cdot 10^{-9} n Z^2 \sqrt{\frac{2Mc^2}{E_{\text{kin}}}} \left\{ 11.8 + \log \frac{E_{\text{kin}}}{Mc^2} \right\} \approx 2 \cdot 10^{-3} n \quad \text{eV/s}$$

$$(18.10)$$

where $Z \sim 50$ is the charge of the fragment, $M \sim 10^2 m_H$ is its mass, n is the concentration of particles in the plasma. This particle concentration must be very high. For example, if the velocity of expansion of the shell is 10^8 cm/s and the mass of the ejected shell is equal to $10^{-2} M_\odot$, about 100 days after the explosion the radius of the shell will be $\sim 10^{15}$ cm and $n \sim 10^9$ cm^{-3}. It is quite possible that n is much higher (see below).

With $n > 10^9$ cm^{-3} the moderation time of the fragments is < 100 s. This indicates that the fragments cannot leave the plasma and consume their energy almost entirely in ionization processes in which electrons with energies of 30 eV are produced. These electrons use almost all their energy to ionize and excite the various components of the plasma, first of all the helium. Very rapidly, within a time of the order of the stopping time of the fragments, a state of quasi-equilibrium is established in the plasma at a relatively high characteristic temperature (30,000–50,000° K). The whole energy of the fragments which is released in the plasma per unit time will then be emitted in the form of a line spectrum, leaving the plasma as radiation quanta.

This high plasma temperature guarantees an effective excitation of the various levels of helium whose excitation potentials are 20 eV and more. This picture of the conditions is in full agreement with McLaughlin's interpretations of the spectra of type I supernovae (cf. § 2). In this interpretation, however, the following difficulty arises. In order to explain the extreme widths of the emission bands corresponding to certain atomic transitions it is necessary to assume macroscopic velocities of the emitting and absorbing atoms of the order of 10^9 cm/s, which is by an order of magnitude higher than the expansion velocity of the filaments in the Crab nebula, and is in contradiction with the relatively narrow [O I] lines observed in the spectrum of IC 4182 (cf. § 2). This difficulty may be avoided if the main part of the radiation of a supernova after the maximum is assumed not to arise in the expanding shell, but in the "bubbling" extended atmosphere which surrounds the exploded star. In this atmosphere (whose dimensions are $\sim 10^{13}$ to 10^{14} cm) move enormous "protuberances" at speeds of $\sim 10^9$ cm/s, upwards and downwards, in which the helium lines are emitted. At these velocities the extended atmosphere must be rapidly dispersed. It is, however, quite possible that the magnetic field which is connected with the star's collapse (cf. § 19) impedes this dispersion. In this atmosphere the plasma density may be rather high, for example, $\sim 10^{11}$ to 10^{12} cm^{-3}. To confine this plasma within a limited volume a field strength $H \sim 10^3$ Oe must be assumed, which is acceptable.

A serious difficulty connected with the hypothesis of Cf^{254} or some modification of it consists in the fact that with the rate adopted for the outbursts of type I supernovae (once per 300 years), under the assumption that in each outburst $1.5 \cdot 10^{-4} M_\odot$ of the isotope Cf^{245} are synthesized in r-processes, the cosmic abundance of the other heavy nuclei synthesized in this process (e.g., uranium) must be a hundred times higher than the abundance observed. It is, however, possible, that this difficulty may be avoided when we assume that only ~ 1 per cent of the Cf^{254} produced in the explosion is ejected into interstellar space. The main mass of this isotope (just as the other products of the g-process) remain in the extended atmosphere surrounding the collapsed star and gradually "deposits" on its surface.

The ideas on the cause of supernova outbursts discussed above permit the conclusion that just before the outburst in the interior of the super-nova a very high temperature of the order of some 10^9 degrees is reached within a short period of time, in a region where the density is high enough. Under these conditions, owing to equilibrium processes, a considerable part of the nuclei is transformed into nuclei of elements of the iron group. After the explosion the iron nuclei produced in this way are thrown out into interstellar space. At the same time heavier nuclei which had been produced during the explosion in the r-process are also ejected. It is obvious that outbursts of supernovae (and perhaps also of galactic nuclei) are the only possibilities for this process to take place under natural astro-physical conditions. One would hardly find another spot in the universe where equilibrium processes of nuclear synthesis can occur, which results in the production of elements of the iron group.

In this way the outbursts of supernovae may play an important part in the evolution of stellar systems, in particular of our own galaxy, since they continuously enrich the interstellar medium with heavy elements.

For this reason one must expect differences in the chemical composition of "old" and "young" stars. Stars of the "first generation," formed from the gas of which the galaxies consisted in the epoch of their development, must be "poorer" in helium and heavy elements than the stars of higher generations which, condensed out of the "secondary" interstellar substance, become essentially "refined" by the ejection of gas from stars which have already travelled a complex evolutionary track. The interstellar medium becomes enriched in helium and light elements by way of ejections of substance from ordinary stars (e.g., from red giants in the process of formation of planetary nebulae) since the fusion of hydrogen to helium and the subsequent reactions of the type

$$3He^4 \to C^{12}, \; C^{12}(\alpha, \gamma)O^{16}, \; O^{16}(\alpha, \gamma)Ne^{20}$$

must take place in most of the stars in the corresponding stages of evolution. The presence of an "iron peak" in the abundance diagram of the elements in the universe, however, cannot be explained by these reactions. Iron and the related elements may be synthesized only under equilibrium conditions, requiring extraordinarily high temperatures and densities. The elements heavier than iron are in all probability synthesized in an r-process. Since the conditions for the synthesis of iron and the heavier elements may be expected to be satisfied in supernova outbursts, it is natural to consider this phenomenon as being responsible for the continuous synthesis of heavy nuclei in our galaxy.

These theoretical conclusions are based on spectrographic observations of stars of various types which have been carried out intensively in the past years. An analysis of the chemical composition of the atmospheres of cluster stars and sub-dwarfs (these objects are known to be older than the sun as their age amounts to $\sim 10 \cdot 10^9$ years) permits the conclusion that the abundance ratio of heavy elements and hydrogen in these stars is ten to a hundred times lower than in the sun.[330,331,332,333,334] The substance from which these "old" stars condensed must therefore have contained much less heavy elements than the substance from which the sun condensed. An analysis of the chemical composition of stars which are younger than the sun show that the relative abundances of heavy elements and hydrogen hardly varied. We may draw the conclusion that, as the evolution of the galaxy proceeds, the process of nuclear genesis (synthesis of nuclei) dies away. The same is true for the process of generation of stars. Though the processes of synthesis of heavy nuclei and of generation of stars are still taking place in our stellar system, their rates are essentially lower than, say, in the first 10^9 years of galactic existence.

On the basis of the conception of the continuous enrichment of the galaxy with heavy elements in supernova explosions, Salpeter sketched the evolution of the fundamental characteristics of our stellar system.[60] His calculations are, of course, preliminary. In particular, they do not take into account the process of periodically repeated explosions of galactic nuclei which are important for the evolution of galaxies. The significance of this process was understood only after Salpeter's paper had been published. Nevertheless, this paper clearly showed what an essential part the outbursts of supernovae play in the evolution of stellar systems.

If in explosions of supernovae, by virtue of the r-process, a great number of heavy nuclei are synthesized, among them also radio-active nuclei, we may, in principle, expect that the remnants of outbursts are still radio-active at present. Haymes, Craddock and Clayton have recently devoted a paper to this interesting problem.[335] The present activity of isotopes with a half-life of about 100 days is, of course, negligibly small. We may expect at present an effect of radio-activity only from nuclei whose half-lives are sufficiently high; for example, of the order of the Crab nebula's age. The calculations made under the assumption that the Cf^{254} hypothesis holds true show that the power of the sources of radio-activity in the present Crab nebula amounts to $1.2 \cdot 10^{36}$ erg; 92 per cent of this energy is set free in the form of kinetic energy of α-particles and fission fragments which, in a series of cases, must be β-active. These calculations were based on the relative abundances of the various heavy nuclei which were synthesized in an r-process in the explosion of a supernova of the type I, using the data obtained by Hoyle and Fowler. Moreover, all isotopes produced as the daughters in subsequent decays were taken into consideration. It must be noted that a considerable number of isotopes must be gamma-active. The radiation must be concentrated mainly in individual narrow spectral lines in the energy interval between 50 keV and 400 keV. The most intense line of the expected gamma spectrum of the Crab nebula, emitted by Cf^{249} and possessing a quantum energy of 390 keV, must hit the earth with a flux of $\sim 5 \cdot 10^{-5}$ quanta/cm$^2 \cdot$s (the distance to the nebula was assumed as equal to $1.7 \cdot 10^3$ psc). The total power which is to be expected as caused by the radio-activity-induced gamma emission of the Crab nebula is of the order of 10^{34} erg/cm$^2 \cdot$s, several times lower than that of its radio emission.

14 + s.

The discovery of this radiation is a very important but at the same time a difficult task. The softer part of this spectrum will be "filled" by the X-ray radiation of the Crab nebula with the continuous spectrum, which is of synchrotron origin (cf. § 14). Precisely in this range Clarke made his balloon observations (cf. § 14). It may be expected that at $hv \sim 400$ keV the X-ray synchrotron spectrum of the Crab nebula is strongly attenuated. The application of a special selection method of gamma radiation as regards the quantum energy and the direction of origin ("gamma telescope") could permit the detection of individual spectral lines in the gamma range.

A positive result of these observations would be of great importance for the understanding of the nature of supernova outbursts as this would be a direct proof of the presence of an r-process during the stellar explosion. Such observations are at present particularly important as only recently Fowler, Hoyle and Burbidge developed an alternative hypothesis on the cause of the explosions of type I supernovae.[336] According to [336] a stellar explosion may be caused by a catastrophic release not of nuclear but of gravitational energy. As already mentioned at the beginning of this section, a non-rotating star whose mass exceeds $2M_{\odot}$ must, after it has used up all its nuclear resources, undergo a catastrophic collapse. Under these conditions there does not exist any equilibrium configuration (not even of a neutron star) so that the compression must be unlimited. Since the gravitational potential per unit mass is proportional to c^2, the consideration of this catastrophic compression (gravitational collapse) must be based on the general theory of relativity.

The energy released in a gravitational collapse per unit mass may reach a value of $9 \cdot 10^{20}$ erg/g which is a hundred times higher than the nuclear energy release in the fusion of 1 g hydrogen to helium. The problem, however, consists in the way of conversion of this energy to the forms which are observed in stellar explosions (kinetic energy of the shell, radiations of all forms).

According to a hypothesis by Hoyle and Narlicar[337] a collapsing star is not compressed to a point (as this results from theory) because of the presence of an assumed "S-field" which becomes effective at very high densities. The "S-field" was introduced by Hoyle and co-workers into a non-evolutional cosmic theory. Owing to the presence of this field the collapsing star which reaches an extraordinarily high density of more than 10^{30} g/cm^3 is no longer compressed but begins to oscillate between certain values of its radius. These oscillations will be damped owing to the high-power neutrino radiation so that the upper limit of the radius will be reduced continuously. At maximum compression the star's radius will be essentially smaller than the Schwarzschild radius and information can in no way be transmitted from the star to the outer world. According to the hypothesis by Hoyle and Narlicar, the star, when oscillating, will intersect the Schwarzschild sphere and at this time information, in particular radiation, can be transmitted to the outer world. According to the hypothesis developed in [336] ex-supernovae of the type I, and particularly the nucleus of the Crab nebula, are collapsed stars in the state of oscillation described above. In particular the activity of the nucleus of the Crab nebula, which has been maintained up to the present time, is explained as the emission of hard corpuscular radiation which appears whenever the radius of the oscillating star exceeds the Schwarzschild radius.

This very fanciful but also elegant hypothesis is, unfortunately, in contradiction with the fundamentals of the general theory of relativity. Though in the proper reference system only a few seconds are needed for the stellar radius to reach the Schwarzschild value, for the outside observer this process takes infinitely longer. We may observe nothing more than an asymptotic approximation of the star's size to the Schwarzschild sphere, from the side of larger values of R, but the Schwarzschild radius can only be reached after an infinitely long period of time (the time of the external observer).

The introduction of the "S-field" is quite arbitrary. The cosmological theory in which this field was adopted has in the past years proved more and more that it cannot hold true. Now even one of the theory's authors, Hoyle, has been forced to reject it. So the hypothesis of the oscillations of a collapsed star about the Schwarzschild radius defies all physical and astronomical bases.

At the same time the collapse of the nucleus of a sufficiently massive star seems to be an inevitable consequence of its evolution. It looks as if a rotation could not prevent the collapse of such a star (cf. [316]). On the other hand, in order to explain the outburst of a type II supernova by nuclear explosion it proves necessary to make use of the gravitational energy which is released in the collapse of a non-degenerate nucleus of a sufficiently massive star (see above). We cannot exclude the possibility that this release of gravitational energy may also play an important part in outbursts of type I supernovae.

The cause of stellar explosions formulated in the most general way is thus a catastrophic release of nuclear and gravitational energy, though many details of this most important process are still unknown to us.

§ 19   Some theoretical problems

At the beginning of the previous section we formulated the fundamental questions which must be answered by a theory that describes all aspects of the problem of stellar explosion. Then we discussed some of the most promising hypotheses explaining the causes of stellar explosions by regular processes occurring in the final stages of evolution of certain stars. But a series of important questions remained unanswered, among them the following:

1. The origin of the enormous quantity of relativistic particles contained in the remnants of supernovae.
2. The origin of the magnetic field in these remnants, in particular the relatively carefully investigated magnetic field in the Crab nebula which is of a quasi-regular nature.
3. The explanation of the permanently high activity of the nucleus of the Crab nebula and, possibly, of other ex-supernovae of the type I.

In this last section we shall discuss briefly the present hypotheses which have been developed in order to answer the above fundamental questions. Over the past few years the point of view has become more and more widely accepted according to which the generation of relativistic particles is an inevitable attribute of every perturbed plasma (cf., for example, [338]). Owing to the instabilities which are specific for such a plasma, the particles in the "tail" of the maxwellian velocity distribution may be accelerated up to relativistic energies. In our opinion, however, such a conception is too general. In individual cases, which are of great theoretical and practical interest, it may just be wrong. It is beyond any doubt that the mechanism and nature of acceleration of charged particles up to relativistic energies may be very different for different cosmic objects.

In § 16 we have already dealt with some examples. Recall that in the active zones of the sun for some reason or other mainly protons are accelerated and in the Crab nebula electrons. The absence of synchrotron radio emission from ordinary novae, which exploded a relatively short time ago and not too far away from the sun, is important (for example, the Nova

Persei of 1901, the Nova Aquilae of 1918 and the Nova Puppis of 1942). If in the case of these novae the number of accelerated particles per unit mass of the shell ejected were the same as in the case of supernovae, we must have observed sources whose fluxes were essentially higher than the fluxes from Cassiopeia A and the Crab nebula, provided that we take into account the law of decline of synchrotron emissivity in expanding sources ($L \propto R^{-2\gamma}$) and the relative proximity of the object. From the negative result of special observations it follows that the radio-frequency radiation fluxes from the remnants of novae are at least 10^4 times weaker than the flux from Cassiopeia A. This may indicate that in the explosion of an ordinary nova almost no relativistic particles are generated, though it is doubtful whether the plasma in such a star is sufficiently perturbed.

In the first years after the synchrotron theory of the radio emission from the remnants of supernovae had been established, some authors assumed that the acceleration of charged particles occurs in the magnetized turbulent shells ejected, by way of a statistical mechanism of Fermi acceleration (cf., for example, [339]). In [113], however, it was shown that owing to the adiabatic expansion of these shells the relative particles contained in them must lose energy.

A statistical mechanism of acceleration may be effective only in the earliest phases of evolution of the shell, perhaps even during the explosion. Later on several theoretical investigations were carried out in which the possibility of generation of a considerable quantity of relativistic particles during a supernova outburst was analyzed. The most interesting paper seems to be that by Colgate and Johnson.[340]

Before we pass over to a consideration of this paper we shall discuss briefly the consequences of a catastrophic release of energy in stellar interiors by way of explosions. Colgate and co-workers considered this problem when they solved the equations of hydrodynamics.[341,342] They started from a stellar model applying to a very late stage of evolution, assuming the mass of the star equal to $10M_\odot$ and a polytropic index equal to 3. With the help of hydrodynamic methods they studied the gravitational collapse of such a star, using the equation of state of matter, describing the transformation of iron nuclei into α-particles which, subsequently, decay into protons and neutrons (cf. the previous section). The real conditions of the collapse were described by means of an artificially introduced efflux of heat which withdraws intrinsic energy from the gas falling towards the centre of the star. The velocity of the gas falling to the star's centre reaches the velocity of free fall. A numerical solution of the hydrodynamic equations permits the conclusion that up to density values of $3 \cdot 10^{11}$ g/cm^3 no "catastrophic" effects occur. At such high densities the equations of state mentioned above cannot be used any longer, since owing to the inverse β-decay of protons into neutrons a fast neutronization of the nuclear matter sets in. The calculations carried out by Colgate and co-workers, however, do not answer the question when the explosion occurs. We cannot exclude the possibility that the moment of onset of the explosion depends on such stellar parameters as the state of its rotation or the nature of its magnetic field, which are not taken into account in the theory considered.

Under such conditions, when one does not know when and in which way the collapse of the star's interior to the centre changes into an explosion, an ejection of parts of the stellar substance, in [341] recourse was made to an artificial model: a fictitious solid core was assumed which was to reject the substance falling to the centre of the star after this substance had reached the highest possible degree of compression. The shock wave arising in the explosion is propagated outwards. Since in this case the density of the substance this wave passes through is continuously reduced, the wave is amplified. It may be assumed that finally the shock wave has become so strong (in the peripheral layers of the star) that its velocity becomes higher than the parabolic velocity. The outer parts of the star will then be ejected into interstellar space.

Though the problem of the formation of a shock wave near the centre of the star which explodes as a supernova is at present still far from being solved, it can hardly be doubted that a catastrophic release of energy in the central region must cause a shock wave which is propagated from the centre to the periphery with increasing velocity. When this wave reaches the surface of the star we observe the phenomenon of a supernova explosion. A mathematical treatment of this problem, taking all real characteristic parameters of the star into account, is a very difficult task. This is a problem which, as yet, is still unsolved, though partial calculations, based on various simplifying assumptions, have been carried out.†

---

† Let us indicate, for example, the paper by V. S. Imshennik and D. K. Nadezhkin[343] who solved numerically the problem of the disintegration of stars of great masses ($M = 15 - 50 M_\odot$). As to the idea, the solution of this problem must describe the explosion of a supernova of the type II. The calculation was based on the spherical-symmetrical equations of gas dynamics, radial heat conduction was taken into account. The authors, solving the gas dynamic equations, determined the energy fluxes from the stellar surface, the effective temperature as a time function, the velocity of the substance, and also the light curves. These results are unfortunately not in agreement with the observations

(*footnote continued on p. 415*)

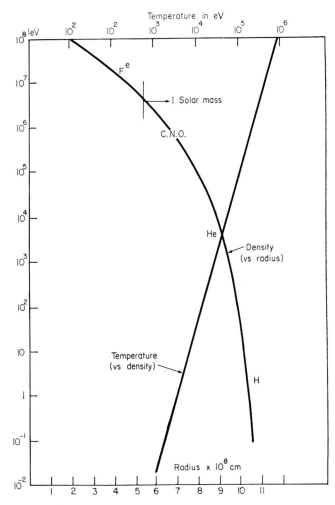

Fɪɢ. 122a   Model of pre-outburst star.[340]

For example, even in the explosion of a very massive star, with $M = 50 M_\odot$, the bolometric absolute magnitude obtained amounts to only -14.6 which is at least five magnitudes lower than the value observed (cf. § 1). The extremely low effective temperature of the supernova does not correspond to reality either ($\sim 5{,}000°$ instead of the $\sim 40{,}000°$ observed). Also the light curve obtained in [343] has nothing in common with the true light curve. The ascending branch, for example, is missing in it. It is possible that the stellar model on which the calculation is based does not correspond to the problem.

Let us now turn to the paper by Colgate and Johnson. Figure 122a illustrates the model of a star just before the outburst which was considered in [326]. The amount of energy released in the centre of the star during the explosion was so chosen that the shock wave propagated towards the periphery was able to impart a parabolic velocity to a mass equal to $1M_{\odot}$. For this to be achieved an energy of $5 \cdot 10^{17}$ erg/g was necessary. The total amount of energy released in the explosion of the star considered must amount to 10^{52} erg. Figure 122b shows the velocity of the shock wave immediately behind the front as a function of the initial density of

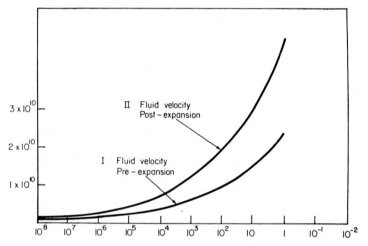

FIG. 122b   Velocity of shock wave as a function of the initial density of matter.[340]

ᴸhe substance in the layer the wave passes through (curve I). The same figure shows also the hydrodynamic velocity of the substance in the star as a function of the density, after the star's expansion caused by the transition of the shock wave (curve II). From curve I we see that the velocity of the stellar substance immediately behind the shock wave front, at a point where $\rho \sim 30$ g/cm^3, increases about tenfold, reaching 10^{10} cm/s. At velocities higher than 10^{10} cm/s relativistic effects must be taken into account. They were also taken into account when determining the values of the hydrodynamic velocities with $\rho < 30$ g/cm^3.

Thus, within the framework of the model considered, the authors found that in the outermost layers of the star the hydrodynamic velocities of the substance behind the shock wave front are so high that the particles constituting this substance reach relativistic velocities. It can be shown that the kinetic energy in a relativistic shock wave per unit mass is determined by

$$u = \left(\frac{1}{2}\right)^{1+\sqrt{3}} \left(\frac{E_0}{\rho_0 c^2}\right)^{0.5(3-\sqrt{3})} \tag{19.1}$$

where $E_0 \sim 30c^2$ erg/cm^3 corresponds to a density $\rho_0 \sim 30$ g/cm^3 at which the wave reaches a relativistic velocity.

The expression for the kinetic energy per gram substance described by the power law, Equation (19.1), corresponds exactly to the integral energy spectrum of cosmic rays. With the polytropic model of the star, being in hydrodynamic and radiation equilibrium, the density at a distance R from the star's centre is in fact proportional to $T^{3.25}$ where T is the temperature at the point R. In the outer layers of the star, where the pressure P is precisely equal to the weight of the column of matter above the level of R, the mass of this substance is proportional to $P = \rho T \rho^{1.31}$. On the other hand, according to (19.1), $u \propto \rho^{-0.64}$; hence we obtain

$$M(<\rho) \propto N(>u) \propto u^{-(1.31/0.64)} \approx u^{-2} \tag{19.2}$$

where N is the number of particles ejected in the outburst, which, before the outburst, had been contained in a region in which the density of the substance was smaller than ρ. It may be assumed that in more accurate calculations the function $N(u)$ is more slanting, e.g., $N \propto u^{-1.6}$, which, as suggested by Colgate and Johnson, results in a better agreement with the integral energy spectrum of the cosmic rays.

The calculations showed that for energies exceeding 10^4 beV per nucleon the initial density of the medium in which the shock wave is propagated must be lower than 10^{-5} g/cm^3, and the surface density of the star in the model considered is smaller than 1 g/cm^2. Under such conditions doubt might be cast on the possibility of propagation of such a strong relativistic shock wave. But owing to the processes of collective interaction (cf. § 8) a hydrodynamic consideration of the problem is admissible up to densities of 10^{-12} g/cm^3 which correspond to a kinetic energy per nucleon of 10^8 beV.

Colgate and Johnson assume that the mechanism described above acts as the main injector of cosmic rays in the galaxy. Assuming that supernovae of the type II explode once every 100 years and that the time of residence of cosmic rays in the galactic corona (volume $\sim 5 \cdot 10^{68}$ cm^3)

14*+

amounts to $5 \cdot 10^8$ years, they determined the equilibrium density of the primary cosmic rays. It may be estimated that the initial density of that layer in the star, whose particles reach an energy of 10 beV per nucleon when a shock wave passes through, must be ~ 1 g/cm^3. The mass of the surrounding shell for which $\rho < 1$ g/cm^3 amounts to $\sim 10^{26}$ g or $6 \cdot 10^{49}$ protons for the model considered. Hence it follows that the equilibrium concentration of relativistic protons in the galactic corona is $\sim 6 \cdot 10^{-13}$ cm^{-3} which agrees with the results of observations.

A difficulty of this theory, to which the authors themselves drew attention, is the fate of the substance of the outer layers of the star, which has been ejected by the shock wave and whose energy density is relatively low; for example, lower than several beV per nucleon. The mass of this substance exceeds by at least one order of magnitude that which may be retained by the interstellar magnetic field. Colgate and Johnson assume that this substance might be retained for a long time by the magnetic field in the immediate proximity of the exploded star. In this way they try to explain the synchrotron radiation of the remnants of supernovae. It is, however, easily proved that this cannot be the case. Since the number of remnants of supernovae of the type II which have not yet dissipated in the interstellar medium does not exceed 10^3 (cf § 7), and the energy of the relativistic particles in each of these objects can in no way be higher than 10^{50} erg, the total amount of energy contained in the remnants of these supernovae cannot be higher than 10^{53} erg and this is three orders below the total energy of cosmic radiation in the galaxy.

Another difficulty for the theory of Colgate and Johnson is the inevitable discontinuation of the increase in energy of the wave when the medium in which the wave is propagated becomes transparent for the X-rays and gamma radiation generated in its front. In paper [95] it was shown that the American authors incorrectly took absorption into account, over-estimating it strongly. In fact, the medium becomes transparent even at a relatively great depth and the increase in energy of the wave ceases long before such high values are reached as were obtained by Colgate and Johnson.

The problem of the possibility of an acceleration of particles of sub-relativistic energies when the shock wave passes through the surface of the star, was also considered by D. K. Nadezhkin and D. A. Frank-Kamenetskiy.[344] They dealt with both the self-modelling and the exact (based on a numerical integration of the equations) solutions to this problem. The self-modelling solution, describing the passage of the shock wave through the interface of the medium whose density decreases according to a power law ($\rho = k_1 x^n$, where x is the distance from the surface and n is the polytropic index), was considered in papers [345] and [346]. The velocity of the front depends on the co-ordinates (considering a unidimensional model) according to the power law

$$u = k_2 x^{-\lambda}(k_2 > 0, \lambda > 0),\qquad(19.3)$$

where λ may be described by an approximate formula

$$\lambda = \frac{n}{2 + \sqrt{2\gamma/(\gamma - 1)}}\qquad(19.4)$$

where n is the polytropic index and γ the specific-heat ratio. It follows from Equation (19.3) that the velocity of the shock wave increases unlimitedly as the distance to the surface of the star decreases. In [344] the mass of substance was estimated which, in the transition of the shock wave, reaches a velocity higher than the parabolic velocity and which must therefore be ejected from the star. The estimate obtained in [344] for the mass of gas ejected by the shock wave, where the gas particles have a velocity close to the velocity of light, is of particular interest. In one special case this problem has already been considered by Colgate and Johnson. For a mass of substance m_q ejected from the star by a shock wave with a velocity higher than qc the expression

$$m_q = \Delta M \left(\frac{u_\pi}{qc}\right)^{(n+1)/\gamma}\qquad(19.5)$$

was obtained in [344];

$$u_\pi = \sqrt{2GM_0/R_0}$$

is the parabolic velocity close to the mean velocity of the shell ejected. With $n \geqslant 3$ and $\gamma = \frac{5}{3}$, $(n + 1)/\lambda \approx 6$. If we further assume a mass of the shell ejected in the outburst of a type II supernova equal to $\Delta M_H \sim M_0 \sim 30 M_\odot$, $u_n \sim 10^8$ cm/s, we find that $m_{0.5} = 2.6 \cdot 10^{-12} M_\odot = 4 \cdot 10^{21}$ g, which rapidly decreases as g increases. Colgate and Johnson obtained a value of m_q which was many orders of magnitude higher. As indicated in [344], the deviation is due to the extremely high value of u_n used by the American authors ($u_n = 1.6 \cdot 10^9$ cm/s with $\Delta M = 1 M_\odot$). D. A. Frank-Kamenetski and D. K. Nadezhkin consider the pre-outburst model of the star used in [340] (a very small object of very

high density) to be inconsistent with reality.   The whole star may hardly
be in such a super-high-density state.   The modern theories of stellar
evolution lead to the concept that a star before outburst must have a very
non-uniform structure, with a very dense and hot nucleus and an
extended shell.   With such a structure the parabolic velocity at the
surface of a pre-outburst star cannot be as high as was assumed in [340].

The hypothesis of Colgate and Johnson on the origin of the cosmic
rays in the galaxy will thus hardly correspond to reality.   Moreover, it
does not answer the important question of the origin of the relativistic
particles contained in the expanding remnants of supernovae.   Nevertheless, the generation of a considerable quantity of relativistic particles seems
actually to take place when the shock wave passes through the surface of
an exploding star.   In this connection it is worth noting that as recently as
1954 I. M. Gordon made an attempt at treating the radiation of supernovae
near the maximum as being due to a synchrotron process.[347,348]   Gordon's
hypothesis, however, does not explain the fundamental fact that this
radiation is mainly concentrated in broad emission bands which cannot
yet be identified in a reliable way (cf. § 2).   No synchrotron mechanism
is able to explain the appearance of these bands, in particular if we take
into account that their character recurs at the various supernovae.

An attempt may be made to explain the continued activity of stars
which exploded long ago by the generation of relativistic particles during
supernova explosions.   In the case of the Crab nebula it is beyond any
doubt that such an activity is observed (cf. § 13).   It may be assumed that
it is also possessed by other objects.   In § 13 we have already sketched a
hypothesis on the continued generation of relativistic particles (chiefly
electrons) in the nucleus of the Crab nebula.   There, however, we did not
consider in detail any possible mechanism of generation.   Let us first enter
into details of the problem of the possible part played by the accretion of
gas of an ex-supernova which we shall consider as a collapsed star.   Such
an accretion was first calculated by Ya. B. Zel'dovich, who drew attention
to the importance of this problem for the investigation of the latest phases
of stellar evolution.[316,349]

The problem of the accretion of interstellar gas by stars was treated
relatively intensively during the forties, in connection with the problems
of stellar cosmogony.   All the fundamental problems of mass accretion
were then solved in a non-relativistic approximation.   The solutions to
these problems are likewise valid in the cases of accretion of interstellar
gas by white dwarfs and neutron stars.   Even with a gravitation potential

of $(0.2\text{--}0.3)c^2$, when the stellar radius is only two to three times the Schwarzschild radius $r_q = 2GM/c^2$, the correction for the effects of general relativity does not exceed 20–30 per cent. Since the non-relativistic calculation implies the very inaccurate quantity of the density of "non-perturbed" interstellar matter surrounding the star as a factor, it is, in the given case, virtually pointless to introduce relativistic corrections. Quite another matter is the problem of the accretion by a collapsed star. In this case the effects of general relativity are essential and must be taken into account.

Let us first consider the non-relativistic problem which is convenient to solve in the two limiting cases: (a) individual particles of the interstellar medium falling onto the star in independent motions and (b) the motion of the medium as a whole.

Let us consider case (a). We shall denote by v_0 the velocity of a particle of mass m at infinity and by n the particle concentration. Assuming v_0 small in comparison to the parabolic velocity v_p at the star's surface, we can replace the particle velocity at the star's surface by v_p. In this case the maximum angular momentum of the particle will be $I = mv_p R_1$ where R_1 is the radius of the star. At a great distance from the star we may write $I = mv_0 b$ where b is the "impact parameter." From the law of conservation of angular momentum we may determine the greatest "impact" distance from which a particle will fall down to the star, $b_{max} = R_1 v_p / v_0$. Since the flux of particles with $b < b_{max}$ is equal to $nv_0 \pi b_{max}^2$, the sought quantity, the rate of growth of the star per unit time owing to mass accretion is obtained immediately:

$$\frac{dM}{dt} = mnv_0 \pi k_1^2 v_0^{-2} \frac{2GM}{R} = 2\pi mn \frac{GMR_1}{v_0} \qquad (19.6)$$

In the case of a hydrodynamic consideration of the problem we shall have (cf. [316])

$$\frac{dM}{dt} = 4\pi r_k^2 v_{cr} \rho_k = r^{(\gamma+1)/2(\gamma-1)} \pi (5 - 3\gamma)^{-(5-3\gamma)/2(\gamma-1)} \cdot \frac{G^2 M^2}{a_0^3} \rho_0 \qquad (19.7)$$

where the subscript "cr" refers to the critical level at which the gas velocity v, which was subsonic at $r < r_{cr}$, becomes sonic, γ is the specific-heat ratio of the gas and a_0 the velocity of individual molecules at infinity. It is an interesting fact that in Equation (19.7) the mass accretion is independent of the star's radius, which is quite natural since the rate of accretion is determined only by the conditions on the level $r_{cr} = GM/a_0^2$. The hydrodynamic consideration is applicable when at the distance r_{cr} the particles' mean free path is smaller than r_{cr}. This condition is satisfied in all the cases we are interested in.

In the case of $r < r_{cr}$ the motion of the gas towards the star will be supersonic. Each element of the gas will move in the field of stellar gravity with a velocity close to the velocity of free fall. The density of the gas will increase in proportion to $r^{-3/2}$. In the case of accretion of gas by a neutron star the falling gas will be stopped at the star's surface by the shock wave. In this process its kinetic energy is converted into thermal energy and emitted as radiation. The total release of energy per unit mass of the gas that falls onto the surface of a neutron star will be equal to $c^2 r_q/2R$. With $R = 3r_q$ it will be equal to $1.5 \cdot 10^{20}$ erg/g, which is twenty times higher than the nuclear energy set free in the fusion of hydrogen into iron. Let us now estimate the power released by virtue of the accretion of interstellar gas by a neutron star. Numerically we shall have

$$\frac{dM}{dt} \sim 10^{15} \left(\frac{M}{M_\odot} \right)^2 \frac{\rho_0}{10^{-24}} \, a_0^{-3} \quad \text{km/s} \qquad (19.8)$$

The sought power which is released mainly in the form of X-rays will be high enough, even if $\rho_0 = 10^{-24}$ g/cm^3 and $a_0 \sim 1$ km/s, namely $\sim 10^{35}$ erg/s. As shown in [316], it is not impossible that the cosmic X-ray sources discovered recently emit according to this mechanism, on condition that $\rho_0 \sim 10^{-21}$ g/cm^3.

In the case of accretion of interstellar gas by a collapsed star we obtain a different picture. Owing to the effects of general relativity which are particularly effective in the vicinity of the Schwarzschild radius, only a very small fraction of the energy set free in a spherical-symmetrical accretion is emitted into outer space. The spherical symmetry causes a serious limitation. In the case of spherical symmetry the macroscopic velocity of the gas at infinity relative to the star is equal to zero. Let us now assume that this velocity $u_0 \gg a_0$. This problem was recently considered by Salpeter[350] who obtained the following picture of the gas motion (cf. Fig. 123). Hence we see that the trajectories of the stream lines of the gas in the field of stellar gravity are curved; the velocity of the gas increases according to Bernoulli's law. Behind the collapsed star in the circumfluent gas stream a shock wave arises whose elongated surface

is shown in Figure 123. When the front of the shock wave hits the moving
gas, the latter will lose the velocity component perpendicular to the front
while the velocity component parallel to the wave front remains unchanged.

The author of [350] used Kepler's laws in order to determine a certain
critical trajectory (dashed in Figure 123) with the critical impact parameter
b_{cr} corresponding to it. With $b > b_{cr}$ the velocity of the gas behind the
shock wave front will, as before, exceed the parabolic velocity and the gas,
streaming around the star, will flow off to infinity. With $b < b_{cr}$ the
gas will fall to the surface of the collapsed star. The rate of accretion is

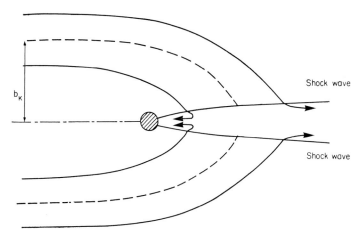

FIG. 123   Schematic diagram of motion of interstellar gas in the neighbourhood of a
collapsed star.[350]

determined by a formula analogous to Equation (19.7), where a_0 must be
replaced by u_0. It is essential that when the gas passes through the shock
wave its kinetic energy be transformed into radiant energy which, in this
case, may be emitted outwards. Thus, an analysis of the non-symmetrical
problem permits the conclusion also that in the case of a collapsed star the
mass accretion results in a very effective radiation which can be emitted
into interstellar space. It must be noted that, in the framework of the
problem considered in [350], energy is released only in the form of radiation
and not in the form of kinetic energy of individual particles or a gas jet.
But we must take into consideration that the model considered by Salpeter

is extremely idealized. So, for example, the influence of the magnetic fields frozen in the interstellar gas has not been taken into account. It is quite possible that accounting for magnetic fields might present a possibility of acceleration of charged particles up to relativistic energies. Such an acceleration (of the type of a Fermi mechanism of first order) may occur in the region of the shock wave behind the star in the circum-fluent gas stream.

In § 14 we considered a hypothesis according to which the nucleus of the Crab nebula, a neutron star or a collapsed star, is a component of a binary system. If the relative orbital velocity is ~ 700 km/s, for an energy release during the passage of the "invisible" star through the periastron of its orbit of $\sim LT/\tau \approx 10^{38} \cdot 10^4 \sim 10^{42}$ erg/s ($T \sim 10^7$ s is the period of revolution of the star, $\tau \sim 10^3$ is the time of passage of the invisible star through the atmosphere of its satellite, i.e., the time of effective mass accretion) it is necessary that $\rho_0 = 2 \cdot 10^{-11}$ g/cm^3 or $N_0 \sim 2 \cdot 10^{15}$ cm^{-3} (cf. Eq. 9.7). Therefore, if our hypothesis holds true, the ex-supernova must in the periastron pass through the lower chromosphere of its non-exploded component or through rather dense jets of gas ejected by it. It may then be assumed that owing to the magnetization of these jets the particles are accelerated and an essential part of the energy is converted into kinetic energy of the particles. But it must be expected that a similar amount of energy will be emitted, mainly in the X-ray range. Thus, if our hypothesis is correct, one has to expect once in several months powerful outbursts of X-ray emission from the Crab nebula, each of which has a duration of $\sim 10^3$ s. During these outbursts the X-ray flux from the Crab nebula may rise by four to five orders of magnitude. At present such special observations would be quite possible. For this purpose photon counters must be mounted on an oriented long-lived artificial satellite and the X-ray flux from the Crab nebula must be measured systematically (the ratio of the average pulse spacing to the average pulse duration should not exceed several minutes). Such a "service" is necessary because the moment of a possible transition of the ex-supernova through the atmosphere of its satellite cannot be known in advance.

Note that the problem of the duplicity of the Crab nebula's nucleus, the ex-supernova, need not necessarily be linked with the problem of generation of relativistic electrons in this nebula. The duplicity may be doubted on the basis of an analysis of the proper motion and the position of the southern star in the central part of the Crab nebula (cf. § 14), whereas the generation of relativistic particles may also be independent of the gas accretion by the collapsed star during its passage through the atmosphere of the non-exploded component. It could be imagined that this generation is due to "intrinsic" causes. In this connection the fact that chiefly relativistic electrons are injected into the Crab nebula deserves, in our opinion, the greatest attention.

When relativistic particles are accelerated in a shock wave, one would think that mainly heavy nuclei, in particular protons, must be accelerated. It is possible that for this reason in the setive zones of the sun mainly protons are accelerated. A. A. Korchak and S. I. Syrovatskiy, in connection with the problem of the origin of cosmic radiation, showed that in the early stages of acceleration by a statistical mechanism mainly nuclei heavier than protons will be accelerated.[351] Thus it is all the more remarkable that this does not hold true in the case of the Crab nebula.

For what reason is it that chiefly the electrons are accelerated? First of all, we cannot say that electrons of such high energies (up to 10^{13} eV) are produced in some processes of interaction between elementary particles. This possibility is rejected by modern physics. We must assume that within a narrow zone around the nucleus of the Crab nebula a macroscopic mechanism is effective in which mainly electrons are accelerated. The exponential spectrum seems to suggest a statistical mechanism.

It is well known that in such a mechanism charged particles can be accelerated if their initial energy E_0 exceeds a certain critical value E_i, called the "injection energy" (cf., for example, [95]). If $E_0 < E_i$ the energy losses of the particles to ionization and excitation of plasma particles will exceed the energy gain due to the acceleration by the statistical mechanism. It will be mainly the electrons that are accelerated if in the zone where the statistical mechanism is effective another mechanism may act by which only electrons of sufficiently high energies are injected. The most natural assumption for such a mechanism would be the β-radio-activity of some isotopes. In the previous section we discussed in detail the hypotheses assuming the presence of considerable amounts of radio isotopes in ex-supernova stars.

So we can now imagine the following model of the Crab nebula's nucleus: The ex-supernova, a collapsed (or neutron) star, is surrounded by a rather extended atmosphere which is in a state of very high-energy turbulent motion, the degrees of magnetization being different for different turbulent elements. We leave the question open, how and whereby this turbulence is maintained. It is possible that at the surface of the star

14**

very powerful active processes take place which may also sustain the turbulence postulated for its extended atmosphere.

Since the activity in the centre of the Crab nebula displays a periodicity of $\sim 10^7$ s (cf. 13), the characteristic parameter of the statistical mechanism is $\alpha = u^2/cl$ (u is the turbulent velocity and l is the characteristic dimension) and must be of the order of 10^{-6} s^{-1}. Let us assume that the initial energy of the electrons produced in β-decay events is $\sim 10^6$ eV. At such energies the ionization losses are essentially higher than the radiation losses. From the condition

$$-\left(\frac{dE}{dt}\right)_u = 7.62 \cdot 10^{-9} n \left\{ 20.1 + 3 \frac{E}{mc^2} \right\} < \alpha E_0 \qquad (19.9)$$

we obtain a value of $n < 5 \cdot 10^6$ cm^{-3} for the particle concentration in the plasma, which seems reasonable. An amount of $\sim 10^{38}$ erg/s is injected on the average from the nucleus into the Crab nebula (cf. § 13), which corresponds to $\sim 10^{40}$ relativistic electrons per second. This quantity must be produced in the nucleus of the nebula; this means that within a period of $3 \cdot 10^{10}$ s (the life-time of the nebula) no less than $3 \cdot 10^{50}$ nuclei must have decayed. Let us assume a value of 10^{51}. The total mass of the nuclei with $A \sim 200$ must then be $\sim 3 \cdot 10^{29}$ g or $1.5 \cdot 10^{-4} M_\odot$, this is 1 per cent of the substance which, according to the calculations carried out in [326], have undergone an r-process. If the extended shell which is supposed to surround the nucleus of the Crab nebula has a diameter of $\sim 10^{15}$ cm, and $n \sim 10^6$ cm^{-3}, it will contain $\sim 10^{52}$ nuclei. There is no reason why an essential part of these nuclei should be β-active. The shell may be in dynamic equilibrium with the star, its substance being continuously regenerated.

The losses due to synchrotron radiation may be essential when the accelerated electrons possess high energies. Moreover, the Crab nebula is supplied with relativistic electrons whose energies are at least 10^{13} eV. Precisely these electrons are responsible for the X-ray emission of this nebula (cf. § 13). In the range of acceleration $\alpha E \approx 10^7$ eV/s for these electrons. On the other hand, the losses due to synchrotron radiation are given by the formula

$$-\left(\frac{dE}{dt}\right)_{\text{synchr.}} = 0.98 \cdot 10^{-3} H_\perp^2 \left(\frac{E}{mc^2}\right)^2 \text{ eV/s} \qquad (19.10)$$

From the condition that $(dE/dt)_{\text{synchr.}} < \alpha E$ we may derive that in the acceleration range $H_\perp < 5 \cdot 10^{-3}$ Oe, which is relatively low. According to the statistical mechanism of acceleration under consideration, the magnetic field strength near the star should be higher. This difficulty may be avoided if we suppose that the acceleration occurs in a magnetic trap with the "plugs" moving towards each other. We know (cf., for example, [95]) that in such a mechanism only the longitudinal component of the momentum of the accelerated particle (in our case the electron) increases, which is reflected in the moving magnetic "plug." In such a process the losses due to synchrotron radiation are vanishingly small. It must be stressed that in both the statistical mechanism and acceleration, owing to reflection in moving magnetic plugs, most of the energy the electrons acquire stems from the kinetic energy of macroscopic motion of plasma in the shell surrounding the ex-supernova. Radio-activity only exercises the function of an injector. When the energy density of the relativistic electrons exceeds the density of the kinetic and magnetic energies of the plasma, they escape from the trap and "spatter" in the nebula, after which the process of acceleration starts anew. It follows from observations that this occurs every couple of months, the total energy of the relativistic electrons accumulated in the trap being $\sim 10^{44}$ to 10^{45} erg.

The above considerations were, of course, not intended as a theory. Their aim was to draw attention to some consequences resulting from the observational fact that mainly relativistic electrons are generated in the Crab nebula. The present theory of the permanent activity of the Crab nebula's nucleus will be established as soon as the modest information on the physical processes in the central part of the Crab nebula, which is today at our disposal, has been completed.

Let us now turn to the difficult problem of the origin of the magnetic field in the remnants of supernovae, in particular of the Crab nebula. Previously it had been suggested (particularly by the author of this book, see [217]) that the magnetic field in the Crab nebula (and analogously in other related objects) is the magnetic field of the interstellar conductive medium, amplified by the chaotic motions. Since the intensity of the interstellar magnetic field ($\sim 10^{-5}$ Oe) is about a hundred times lower than the intensity of the magnetic field in the Crab nebula (cf. § 11), in the framework of this hypothesis the structure of the magnetic lines of force must be very complex. This is in contradiction with the observed quasi-regular structure of the magnetic field in the Crab nebula (see, for example, Fig. 100) which clearly demonstrates that the "coefficient of entanglement" is small. S. B. Pikel'ner, who analyzed this problem,[352] also advanced a series of theoretical arguments against the hypothesis on the "interstellar" origin of the Crab nebula's magnetic field.   For example, from the fact that the mean gas density in the shell of the nebula $< 10^{-24}$ g/cm^3 (cf. § 13) and the condition that kinetic energy density of the gas is not lower than the magnetic energy density (and this is a necessary condition for the hypothesis of "entanglement"), it follows as a necessary condition that the velocity of the random motions in the plasma caused by hydrodynamic forces must exceed the velocity of expansion of the nebular filaments which, obviously, is impossible.   The fact that the relativistic particles are confined in the nebula also speaks against the "interstellar" origin of the magnetic field in the Crab nebula.   If the field in the nebula were partly an interstellar field, then, taking the quasi-regular character of the magnetic field in the nebula into account, the relativistic particles would leave it after several years.   Taking the beam instability of the relativistic particles into account (see § 16) does not essentially alter this conclusion.

More probable is the assumption that the expanding shell which appeared after the supernova explosion drove the interstellar gas back, together with the magnetic field "frozen" in it.   Only an insignificant fraction of the original magnetic flux may have remained in the interior of the nebula, together with the relatively dense "clusters" of interstellar medium compressed by the magnetic field of the remnant of the outburst.   This seems to offer the most likely explanation of the "stationary" condensations in Cassiopeia A (cf. § 6).

It must also be stressed that the magnetic field of the exploded star, which is ejected together with the shell in its expansion process, will very rapidly become smaller.   In fact, even if $H_0 \sim 10^6$ Oe and the stellar radius is $\sim 10^{10}$ cm, we obtain, assuming conservation of the magnetic flux, a present value of $H \sim 10^{-10}$ Oe in a nebula whose dimensions have increased to 10^{18} cm; this value is negligibly small.   It is, on the other hand, impossible, for reasons of energy conditions, to assume $H_0 \sim 10^{13}$ Oe (the magnetic energy of the star would then be obtained as $\sim 10^{56}$ erg which is two orders of magnitude higher than the energy equivalent of the whole mass of the star).

In view of this situation it is necessary to conclude that a magnetic field is in some way produced in the nebula after the explosion of the supernova.   The problem is to find the mechanism by which this field is amplified.   The author of [352] considers the possibility of the production of a magnetic field in various parts of the nebula by thermal currents and also by currents consisting of cosmic particles ($N_p = N_e$) emitted by their sources, e.g., the ex-supernova star, and also in their diffusion. But accounting for self-induction, as is usual in cosmic electrodynamics, eventually reduces the rate of growth of the field. S. B. Pikel'ner also calculated the amount of thermal energy which is released in the various mechanisms of field production considered in his paper; the value he obtained is quite considerable. This indicates that the process in which the magnetic field is produced has a very low "efficiency." It seems likely to us that the energy of the relativistic particles and the gaseous component of the nebula is insufficient for the production of the magnetic field, especially if we take into account that the magnetic field energy is of the same order of magnitude as the energy of the relativistic particles and the gas contained in the nebula. In order to obtain a higher efficiency it must be supposed that the number of neutral atoms in the Crab nebula is at least equal to that of the ionized particles. If there are many neutral atoms in the nebula, then, as shown in the calculations carried out in [352], the dissipation of the currents amplifying the field will occur much more rapidly, and this indicates that the efficiency of the process of field generation rises considerably.

Summing up, it must be said that, though the analysis of the problem of magnetic field generation in the Crab nebula carried out in [352] did not lead to its solution, it is very valuable, as it revealed the difficulties we meet with when attempting to solve this important problem.

A new approach to the understanding of the causes of the appearance of a magnetic field in the Crab nebula and in other remnants of supernovae is contained in the interesting paper [353] by N. S. Kardashev. After the discovery of the quasi-stellar radio sources and the first attempts at explaining them, this paper has stimulated considerably the interest in the various aspects of the problem of the gravitational collapse of stars. Yet before Kardashev's paper was published. V. L. Ginzburg drew attention to the fact that the collapse of a star must be accompanied by an essential intensification of its magnetic field.[354,355] Since the substance of solar-type stars has a very high conductivity ($\sim 10^{16}$ s^{-1}), the time of attenuation of its magnetic field

$$t_m \approx \frac{4\pi\sigma R^2}{c^2} \tag{19.11}$$

must be very high. Substituting $R = R_\odot$, we obtain $t_m \sim 2 \cdot 10^{10}$ years, which is several times greater than the age of the sun. When the star in the process of evolution transforms to a neutron star, the conductivity will be increased further and, accordingly, t_m will be $\sim 10^6$ years (as the stellar radius drops to $\sim 10^6$ cm), i.e., it will still be high.

The above considerations indicate that the magnetic lines of force "stick" to the stellar substance (i.e., they are "frozen" in it). Under these conditions the magnetic flux is conserved during the star's compression, i.e., $H \propto R^{-2}$, and the total magnetic energy W_m depends on the radius of the star in precisely the same way as the gravitational energy, i.e., it is proportional to R^{-1}. Since in "normal" stars the total magnetic energy is much lower than the gravitational energy, this relationship must remain unchanged during the collapse.

As the radius of a collapsing star approaches r_q for a "co-moving" observer on the star, the magnetic field may reach extremely high intensities, e.g., 10^{10} Oe. For the external observer, however, the picture would be different. According to [355] the magnetic moment of the collapsing star is given by the expression

$$d = \frac{d_0 r_q}{R_0 3 \ln\left[r_q/(R - r_q)\right]} \tag{19.12}$$

where d_0 is the magnetic moment of the star when its radius is equal to R_0. It then follows from Equation (19.11) that as $R \to r_q$, $d \to 0$, whereas in the classical theory $d \propto R$. Substituting the t-dependence of R in Equation (19.11) we find that

$$d = \frac{d_0 r_q^2}{3R_0 ct} \tag{19.13}$$

i.e., for an external observer the magnetic moment will asymptotically tend to zero as $t \to \infty$.

In [355] it has also been shown that as R approaches r_q the tangential component increases much more rapidly than the radial component. It should also be mentioned that I. D. Novikov showed that the variation of the magnetic field of a star during its contraction induces an electrical field.[356] Under these conditions a collapsing star emits a considerable amount of electromagnetic energy in the form of a single pulse of the duration r_q/t. According to [356] the amount of energy emitted is determined by the expression

$$\mathscr{E} = \frac{\phi^2}{15r_q}\left(\frac{r_q}{R}\right)^{2.5} \tag{19.14}$$

where $\phi = d_1/R$, d_1 denoting the dipole moment of the star's external magnetic field. When the collapsing star resembles the sun, $\phi \sim 3 \cdot 10^{21}$ cm^2, $r_q \sim 3 \cdot 10^5$ cm and $\varepsilon \sim 3 \cdot 10^{36}$ $(r_q/R)^{2.5}$ erg. Practically the whole energy of the external magnetic field will then be emitted.

The magnetic effects described above which accompany the gravitational collapse of a star imply a topological division of the star's magnetic field into two parts: the external and the internal fields (cf. Fig. 124). The external field does not "adhere" any longer to the "parent" star; together with the ejected shell it moves out into interstellar space.

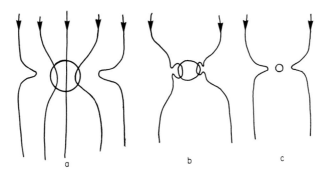

Fɪɢ. 124   Magnetic field configuration around a collapsed star (a, b, c). Evolution of field topology.[353]

N. S. Kardashev assumes that in this way the magnetic field of the remnants of type II supernovae is produced, which remnants, as we saw in § 6, have a shell structure. On the other hand, in § 18 we advanced arguments in favour of the conclusion that in the case of outbursts of supernovae of the type II a gravitational collapse should take place.

According to N. S. Kardashev we may expect quite different conditions when a star of a relatively small mass, e.g., $< 1.5 M_\odot$, suffers a collapse. In the case of a collapse the star may assume a neutron configuration. In the process of an adiabatic compression (with $\gamma = \frac{4}{3}$) the magnetic energy and the gravitational energy increase proportionately to $1/R$, whereas the kinetic energy of rotation increases as $1/R^2$. This may result in a rotational instability arising when the rotational energy (which, originally, was relatively low) is of the same order of magnitude as the gravitational energy. The star assumes the form of an ellipsoid of revolution and, beginning from its equatorial zone, a violent ejection of mass sets in. The emerging jets of conductive gases will extend and twist the magnetic lines of force. The same rotational moment of the star will be imparted to the gas disc which starts rotating more and more rapidly. Since the star rotates much more rapidly than the disc the lines of force between the disc and the star are coiled up, forming a spiral. For this reason the magnetic field in the gaseous disc will be continuously intensifield. An analogous mechanism had been suggested by Hoyle in order to explain the anomalous distribution of the rotational moment in the solar system between the sun and the planets.[357] In N. S. Kardashev's paper, however, attention was paid mainly to the intensification of the magnetic field in the gaseous disc forming around the condensed star.

Let us now try a rough quantitative estimate of the effectiveness of this mechanism of field intensification in the large region around the collapsed neutron star, which is assumed to be an ex-supernova of the type I. The gravitational energy of a homogeneous sphere is $\Omega = 0.6\ GM/R$, its rotational energy is $W_r = 0.2\ MV_0^2(R_0/R)^2$ and the magnetic energy (without taking the twisting effect into account) is

$$W_m = \frac{4}{3}\pi R^3 \frac{H_0^2}{8\pi}\left(\frac{R_0}{R}\right)^4$$

where V_0, H_0 and R_0 are the initial values of the equatorial velocity of rotation, the magnetic field at the surface of the star and the radius. The condition of the rotational instability reads as follows:

$$\Omega = 2W_r \qquad (19.15)$$

From the condition (19.14) we find that the radius R_r at which the rotational instability sets in will be equal to

$$\frac{R_r}{r_q} = \frac{1}{3}\left(\frac{cV_0R_0}{GM}\right)^2 \qquad (19.16)$$

The period of stellar rotation will be equal to

$$t = \frac{2\pi R}{V} = \frac{8\pi}{9}\frac{(V_0R_0)^3}{(GM)^2} \qquad (19.17)$$

Now we take into account that after n revolutions the magnetic flux in the gaseous disc has increased n-fold. We shall then have the following expression for the magnetic flux in the disc:

$$Hl^2 = H_0R_0^2n \qquad (19.18)$$

where H and l denote the mean magnetic field strength and the diameter of the gas shell (disc), $n = t/\tau$, t being the time after the explosion. Finally, we shall have

$$H = \frac{H_0 R_0^2 t}{l^2 \pi} \tag{19.19}$$

The pre-outburst characteristic parameters of a star similar to the sun are assumed as follows: $M \sim 2 \cdot 10^{33}$ g, $R_0 = 10^{11}$ cm, $H_0 \sim 1$ Oe, $V_0 \sim 10^6$ cm/s, $r_q = 3 \cdot 10^5$ cm, $R_r \sim 1.7 \cdot 10^2$, $r_q = 5 \cdot 10^7$ cm, $W_r = 1.6 \cdot 10^{51}$ erg, $W_m = 3.3 \cdot 10^{35}$ erg, $V_r = V_0 R_0 / r_q = 2 \cdot 10^9$ cm/s, $\tau = 0.16$ s; from these, together with the observed characteristic parameters of the Crab nebula, $l = 2.5 \cdot 10^{18}$ cm, $t = 3 \cdot 10^{10}$ s, we obtain $H \sim 3 \cdot 10^{-4}$ Oe, which agrees with the value obtained from an analysis of the synchrotron radiation emitted by the Crab nebula.

From N. S. Kardashev's theory it follows that the magnetic field of the Crab nebula is still being intensified, even now. The acceleration of the shell caused by the magnetic pressure and the pressure of the cosmic rays is defined by the equation (cf. § 14)

$$\frac{d^2 l}{dt^2} = \frac{2H^2}{8\pi} \frac{4\pi l^2}{M_0} \tag{19.20}$$

where M_0 is the mass of the shell.

The process of expansion of the shell is therefore described by a differential equation of the form

$$l^2 \ddot{l} = at^2 \tag{19.21}$$

where $a = H_0^2 R_0^4 / M_0 \tau^2$. A particular solution to (19.20) will read $l = at^{4/3}$, where $a = 4A^3/9$. The magnetic energy enclosed in this expanding shell will increase with time according to the law

$$W_m = \frac{H^2}{8\pi} \frac{4}{3} \pi l^3 = \frac{H_0^2 R_0^4 t^2}{\sigma l \tau^2} = \frac{2}{27} A^2 M_0 t^{2/3} \tag{19.22}$$

whereas the kinetic energy of the expansion

$$W_k = \frac{M_0 \dot{l}^2}{2} = \frac{8}{9} A^2 M_0 t^{2/3} \tag{19.23}$$

so that the ratio W_m / W_k remains constant and equal to about 0.10. This is close enough to the observed value.

In [353] the time of Joulean attenuation of the magnetic field near the surface of the ex-supernova star was also estimated:

$$t_{ei} = 3 \cdot 10^{-21} T^{3/2} R_r^2 \tag{19.24}$$

where $T \sim 10^6 \,^\circ\mathrm{K}$ is the temperature of the neutron star (it has already dropped essentially, in the beginning it was $(1\text{–}3) \cdot 10^7 \,^\circ\mathrm{K}$). Since $R_r \sim 5 \cdot 10^7$ cm, $t_{ei} \sim 7.5 \cdot 10^3$ years, i.e., essentially greater than the age of the present Crab nebula.

It must be noted that Equation (19.20) does not contain a term describing the deceleration of the shell. But in such a young object as the Crab nebula effects due to deceleration of the shell are negligibly small. In the course of time the magnetic connection between shell and star may be disturbed by various types of instabilities. This may, generally speaking, reduce the time within which the lines of force are twisted and the field is increased.

The true magnetic field in the Crab nebula may of course differ essentially from the ideal spiral structure that follows from the simple theory stated above. The presence of a great number of magneto-hydrodynamic waves must distort the structure of the field so that it becomes quasi-regular. It is well known that in the present Crab nebula such waves are actually observed. It can be assumed that in an earlier epoch of evolution the magneto-hydrodynamic perturbations in the Crab nebula were considerably stronger. Together with the regular process of "coiling" of the lines of force the magneto-hydrodynamic processes determine the magnetic field structure in the present Crab nebula.

Summing up, we must say that the good agreement between the calculated value of the magnetic field intensity in the Crab nebula and the observed value, and also the logicality, simplicity and elegance of the analysis favour N. S. Kardashev's theory. In the framework of this theory, for example, the fundamental differences to be observed between the remnants of type I and type II supernovae find a natural explanation.

It must, however, be mentioned that we do not yet possess a detailed and generally accepted theory explaining the origin of the magnetic field in the remnants of supernovae. The same is true for the other basic problems formulated at the beginning of this section. But we have every reason to assume that new observations will stimulate the theoretical investigations so that sufficiently well-supported answers will be found to the fundamental problems connected with the outburst of supernovae.

References

1. A. M. Clerke. *The System of Stars*. London, Adam & Black, 1905.
2. K. Lundmark. Svenska Vetenkapsakad. *Handlingar* **60**, No. 8, 1920.
3. H. Shapley and H. Curtis. *Bull. Nat. Res. Council* **11**, Pt. 3, 171, 1921.
4. A. J. Cannon. Spectrum of Z Centauri. *Harvard Ann.* **76**, 37, 1916.
5. W. Baade and F. Zwicky. *Proc. Nat. Ac. Sci. U.S.* **20**, 254, 1934; *Comm. Mt. Wilson Obs.* **114**.
6. F. Zwicky. *Ap. J.* **88**, 529, 1938.
7. F. Zwicky. *Ap. J.* **96**, 28, 1942.
8. F. Zwicky. *Handbuch der Physik* **51**, 776, 1958.
9. W. Baade. *Ap. J.* **88**, 285, 1938.
10. R. Minkowski. *Publ. Astr. Soc. Pacific* **53**, 130, 194, 224, 1941.
11. F. Zwicky. *Ann. d'Ap.* **27**, 300, 1964.
12. W. Baade. *Ap. J.* **102**, 309, 1945.
13. R. Minkowski. *Ann. Rev. of Astronomy and Astrophys.* **2**, 247, 1964.
14. P. Wildt. *Publ. Astr. Soc. Pacific* **74**, 97, 1960.
15. H. Arp. *Ap. J.* **133**, 883, 1961.
16. D. Michalas. *Publ. Astr. Soc. Pacific* **75**, 256, 1963.
17a. F. Bertola. *Ann. d'Ap.* **27**, 329, 1964.
17b. S. Van den Bergh. *Ann. d'Ap.* **22**, 123, 1959.
17c. Yu. P. Pskovskiy. *A. Zh.* **38**, 656, 1961.
17d. C. Bertaud. *Ann. d'Ap.* **24**, 516, 1961.
18. I. Balanowsky. *A.N.* **215**, 922, 1921.
19. R. Minkowski. *Ann. d'Ap.* **27**, 328, 1964.
20. B. A. Vorontsov-Bel'yaminov. *Gazovyye tumannosti i novyye zvezdy (Gas Nebulae and Novae)*. Moscow–Leningrad, 1948.
21. P. Couderc. *Ann. d'Ap.* **2**, 271, 1939.
22. F. Zwicky. *Morphological Astronomy*. Göttingen, Springer, 1957.
23. I. S. Shklovskiy. *A. Ts.* 1964.
24. R. Hayward. *Publ. Astr. Soc. Pacific* **76**, 35, 1964.
25. R. Minkowski. *Ap. J.* **89**, 156, 1939.
26. M. Bloch, D. Chalonge and J. Dufay. *Ann. d'Ap.* **27**, 315, 1964.
27. R. Minkowski. *Publ. Astr. Soc. Pacific* **52**, 206, 1940.
28. V. G. Gorbatskiy and I. N. Mishin. *Nestationarnyye zvezdy (Variable Stars)*. Moscow, Gostekhizdat, 1963.
29. F. Zwicky. *Ap. J.* **139**, 514, 1964.
30. C. Payne-Gaposhkin and F. Wipple. *Proc. Nat. Ac. Sci. U.S.* **26**, 264, 1940.
31. F. Bertola. Contr. Dell'osservatorio Astrofisico dell'Universita di Padova in Asiago, No. 135. Pavia, 1963.
32. D. B. McLaughlin. *Publ. Astr. Soc. Pacific* **75**, 133, 1963.
33. R. Minkowski. *Publ. Astr. Soc. Pacific* **75**, 505, 1963.
34. E. Biot. Connaissance des temps pour l'an 1846; Additions, p. 61.
35. A. Humboldt. *Kosmos.*, Vol. 3. Stuttgart and Tübingen, 1850.
36. E. Williams. *Observations of Comets from B.C. 611 to A.D. 1640*. London, 1871.

37. E. Zinner. *Sirius* **52**, 26, 1919.
38. K. Lundmark. *Publ. Astr. Soc. Pacific* **33**, 225, 1921.
39. P. P. Parenago and I. S. Shklovskiy. *A. Ts.*, No. 131, I, 1952.
40. I. S. Shklovskiy. *D.A.N.* **94**, 417, 1954.
41. Hsi Tse-tsung. *Smithsonian contr. to Astrophys.* **2**, 109, 1958.
42. B. Goldstein. *A.J.* **76**, 105, 1965.
43. B. Goldstein. preprint Yale University, 1965.
44. I. S. Shklovskiy. *Kosmicheskoye radioizlucheniye (Cosmic Radio Emission).* Moscow, Gostekhizdat, 1956.
45. E. Schönfeld. *A.N.* **127**, 153, 1891.
46. C. O. Lampland. *Publ. Astr. Soc. Pacific* **33**, 79, 1921.
47. I. C. Duncan. *Proc. Nat. Ac. Sci. U.S.* **7**, 170, 1921.
48. E. Hubble. *Astr. Soc. Pacific Leaflet*, No. 14, 1928.
49. K. Lundmark. In the book: *Festskrift Tillägnat Ö. Bergstrand.* Uppsala, 1938, 97.
50. Y. Yba. *Pop. Astronomy* **42**, 251, 1934.
51. J. J. Duyvendak. *Publ. Astr. Soc. Pacific* **54**, 91, 1942.
52. W. C. Miller. *Astr. Soc. Pacific Leaflet*, No. 314, 1955.
53. N. U. Mayall. *Science* **137**, No. 3123, 1962.
54. N. U. Mayall and J. H. Oort. *Publ. Astr. Soc. Pacific* **54**, 95, 1942.
55. W. Baade. *Ap. J.* **102**, 309, 1945.
56. S. Boehme. *A.N.* **262**, 479, 1937.
57. E. Schoenfeld. *A.N.* **65**, 7, 1865.
58. O. Schlier. *A.N.* **254**, 181, 1934.
59. W. Baade. *Ap. J.* **97**, 119, 1943.
60. E. Salpeter. *Ap. J.* **129**, 608, 1959.
61. I. S. Shklovskiy. *A. Zh.* **37**, 369, 1960.
62. A. Blaauw. *B.A.N.* **15**, 265, 1961.
63. J. H. Oort and L. Spitzer. *Ap. J.* **121**, 6, 1955.
64. J. H. Oort. In the book: *Gas Dynamics of Cosmic Clouds.* Amsterdam, North Holland, Publ. 1955, 147. (I.A.U. Symp. No. 2.)
65. G. N. Duboshin. *A. Zh.* **5**, 138, 1928.
66. N. F. Reyn and N. D. Moiseyev. *Uspekhi astr. nauk* **2**, 5, 1941.
67. J. Boersma. *B.A.N.* **15**, 291, 1961.
68. A. Sandage. In the book: *Stellar Populations.* Amsterdam–New York, 1958, 149. (*Specola astr. Vaticana Astr. Ric.* **5**.)
69. M. Schwarzschild and R. Härm. *Ap. J.* **128**, 348, 1958.
70. L. G. Henyen, L. Le Levier and R. Levee. *Ap. J.* **129**, 2, 1959.
71. E. R. Mustel'. *A. Zh.* **39**, 146, 1962.
72. J. H. Oort. *M.N.* **106**, 159, 1946.
73. G. A. Shayn and V. F. Gaze. *Izv. Kr. AO* **9**, 123, 1952.
74. G. A. Shayn and V. F. Gaze. *Izv. Kr. AO* **15**, 11, 1955.
75. G. A. Shayn and V. F. Gaze. *Atlas diffuzuykh gazovykh tumannostey (Atlas of Diffuse Gaseous Nebulae).* Moscow, 1952.
76. F. Smith. *Nature* **168**, 555, 1951.
77. W. Baade and R. Minkowski. *Ap. J.* **119**, 206, 1954.
79. W. Baade and R. Minkowski. *Ap. J.* **119**, 214, 1954.

80. R. Minkowski. In the book: *Radio Astronomy*. Cambridge, 1957, 107. (I.A.U. Symp. No. 4.)

81. R. Minkowski. In the book: *Paris Symposium on Radio Astronomy*. Stanford University Press, 1959, 315.

82. R. Minkowski and L. Aller. *Ap. J.* **119**, 232, 1954.

83. J. W. Chamberlain. *Ap. J.* **117**, 399, 1953.

84. S. B. Pikel'ner. *Izv. Kr. AO* **12**, 93, 1954.

85. I. S. Shklovskiy. *Solnechnaya Korona* (*Solar Corona*). Moscow–Leningrad, Gostekhizdat, 1951.

86. A. A. Boyarchuk, R. Ye. Gershberg and V. I. Pronik. *Izv. Kr. AO* **29**, 292, 1963.

87. R. Parker. *Ap. J.* **139**, 493, 1964.

88. B. E. Westerlund and D. S. Mathewson. Preprint 1965.

89. J. Hey, J. Phillips and S. Parsons. *Nature* **157**, 296, 1946.

90. G. R. Whitfield. *M.N.* **117**, 680, 1957.

91. R. Hanburry Brown, R. Jennisson and M. Das Gupta. *Nature* **170**, 1061, 1952.

92. F. Smith. *Nature* **170**, 1065, 1952.

93. M. Ryle, B. Elsemore and A. Neville. *Nature* **205**, 1259, 1965.

94. J. Lequeux. *Ann. d'Ap.* **25**, 221, 1962.

95. V. L. Ginzburg and S. I. Syrovatskiy. *Proiskhozhdeniye kosmicheskikh luchey* (*Origin of Cosmic Rays*). Moscow. *Izd. AN SSSR*, 1963.

96. V. V. Vladimirskiy. *ZhETF* **18**, 393, 1948.

97. A. A. Korchak. *Trudy FIAN* **17**, 149, 1962.

98. G. Westerhout, W. Seeger and J. Brown. *B.A.N.* **16**, 213, 1962.

99. C. Mayer, T. McCullough and R. Sloanaker. *Ap. J.* **139**, 248, 1964.

100. J. Hagen, A. Lilley and E. McClain. *Ap. J.* **122**, 361, 1955.

101. S. Weinreb, A. Barret, M. Meeks and J. Henry. *Nature* **200**, 829, 1963.

102. I. S. Shklovskiy. *D.A.N.* **92**, 948, 1953.

103. I. S. Shklovskiy. *Kosmicheskoye radioizlucheniye* (*Cosmic Radio Emission*). Moscow, Gostekhizdat, 1956.

104. A. Boischot. *C.R.* **255**, 3374, 1962.

104a. P. Leslie. *Observatory* **80**, 23, 1960.

105. J. Crowther. *Observatory* **85**, 110, 1965.

106. D. Mathewson, M. Large and C. Haslam. *M.N.* **121**, 543, 1960.

107. D. E. Harris. *Ap. J.* **135**, 661, 1962.

108. S. Kenderline. *M.N.* **126**, 55, 1963.

109. R. Davis, G. Verschuur and P. Wildt. *Nature* **196**, 563, 1962.

110. D. E. Hogg. *Ap. J.* **140**, 992, 1964.

110a. I. R. Dickel, G. P. McGuire and K. S. Yang. *Ap. J.* **142**, 798, 1965.

111. K. Henize. *Ap. J. Suppl.* **2**, No. 22, 315, 1956.

112. B. Mills, O. Slee and E. Hill. *Austr. J. Phys.* **14**, 497, 1961.

113. V. L. Ginzburg, S. B. Pikel'ner and I. S. Shklovskiy. *A. Zh.* **32**, 503, 1955.

114. K. Kellerman. *Ap. J.* **140**, 969, 1964.

115. R. G. Conway, K. I. Kellerman and R. J. Long. *M.N.* **125**, 261, 1963.

116. I. S. Shklovskiy. *A. Zh.* **37**, 256, 1960.

117. J. A. Högbom and J. R. Shakeshaft. *Nature* **189**, 561, 1961.

118. D. S. Heeshen and B. L. Meredith. *Nature* **190**, 705, 1961.
119. C. H. Mayer, T. P. McCullough and R. M. Sloanaker. *Ap. J.* **141**, 867, 1965.
120. V. P. Lastochkin and K. S. Stankevich. *A. Zh.* **41**, 769, 1964.
121. I. W. Findlay, H. Hvatum and W. B. Waltman. *Ap. J.* **141**, 873, 1964.
122. V. I. Slish. *Nature* **199**, 682, 1963.
123. I. S. Shklovskiy. *A. Zh.* **37**, 222, 1956.
124. I. S. Shklovskiy. *A. Zh.* **34**, 403, 1957.
125. R. Rishbeth. *Austr. J. Phys.* **11**, 550, 1956.
126. R. Hanburry Brown and C. Hazard. *M.N.* **113**, 123, 1953.
127. B. Mills. In the book: *Paris Symposium on Radio Astronomy.* Stanford University Press, 1959, 431.
128. P. P. Parenago. *Kurs zvezdnoy astronomii (Course of Stellar Astronomy).* Moscow, Gostekhizdat, 1954.
129. A. Sandage. *Ap. J.* **125**, 422, 1957.
130. S. S. Moiseyev and R. Z. Sagdeyev. *D.A.N.* **146**, 329, 1962.
132. I. S. Shklovskiy. *A. Zh.* **39**, 209, 1962.
133. L. I. Sedov. *Metody podobiya i razmernosti v mekhanike (Methods of Similitude and Dimensionality in Mechanics).* Moscow, Gostekhizdat, 1957.
134. C. Heiles. *Ap. J.* **140**, 470, 1964.
135. C. W. Allen. *Astrophysical Quantities.* London, Athlone Press, 1963.
136. R. L. Blake, T. L. Chubb, H. Friedmann and A. N. Unzicker. *Ann. d'Ap.* **28**, 583, 1965.
137. I. S. Shklovskiy. *A. Zh.* **41**, 676, 1964.
140. T. K. Menon. *Ap. J.* **127**, 28, 1958.
141. R. Ye. Gershberg. *Izv. Kr. AO* **30**, 90, 1963.
142. G. A. Shayn and V. F. Gaze. *A. Zh.* **30**, 135, 1953.
143. H. van der Laan. *M.N.* **124**, 125, 1962.
144. C. H. Costain. *M.N.* **120**, 248, 1962.
145. H. van der Laan. *M.N.* **124**, 179, 1962.
145a. C. Messier. *Mém. Acad. Sci. Paris,* 1759, p. 165.
145b. C. Messier. *Mém. Acad. Sci. Paris,* 1771, p. 435.
145c. W. Herschel. *Philosophical Transactions,* 1818, p. 435.
145d. Ross. *Philosophical Transactions,* 1844, p. 322.
146. V. M. Slipher. *Harvard Bull.,* No. 743, 1921.
147. R. F. Sanford. *Publ. Astr. Soc. Pacific* **31**, 108, 1919.
148. E. Hubble. *Ap. J.* **56**, 162, 1922.
149. D. Barbier. *Ann. d'Ap.* **8**, 35, 1945.
150. A. Ya. Kipper. In the book: *O razvitii sovetskoy nauki v Estonskoy SSR (On the Development of Soviet Science in the Est. SSR), 1940–1950.* Tallin, 1950.
151. L. Spitzer and J. Greenstein. *Ap. J.* **114**, 407, 1951.
152. N. U. Mayall. *Publ. Astr. Soc. Pacific* **49**, 101, 1937.
153. L. Woltier. *B.A.N.* **13**, 301, 1957.
154. K. Graff. *Mitteil. Wiener Sternwarte* **4**, No. 4, 1948.
157. J. C. Duncan. *Mt. Wilson Observ. Communications,* No. 76, 1921.
158. J. C. Duncan. *Ap. J.* **89**, 482, 1939.

159. A. N. Deych and V. V. Lavdovskiy. *Tsirk. Gl. astr. obs. v Pulkove* No. 30, 21, 1940.
160. W. Baade. *Ap. J.* **96**, 188, 1942.
161. Walnaven. (Reference not available).
162. R. Minkowski. *Ap. J.* **96**, 199, 1942.
163. L. Woltier. *B.A.N.* **14**, 39, 1957.
164. D. Menzel *et al. Coll.*: *fizicheskiye protsessy v gazovykh tumannostyakh* (*Physical Processes in Gaseous Nebulae*). Moscow, I.L. (Publ. of Foreign Literature), 1948.
165. D. H. Menzel and L. H. Aller. *Ap. J.* **94**, 30, 1941.
166. M. J. Seaton and D. Osterbrock. *Ap. J.* **125**, 66, 1957.
167. D. Osterbrock. *Publ. Astr. Soc. Pacific* **69**, 227, 1957.
168. J. Bolton and G. Stanley. *Nature* **162**, 141, 1948.
169. J. Bolton and G. Stanley. *Austr. J. Sci. Res. A* **2**, 139, 1949.
170. G. Stanley and O. Slee. *Austr. J. Sci. Res. A* **3**, 234, 1950.
171. L. L. Bazelyan and S. Ya. Braude et al. *Izv. visshikh uch. zaved. Radiofizika* **6**, 897, 1963.
172. D. F. Burke and K. L. Franklin. In the book: *Radio Astronomy.* Cambridge, 1957, 151. (I.A.U. Symp. No. 4.)
173. G. R. Whitfield. *M.N.* **120**, 581, 1960.
174. R. Adgie and F. Smith. *Observatory* **76**, 181, 1956.
175. G. R. Whitfield. *M.N.* **117**, 680, 1957.
176. B. Y. Mills and O. B. Slee. *Austr. J. Phys.* **10**, 162, 1957.
177. G. Stanley and O. B. Slee. *Austr. J. Sci. Res. A* **3**, 234, 1950.
178. J. D. Kraus, H. G. Ko and S. Matt. *A.J.* **59**, 439, 1954.
179. C. L. Seeger, G. Westerhout and H. C. van der Hulst. *B.A.N.* **13**, 389, 1956.
180. D. S. Heeshen. *Ap. J.* **133**, 322, 1961.
181. N. G. Roman and B. S. Yapslee. *P.I.R.E.* **46**, 199, 1958.
182. J. H. Piddington and G. H. Trent. *Austr. J. Phys.* **9**, 74, 1956.
183. J. Denisse, J. Lequeux and E. Le Roux. *C.R.* **244**, 3030, 1956.
184. D. E. Harris. *Calif. Inst. Tech. Rep.* No. **6**, 1961.
185. P. Mezger. *Zschr. f. Ap.* **46**, 234, 1958.
186. G. Westerhout. *B.A.N.* **14**, 488, 1958.
187. J. P. Hagen, E. F. McClain and M. Hupburn. *P.I.R.E.* **42**, 1811, 1954.
188. R. M. Sloanaker and J. Nichols. *A.J.* **65**, 105, 1961.
189. A. D. Kuz'min, M. T. Levchenko and R. N. Noskova. *A. Zh.* **37**, 965, 1960.
190. V. M. Plechkov and V. A. Razin. In the book: *Trudy 5-go soveshch. po vopr. kosmogonii.* (*Transactions of the 5th Conference on Problems of Cosmogony*). Moscow, 1956, 430.
191. N. W. Broten and W. J. Medd. *Ap. J.* **132**, 279, 1960.
192. F. Haddock, V. Mayer and R. Sloanaker. *Ap. J.* **119**, 456, 1954.
193. A. M. Karachun, A. D. Kuz'min and A. Ye. Salomonovich. *A. Zh.* **38**, 83, 1961.
194. N. L. Kaydanovskiy, N. S. Kardashev and I. S. Shklovskiy. *D.A.N.* **104**, 517, 1955.
195. D. H. Staelin, A. H. Barret and B. R. Kusse. *A.I.* **69**, 69, 1964.
196. A. H. Barret. *Ap. J.* **134**, 945, 1961.

197.   C. W. Tolbert and A. W. Straiton. *A.J.* **70**, 2, 1965.

198.   C. W. Tolbert. *Nature* **206**, 1304, 1965.

199.   A. D. Kuz'min and A. Ye. Salomonovich. *D.A.N.* **140**, 81, 1961.

200.   C. W. Tolbert and A. W. Straiton. *Nature* **204**, 1242, 1964.

203.   B. Mills. *Nature* **170**, 1063, 1952.

204.   B. Mills. *Austr. J. Phys.* **6**, 452, 1953.

205.   J. Baldwin. *Observatory* **74**, 120, 1954.

206.   V. A. Udal'tsov and V. V. Vitkevich. *A. Zh.* **25**, 5, 1958.

207.   C. Costain and B. Elsmore. *M.N.* **118**, 380, 1956.

208.   J. Tuominen and M. Karras. *Ann. Acad. Sci. Fennicae (A)* **6**, 6, 1957.
       Repr. Radioastr. Station Helsinki, No. 5.

209.   B. Andrew, H. Branson and D. Wills. *Nature* **203**, 494, 1964.

210.   A. Hewish and S. Okoye. *Nature* **203**, 494, 1964.

211.   A. Hewish and S. Okoye. *Nature* **207**, 59, 1965.

212.   G. P. Apushkinskiy and Yu. N. Pariyskiy. *A. Zh.* **36**, 739, 1959.

213.   Yu. N. Pariyskiy. *Izv. GAO v Pulkove* **21**, 164, 45, 1960.

214.   V. A. Gol'nev and Yu. N. Pariyskiy. *A. Zh.* **42**, 305, 1965.

215.   A. R. Thompson and T. Krishnan. *A.J.* **141**, 19, 1965.

216.   N. R. Labrum, T. Krishnan, W. J. Payten and E. Harting. *Austr. J. Phys.*
       17, 323, 1964.

217.   I. S. Shklovskiy. *A. Zh.* **30**, 15, 1953.

218.   G. Westerhout. *B.A.N.* **12**, 309, 1956.

219.   C. Mayer, T. McCullough and R. Sloanaker. *Ap. J.* **126**, 468, 1957.

220.   A. D. Kuz'min and V. A. Udal'tsov. *A. Ts.*, No. 187, 1957.

221.   J. Hollinger, C. Mayer and R. Mennella. *Ap. J.* **140**, 650, 1964.

222.   D. Morris and V. Radakrishnan. *Ap. J.* **137**, 169, 1963.

223.   N. S. Soboleva, V. A. Prozorov and Yu. N. Pariyskiy. *A. Zh.* **40**, 1, 1963.

224.   D. Morris, V. Radakrishnan and G. Selestad. *Ap. J.* **139**, 758, 1964.

226.   J. Holetschek. *Ann. Wiener Sternwarte* **20**, 40, 1907.

227.   C. Würtz. *Lund Obs. Medd.* (2), No. 29, 1923.

228.   J. Greenstein and R. Minkowski. *Ap. J.* **118**, 1, 1953.

229.   T. G. Cowling. Nuclear Processes and Stellar Structure: General Survey.
       Mém. Soc. Roy. Sci. Liege **14**, 75, 1954.

230.   I. S. Shklovskiy. *D.A.N.* **90**, 983, 1953.

231.   V. A. Dombrovskiy. *D.A.N.* **94**, 21, 1954.

232.   G. A. Shayn, S. B. Pikel'ner and R. N. Ikhsanov. *A. Zh.* **32**, 395, 1955.

233.   M. A. Vashakidze. *A. Ts.*, No. 147, 1954.

234.   E. Ye. Khachikyan. *D.A.N. Arm. SSr* **21**, 63, 1955.

235.   J. Oort and Th. Walraven. *B.A.N.* **12**, 285, 1956.

235a. W. Baade. *B.A.N.* **12**, 312, 1956.

236.   C. R. O'Dell. *Ap. J.* **136**, 809, 1962.

236a. Th. Walraven. *B.A.N.* **13**, 293, 1957.

236b. *Publ. of the Lick Obs.* **8**, 1908.

237.   V. Shcheglov. *A. Zh.* **34**, 675, 1957.

237a. W. Hiltner. *Ap. J.* **125**, 300, 1957.

238.   V. I. Moroz. *A. Zh.* **37**, 265, 1960.

239.   V. I. Moroz. *A. Zh.* **40**, 982, 1963.

240. E. S. Brodskaya. *Izv. Kr. AO* **31**, 1964.
241. R. Giacconi, H. Gursky, F. Paolini and B. Rossi. *Phys. Rev. Lett.* **9**, 439, 1962; **11**, 530, 1963.
242. S. Bowyer, E. Byram, T. Chubb and H. Friedman. *Nature* **201**, 1307, 1964.
243. D. Morton. *Ap. J.* **140**, 460, 1964.
244. P. I. Bakulin and I. S. Shklovskiy. *A. Zh.* **32**, 29, 1955.
245. S. Bowyer, E. Byram, T. Chubb and H. Friedman. *Science* **146**, 912, 1964.
246. S. Bowyer, E. Byram, T. Chubb and H. Friedman. *Science* **147**, 394, 1965.
247. G. W. Clark. *Phys. Rev. Lett.* **14**, No. 4, 91, 1965.
248. V. I. Pronik. *Izv. Kr. AO* **30**, 104, 1937.
249. V. L. Ginzburg. *U.F.N.* **60**, 243, 1953.
250. V. L. Ginzburg. *U.F.N.* **62**, 37, 1957.
251. S. B. Pikel'ner. *A. Zh.* **33**, 785, 1956.
252. G. Burbidge. In the book: *Paris Symposium on Radio Astronomy.* Stanford University Press, 1959, 541.
254. V. I. Slysh. *A. Zh.* **42**, 689, 1956.
255. A. A. Korchak and S. I. Syrovatskiy. *A. Zh.* **37**, 885, 1961.
256. G. Burbidge. *Ap. J.* **124**, 416, 1956.
257. G. Cocconi. In the book: *Trudy mezhd. konferentsii po kosm. lucham (Transactions of the International Conference on Cosmic Rays).* Vol. 2, 327, 1960.
258. A. Ye. Chudakov, V. L. Dadykin, V. I. Zatsepin and N. M. Nesterova. *Trudy F.I.A.N.* **26**, 118, 1964.
259. F. Hoyle. Preprint Caltech, 1964.
260. A. N. Deych. Chastnoye soobshcheniye (Private Communication).
261. P. P. Parenago. *A. Zh.* **27**, No. 3, 1950.
262. I. S. Shklovskiy. *D.A.N.* **160**, 54, 1965.
263. R. Kraft. *Ap. J.* **139**, 457, 1964.
264. V. V. Zheleznyakov. *Radioizlucheniye Solntsa i planet (Radio Emission from the Sun and the Planets).* Moscow, "Nauka," 1964.
265. Humeson. (Reference not available).
266. R. Minkowski. *Ap. J.* **97**, 128, 1943.
267. R. Hanburry Brown and C. Hazard. *Nature* **170**, 364, 1952.
268. J. R. Shakeshaft, M. Ryle and J. Thomson. *Mem. R. Astr. Soc.* **67**, Pt. 3, 106, 1956.
269. P. Maltby and A. Moffet. *Ap. J. Suppl.* **7**, No. 67, 1962.
270. J. Baldwin and D. Edge. *Observatory* **77**, 139, 1957.
271. D. Edge, J. Shakeshaft, N. Adam, J. Baldwin and S. Archer. *Mem. R. Astr. Soc.* **68**, 37, 1959.
272. A. D. Kuz'min. *Trudy F.I.A.N.* **17**, 1962.
273. H. Rishbeth and A. Little. *Observatory* **77**, 71, 1957.
273a. K. Kellerman. *Publ. Owens Valley Radio Observatory* **1**, No. 1, 1964.
273b. B. W. Wilson. *Obs. Owens Valley Radio Observatory*, No. 2, 1963.
274. J. Bologna, E. McClain, R. Sloanaker and W. Rose. *A.J.* **68**, 681, 1958.
275. V. Radakrishnan. In the book: *Physics of Nonthermal Radio Sources.* N.A.S.A. Goddard Inst., 1964, 55.
276. J. A. Seilstad. *Observ. Caltech Radio Observatory*, No. 7, 1963.

277. H. Arp. *Ap. J.* **139**, 1378, 1964.
278. Yu. P. Pskovskiy. *A. Zh.* **42**, 683, 1965.
279. F. Zwicky and E. Herzog. *Catalogue of Galaxies and Clusters of Galaxies* **2**. Zürich, 1963.
280. M. Schmidt. *Ap. J.* **41**, 1, 1965.
281. Yu. P. Pskovskiy. *A. Zh.* **42**, 683, 1965.
282. B. A. Vorontsov-Vel'yaminov and V. P. Arkhipova. *Morfologicheskiy katalog galaktik (Morphological Catalogue of Galaxies)*. Part 2, Moscow, 1964.
283. P. Maltby and A. Moffet. *Observ. Caltech Radio Observatory* No. 1, 1962.
284. A. Penzias and R. Wilson. *Ap. J.* **142**, 419, 1965.
285. R. Dicke, P. Pibles, P. Roll and D. Wilkinson. *Ap. J.* **142**, 414, 1965.
286. I. S. Shklovskiy. *D.A.N.* **91**, 475, 1953; *A. Zh.* **30**, 577, 1953.
287. P. Meyer and R. Vogt. *Phys. Rev. Lett.* **6**, 193, 1961.
288. T. L. Cline, G. H. Ludwig and F. B. McDonald. *Phys. Rev. Lett.* **13**, 786, 1964.
289. J. Heureux and P. Meyer. Preprint E. Fermi Inst., 1965.
290. J. W. Schmocker and J. A. Earl. *Phys. Rev.* **138**, 300, 1965.
291. L. Bolton and K. Westfold. *Austr. J. Sci. Res. A* **3**, 19, 1950.
292. I. S. Shklovskiy. *Russ. Astr. J.* **29**, 418, 1952.
292a. E. Baldwin. *Observatory* **83**, 153, 1963.
293. D. S. Mathewson and M. Rome. *Observatory* **83**, 20, 1963.
294. B. Mills and I. Glanfield. *Nature* **208**, 10, 1965.
295. B. Mills. *Publ. Astr. Soc. Pacific* **71**, 267, 1959.
296. S. B. Pikel'ner and I. S. Shklovskiy. *Ann. d'Ap.* **22**, 913, 1959.
297. G. Westerhout. In the book: *Paris Symposium on Radio Astronomy*. Stanford University Press, 1959, 447.
298. A. J. Turtle, J. F. Pugh, S. Kenderlin and I. Pauliny Toth. *M.N.* **124**, 296, 1962.
299. V. L. Ginzburg and S. I. Syrovatskiy. *Dokladna konferentsii po kosmicheskim lucham (Paper of Conference on Cosmic Rays)*. Moscow, October 1965.
300. B. Mills. *Astr. J. Phys.* **8**, 368, 1955.
301. G. Burbidge and F. Hoyle. *Ap. J.* **138**, 57, 1963.
302. V. L. Ginzburg and S. I. Syrovatskiy. *A. Zh.* **41**, 430, 1964.
303. I. S. Shklovskiy. *A. Zh.* **41**, 176, 1964.
304. I. S. Shklovskiy. *U.F.N.* **77**, 3, 1964.
305. A. Unsöld. *Zschr. f. Phys.* **141**, 70, 1955.
306. V. I. Krasovskiy and I. S. Shklovskiy. *D.A.N.* **116**, 197, 1957.
307. C. Halsam, M. Large and M. Quigley. *M.N.* **127**, 273, 1964.
308. R. Davis, R. Hanbury Brown and J. Meaburn. *Observatory* **83**, 179, 1963.
309. T. A. Lozinskaya and P. V. Shcheglov. *A. Ts.*, No. 327, 1965.
310. R. Hanburry Brown, R. Davis and C. Hazard. *Observatory* **80**, 191, 1960.
311. J. H. Blythe. *M.N.* **117**, 652, 1957.
312. T. A. Lozinskaya. *A. Ts.*, No. 299, 1964.
313. M. Quigley. *Observatory* **85**, 135, 1965.
313a. M. L. Large, M. Quigley and C. Halsam. *M.N.* **124**, 405, 1962.
314. F. Hoyle and F. Fowler. *Ap. J.* **132**, 565, 1960.

315. Ya. B. Zel'dovich and I. D. Novikov. *U.F.N.* **84**, 377, 1964.
316. Ya. B. Zel'dovich and I. D. Novikov. *U.F.N.* **86**, 447, 1965.
317. R. H. Fowler. *M.N.* **87**, 114, 1926.
318. J. Frenkel. *Zschr. f. Phys.* **50**, 234, 1928.
319. S. Chandrasekhar. *Stellar Structure*, Chap. XI. University of Chicago Press, 1938.
320. J. R. Oppenheimer and G. M. Volkoff. *Phys. Rev.* **55**, 374, 1939.
321. J. R. Oppenheimer and H. Snyder. *Phys. Rev.* **56**, 456, 1939.
322. I. S. Shklovskiy. *A. Zh.* **42**, 287, 1965.
325. W. Baade, R. Christy, G. Burbidge, W. A. Fowler and F. Hoyle. *Publ. Astr. Soc. Pacific* **68**, 196, 1956.
326. E. M. Burbidge, G. Burbidge, W. A. Fowler and F. Hoyle. *Rev. Mod. Phys.* **29**, 547, 1957.
327. L. Borst. *Phys. Rev.* **78**, 807, 1950.
328. E. Anders. *Ap. J.* **129**, 327, 1959.
329. S. A. Johansson. *Nuclear Phys.* **12**, 449, 1959.
330. H. M. Johnson. *Publ. Astr. Soc. Pacific* **71**, 425, 1959.
331. L. Goldberg, E. Müller and L. Aller. *Ap. J. Suppl.* **5**, No. 15, 1, 1960.
332. H. C. Arp. *Ap. J.* **135**, 311, 1962.
333. M. Burbidge and G. Burbidge. *Ap. J.* **124**, 116, 1956.
334. L. H. Aller and J. R. Greenstein. *Ap. J. Suppl.* **5**, No. 46, 139, 1960.
335. R. C. Haymes, W. L. Craddock and D. D. Clayton. Preprint COSPAR. Conf. Buenos Aires, May 1965.
336. F. Hoyle, W. A. Fowler, G. R. Burbidge and M. Burbidge. *Ap. J.* **139**, 909, 1964.
337. F. Hoyle and I. Narlicar. *Proc. Roy. Soc. (A)* **273**, 4, 1963.
338. V. L. Ginzburg. Dokl. na konferentsii po kosmicheskim lucham (Paper of Conference on Cosmic Rays). Moscow, 1965.
339. V. L. Ginzburg. *D.A.N.* **92**, 723, 1963.
340. S. A. Colgate and M. N. Johnson. *Phys. Rev. Lett.* **5**, 235, 1960.
341. S. A. Colgate, W. H. Grassberger and R. A. White. *J. Phys. Soc. Japan. Suppl. A* **3**, 157, 1957.
342. W. H. Grassberger. Univ. Calif. Lawrence Rad. Laborat. Repr. 6196, 1960.
343. V. S. Imshennik and D. K. Nadezhkin. *A. Zh.* **41**, 829, 1964.
344. D. K. Nadezhkin and D. A. Frank-Kamenetskiy. *A. Zh.* **41**, 842, 1964.
345. G. M. Gandel'man and D. A. Frank-Kamenetskiy. *D.A.N.* **107**, 811, 1956.
346. A. Sakurai. *Comm. Pure Appl. Mathematics* **13**, 353, 1960.
347. I. M. Gordon. *D.A.N.* **94**, 413, 1954.
348. I. M. Gordon. *Trudy Astr. Obs. Kharkovskogo un-ta 1–2* **15**, 1957.
349. Ya. B. Zel'dovich and I. D. Novikov. *D.A.N.* **158**, 811, 1964.
350. E. Salpeter. *Ap. J.* **140**, 796, 1964.
351. A. A. Korchak and S. I. Syrovatskiy. *D.A.N.* **122**, 792, 1958.
352. S. B. Pikel'ner. *A. Zh.* **38**, 21, 1961.
353. N. S. Kardashev. *A. Zh.* **41**, 807, 1964.
354. V. L. Ginzburg. *D.A.N.* **156**, 43, 1964.
355. V. L. Ginzburg and L. M. Ozernoy. *Zh.E.T.F.* **47**, 1030, 1964.
356. I. D. Novikov. *A. Ts.* No. 290, 1964.

357. F. Hoyle.   *Voprosy kosmogonii* (*Problems of Cosmogony*).   Moscow, 1960, 15.
358. S. van den Bergh.   *Publ. Astr. Soc. Pacific* **90**, 359, 1957.
359. M. Ryle and F. Smith.   *Nature* **162**, 462, 1948.
360. F. Bertola.   Contr. dell'osservatorio Astrofisico dell'universita di Padova,
      No. 142, 1963.